HAMAM BALKANIA

HAMAM BALKANIA

A Novel

and Other Stories

Vladislav Bajac

Translated from the Serbian by
Randall A. Major

First published in 2014 by
Istros Books
London, United Kingdom
www.istrosbooks.com

© Vladislav Bajac, 2008
English translation © Randall A. Major, 2009

Cover photograph '16th-Century Ottoman Hamam' by Anthony Georgieff
    anthony@vagabond.bg
    www.vagabond.bg
Artwork & Design@Milos Miljkovich, 2013
Graphic Designer/Web Developer – miljkovicmisa@gmail.com

This novel was first published in English by *Geopoetika*, 2009, as part of the
Serbian Prose in Translation/Srpska proza u prevodu series, financed by the
Serbian Ministry of Culture. First published in Serbian as *Hamam
Balkanija* by Arhipelag, Belgrade, in 2008.

ISBN: 978-1-908236-14-2

Printed in England by
CMP (UK), Poole, Dorset
www.cmp-uk.com

Supported using public funding by
LOTTERY FUNDED
ARTS COUNCIL
ENGLAND

The names in this book are fictional.
All the characters as well,
including the omniscient author.

THE HAMAM
OR THE SKILL OF LIVING

It is quite probable that the famous phrase 'miracle of nature' originates with the ancient Greek materialist philosopher Epicurus (341–270 BC). And this is why: he based his ethics and his view of human happiness on the belief that 'without a knowledge of nature it is impossible to achieve the light of enjoyment'. According to him, the greatest good is blissful pleasure. To have these postulates as a goal was not related to the vulgar pleasures of merrymakers or to immoderate gastronomic satiation, as those unfamiliar with him conclude, but rather referred primarily to the elimination of physical suffering and disturbances of the soul.

The attainment of spiritual tranquillity is founded on a naturalistic and individualistic basis.

Epicurus' belief in hedonism was so firm that it could not be shaken even by the dark times of the dissolution of Alexander's empire (and Epicurus had witnessed its grandeur and power), the consequences of which were anything but pleasurable. In spite of it all, he claimed that 'the words of philosophers that do not heal human suffering are of no value. Because, just like medicine that is not able to rid the body of illness, of equal uselessness is a philosophy that is unable to rid the soul of suffering'.

Thus, anyone who knew how to avoid physical pain and spiritual disharmony, who knew that sensual pleasure and spiritual joy (as a unity) are the greatest values of living and, therefore, who knew the very skill of living – such people belonged to the Epicurean brotherhood, maintained to this very day.

His spiritual father was Aristippus (435–355 BC), the founder of the Cyrenaic school, born in Cyrene, the most beautiful and advanced Hellenic settlement in Libya. Pindar described this spot as a remarkably well-situated hill, covered with springs that were utilised to artificially irrigate its garden terraces. These picturesque surroundings were dotted with olive orchards, vineyards and the famous silphium plantations, and also with vast meadows covered with sheep, goats and horses – the last ultimately giving rise to the noble Arabian breed. In spite of their hard-fought battles with the Egyptians and Libyans, the Cyrenians maintained a highly developed trade that made their homeland one of the wealthiest of the Hellenic states. Therefore, its citizens did not have to expend all their energy working, but also became skilfully familiar with the luxury and pleasure 'that come from plenitude and a refined sense of living'. This is the place that seems to be the ancient prototype of the utopian city-states, and most certainly of the societies of Sir Thomas More and Tommaso Campanella.

It is no wonder that the thinker who promoted pleasure as the central principle of life, Aristippus, was born in none other than Cyrene. Indeed, he remained known as the philosophy's progenitor, but under a different name: hedonism. He pronounced pleasure to be the only good and maintained that pain was the only evil. The feeling of pleasure, he claimed, is expressed in movement, 'The gentle movement of feeling, like a breeze suitable for a sailboat, is the source of satisfaction; the rough movement of feeling, like a storm at sea, is the source of dissatisfaction; the absence of the movement of feeling, like a calm sea, is the source of indifference, equal to someone else's satisfaction or dissatisfaction.' However, Aristippus did not in any way believe it was possible to reduce man as a whole to the hunt for momentary physical pleasures, on the contrary, he taught that a wise man, controlling himself with reason, does not become a slave to pleasures, but rather controls them. He testified to this position through his relationship, in no way indifferent, to his hetaera, or concubine, Lais, in his most famous claim, 'I possess Lais, but she does not possess me'.

Quite close to this idea was the ethical school of eudemonism (after the ancient Greek goddess of happiness and well-being) that believed happiness and well-being to be the guiding motive, the reason and goal of all our actions. Furthermore, a heavy emphasis on individualism is the common element of all kinds of hedonism, from the harshly sensual to the rationally spiritual.

The history that followed, that came about after these Hellenistic 'schools of pleasure', shows that some of its most important and well-remembered creators, along with many anonymous and now-forgotten individuals, attempted to become pleasure-seekers, even through personal and national tragedies. They zealously tried to feel satisfaction even in the broadest and most absurd range of the understanding of the meaning of hedonism, even taking pleasure in physical beauty, or even death.

If nothing else, they proved the constancy of the role of ethical relativism.

BEFORE THE BEGINNING

Višegrad, like any other place, has its own daily life. Yet, like few others, it also has its own abstract life. My experience with the metaphysics of Višegrad began in April, 1977, on approaching the town, before I ever saw the famed bridge on the Drina, which has fixed the town's place in history forever. In my little haiku notebook, which I still have, I noted down a geo-poetic commentary 'on the gravel of Višegrad' with the poem that I saw through the window of the bus:

> A stone between them
> two sunbathed firs, a parting
> made in the forest.

My host and friend from my university days, Žarko Čigoja, thought that the bridge of Mehmed-pasha Sokollu (as it is written in Turkish) from 1571 – the bridge Andrić wrote about – was enough of a prize and a pleasure, for that occasion, so that he did not even show me the other attractions of his hometown. He could not even imagine how selfish I was, actually even unhappy, that I had to share this magnificent bridge with others. I did not know then, that deeper knowledge of the secrets of the environs of Višegrad would have to be earned by future experience. Once again, a secret brotherhood was in question and I would have to wait twenty-six whole years to enter that brotherhood. It was worth it. It was actually Ivo Andrić who taught me to wait; through reading him again. During my literature studies I was not yet able to connect his masterpiece with real life: too flippantly had I passed over his notes on the beginnings of the bridge's construction – on its very essence – on the "transportation of stones from the quarries that were opened in the hills near Banja, an hour's walk from the town". What is more, the two most important literary bridges in all of Bosnia – this one on the River Drina and the other on the River Žepa – were built of the very same white stone mentioned in my haiku poem: with the love and money of Mehmed-pasha Sokolović and Jusuf Ibrahim, both Turkified or Islamised Serbs, made eternal in the humble and wise words of Andrić, the man who attributed his own life's motto to his literary hero: *there is safety in silence.*

When I complained to a friend that I had perhaps dried up in my writing, he told me not to worry in the slightest. He had a certain cure for that illness. He was, actually, expecting the arrival of the Turkish writer, Orhan Pamuk, with the same diagnosis, so that the two of us could be cured at the same time with his prescription.

The only thing I knew about *Banja*, about Sokollu's Spa, the Spa of Višegrad, as everyone called it, besides being the source of crystalline calcium carbonate used to build the bridge in Višegrad, was that there was a medicinal spring in this place three miles from the town. It was here that Mehmed-pasha Sokollu, in his waning years in 1575, built a domed Turkish bath, wanting to give something (more) to his birthplace. In a brochure from 1934, I read that the radioactive waters (at an altitude of more than 1200 feet) treated rheumatism, neuralgia and 'women's disorders'. The brochure further claimed that the spa waters have an especially beneficial effect on barren women. 'When a barren wife hails at the spa, and then begets a child, the village round doth shake its head, saying: By God, if she hadn't hailed at the spa and her incantations said, she never ever would have bred...'

So it was that I also travelled through the thick forest to the spa, which I nicknamed 'the Maidenhair' after the magical looking rare grass that grows only there. I was happy to meet up with my old acquaintance, Orhan Pamuk, himself a native of Istanbul. And I was mildly surprised that he too, was suffering from a dry spell, because he was known to be a prolific writer. If perchance in some period of his writing life he did not publish a book for a long while, the one that followed was sure to be a hefty baby.

I gave birth to my children less often, and most often they were of medium weight. Such was my rhythm. However, in the last couple of years I had not conceived a single one, and I was getting seriously worried. That was why I went to visit the stone that gave birth to water: such fertility revived my faith. The stone on which I stepped had been polished for more than four centuries and was now the colour of grass and moss. The water, hot but not boiling, was of a heavenly warmth. and my body was turning into a ghost: alive yet dead. Pamuk and our host tried to talk through the water vapour, but the words disappeared in the glass windows of the dome and lost all their meaning. Our eyelids closed, but our eyes did not go to sleep. I push my way through the powerful water, to sit under the heavy stream that rushes from the mountain into the small pool, across my back. I am beaten as I never have been before. And I am happy to the point of silliness. This is the meeting point of the Cabbala, Zen, Sufism, Orthodox Aestheticism, the Catholic erasure of the fear of sin, the artistic heights of Islam... Just as the maidenhair fern can grow nowhere else but here, only here does the water arrive from a depth of 590 feet and from a more important historical depth of thirty-eight thousand years. An age sufficient to quell counts about its reason for existence or for speaking to the world.

It is also the reason for my relationship with the past. The antiquity that is inhaled here is completely authentic and cannot be resisted. The spirit first loses its orientation, and then the concept of time, and then the body also loses its orientation, and then its concept of space. This peculiar nirvana transformed me into a large question mark: were the barren women at this bath, perhaps, serviced by a man who was renowned for his healthy seed? Was this bath perhaps a male harem for desperate barren women? What kind of pleasure this tucked-away pool must have been for beys, pashas, viziers or sultans, regardless of whether they were the hosts or guests here. Whichever of the genders served these active waters and their bathers – it is noted in a long-lost text, that making love under this mountain stream (at a temperature of 95 degrees) is on par with the pleasure in the beauties of the heavenly gardens, Valhalla and Jannah.

This *hamam* could have been an ideal place for a caravansary, for surely travellers would have parted with their money here. Yet, nature (and perhaps fate) wished to hide it from the busy byways, and so placed it at an altitude that discouraged the weary traveller from the very thought of climbing up to it. That is why the stones of the *hamam* were polished by decades and centuries, and largely not by the hand of man. Although, it must be admitted, that hand got involved wherever and whenever it could: thus it is possible to find quotations in old manuscripts that overlap with the present: 'Next to the spa stands a building where a popular investor maintains a restaurant and has rooms for overnight stay. In front of that building there is a large veranda in front of which spread magnificent panoramas of nature.'

I don't know who the popular investor is nowadays, but he has not deprived himself either of the 'restaurant' nor of the 'veranda'. For, it is true, the satisfaction of bathing in the tiny heavenly pool would not be complete if one does not go to the restaurant veranda afterwards, across a large hanging balcony without glass, above a deep mountain ravine that expands your thoughts with its marvellous views: thoughts that do not seem, reflecting off the Bosnian hills and vales that stand shoulder to shoulder with you, to return to you infertile. And the food! Along with the local specialities, you will be served royal young trout, just pulled from the nearby rapids, ordered by telephone only an hour before. This is trout that has gone all winter without eating, and has just begun to feed on pristine food.

However, the modern structure of this restaurant should not be confused with the caravansary in the 16th century. That, it is not. Today, for those who wish to enjoy these marvels for a while longer, there is a hotel – a rehabilitation centre called 'Maidenhair', with all the necessary comforts and also a modern pool, which is also filled with the thermal waters. The source of their radioactivity is radon, and where there is radon there will also be doctors and physiotherapists. Clearly, you do not have to be ill or concerned about your health to come to this place. In fact, by going there healthy, you prove to yourself that you have not yet rid yourself of hedonism.

Even Mehmed-Pasha himself did not make a caravansary of the hamam, of 'the beautiful spa with its dome roof'; he built one nearby: "next to the River Drina as Sokollu's stone inn or caravansary, which could take about ten thousand horses and camels under its roof". Do you think the numbers are exaggerated? I wouldn't say so. If they are, then they are not far from true. Just imagine what a task it was like to build a bridge like the one in Višegrad in the 1570s! In Mehmed-Pasha's time Višegrad had about seven hundred homes, a mosque named *Selimiye*, a fountain, about three hundred shops, an imaret (hospice) that served the village's poor, and a Dervish monastery – a *tekya*. In the village of Sokolovići (which got its name after the pasha, or the pasha got his name after the village, it makes no difference), there was a mosque called Sokolović mosque, but there was also a place for a Christian church where, according to legend, the pasha built a church dedicated to his Orthodox mother. This, of course, should not surprise anyone, if it is generally known that it was actually Mehmed-Pasha Sokollu who, as a vizier of the Turkish Dīvān, in 1557, personally had the Serbian Patriarchate at Peć renovated and then placed his brother Makarije at the head of the church, as the sources say, at the moment, 'when Orthodoxy was in chaos and disarray, and the national idea of the Serbian people was beginning to wane in the heavy shackles of its slavery'. Some historians hold the position that, with the latter, 'the great vizier through this decree preserved the Serbian people from final extinction and destruction'. This cannot be far from the truth if one knows to what extent the Serbian people of the time, no longer having their own independent state, lent importance to the only existing replacement for statehood – the Serbian Orthodox church. This is the reason for the widely held qualification that Mehmed-Pasha Sokollu was 'an unshakeable Moslem and, at the same time... a good patriot who paid his dues to his people with dignity'. He believed that he made peace between Islam and his Bosnian homeland; his Serbian roots and the Orthodox Christian faith.

And that is why (in my mind) it was there, at the hamam, at that particular time, that most popular and controversial contemporary Turkish writer, Orhan Pamuk showed up with me – because, if there is any ideology in novel writing, he dedicated his books to the relations between East and West, and thereby continued down the path followed by some of his ancestors. And there is another reason: his masterpiece novel *My Name is Red* deals with the Ottoman Empire and in part with Mehmed-Pasha's time, and also with the consequences of that time. For his explanation of that period, Pamuk deserved a virtual (or perhaps for him, Dervish's) bath – for there is never enough cleanliness and purification. Nor is there enough enjoyment, or *akshamluk* 'the Bosnian custom of sitting on the grass in the evening, usually by a body of water, drinking brandy, singing and talking'.

What kind of writers would we be if we did not, sometimes, next to the hamam, enjoy a bit of *akshamluk* ourselves? While understanding this word's hedonistic and philosophical meaning.

One of the writers' main problems, is that they often confuse reality and imagination. That is the source of the famous loss of the boundary between what happened and what was experienced. And that is how I began to temporally mix my encounters with people close to me; it is in fact, how I brought those who lived five centuries before me closer to my own time, and transferred myself and my friends (or characters, it makes no difference) with ease into lives centuries older than we are.

It was one of the ways of fulfilling the writer's dream about the temporal omnipotence of words.

Because of that dream, books come into being.

THE END

He wished that someone would kill him. Yes, that is right. Simply – to be killed. In the past year so much that he cared about and so many that he loved had disappeared from his life. This was, of course, no accident. It was all carefully planned and likewise carried out. He had to admit – his opponent executed it all without error, and thus, from the standpoint of the skill and expertise of what had been done, he had absolutely nothing to object to. Except for the very basis of the idea: why had his enemies set the entire machinery in motion and spent so much time, money and energy in order to obliterate everything dear to him, when it would have been much quicker, cheaper and easier to kill him and him alone?

Yet, in fact, he knew the reason. What they really wanted was for him to constantly ask that question and, not finding an answer, to ultimately feel so alone and abandoned that he wished to live no longer. Because watching those near, dear and loyal to him disappearing one by one before his very eyes, that had to hurt, and it went on and on. If they had killed him *first* and *immediately*, there would be none of the suffering they wished him to go through. To be honest, after so many decades in authority, at the very top, he had to expect such a decline. So it had been, it seems, from the beginning of the world; one's rise is most often associated with one's fall. Whoever reached the top, must also find the bottom, in whatever sequence. But whether everyone actually had to fall to the bottom after being at the top, that is questionable. It did fall to him. Or it was, as they say, his destiny. Or had he actually brought on his own decline.

To be fair, his fall was actually rather literal. No one replaced him, overthrew him or passed him by in a new distribution of authority (even if such things had been planned). He fell from a single, sudden stab of a knife right in the heart and now, there he was, lying in a pool of blood, watching his entire past life as if he were summarising it before death so that he would not forget it.

What more could he ask, his wish was fulfilled: someone had killed him.

Strange, how death can be a relief. Certainly, his murderers had not done this to show him compassion. During his reign, violent death had been a normal, everyday phenomenon; the nuances were just in the type or degree of the morbidity and brutality. The Empire had required violence at all times and in all forms. While he was a grand vizier, taking others' lives was not in any way characteristic of him as a leader or, God forbid, as a person. It was part of protecting the system; it was not even a matter of safeguarding his own authority. It was a mechanism, centuries in the making, that no single individual, no matter from what position of authority he acted, could disturb, much the less change, even if he wanted to. In the battles, wars, campaigns and conquests, death was commonplace. It occurred frequently in peacetime as well, only just not as widely spread.

After all, was he not famed as a grand vizier also because he ruled during the reign of three sultans! Who else could make such a claim? A rarity was a vizier who could survive the enthronement of one sultan, and no one ever connected three in a row! All death had originated from the highest ruler: did not every sultan, when taking the throne, by an unwritten law, first kill all his brothers (some also killed their own children) so that they did not threaten his reign *with their very existence*?

It would also not be true to say that he *was waiting for* his own death. It simply did not surprise him. About Death itself he knew everything: it would be difficult to find someone who could outdo him in his knowledge of its causes and effects, its kinds and types. Perhaps he would not excel at questions of its usefulness: not one of his teachers or rulers had instructed him about such secrets because the question of purpose would never be asked by such people.

'Wishing' to die did not also mean that he 'longed' for it. His wishing allowed him to peacefully await his own fate. It removed all unnecessary uncertainty.

Now everything stopped being important, and especially everything that required additional time for reflection. There was just not enough time for anything. Except for death.

THE VERY BEGINNING

Since I had inwardly proved to myself that I had not 'dried up' as a writer, I could begin in reality to struggle in solving a dilemma. *Which of the three planned books should I start to write?* I will not mention the other two anticipated books because I have, obviously, started writing the frontrunner. Of course, subtle reasons were in this book's favour because I had also done most of the serious and necessary preparatory work for the other two future books from the narrow selection.

Of those subtle reasons, the scales were tipped by those that I would group under 'local-patriotic' reasons. Namely, in a recent conversation with a colleague on the topics of nationalism and globalism in literary themes, I realised for the first time the fact that the fervent defenders of the 'domestic novel' had labelled me 'cosmopolitan', a term that they used with condescension. Yet in this conclusion they ignored the fact that in four out of my five published novels, the action at least begins or takes place entirely in Belgrade and/or Serbia, and that of my seven books of prose (not counting this one, of course) six contain the same topography! And yet, the fault-finding had no end: perhaps those books in their essence or message were too cosmopolitan, so even local geography or local action could not help them. They did not manage to rise to the level of national myths, which was, to be honest, not part of their conception either.

The chosen topic hid new traps, not only compositional but also those mentioned earlier – ideological. However, if a writer puts too much stock in all that, he probably would never write anything (worthwhile). Thus, I resolved to write about a Serb *who became something else*. This 'something else' was what interested me. Not really the 'Serb' part although, even if I wanted to, I could not separate that from 'Something Else-ness'. If I were to delve into it really deeply, I would have to admit that I was actually and essentially interested only in the existence of the *transition* from One into Something Else: the very act in itself.

So, I started researching, investigating, gathering, selecting, accepting and rejecting my materials. Yet, a method had to be chosen for this gathering activity, or at least the order of steps to be taken. Facts as a sort of leitmotif of the process could pop up from anywhere and then be added to the already existing ones. One of my methods was to follow the traces of the protagonists. Thus, over several years (in parallel with other ways of studying this topic) I basically passed through the most important regions where Sokollu Mehmed Pasha had been or had worked: Višegrad with its environs and the wider area of eastern Bosnia and western Serbia (including the Drina River that divides/joins them), Herzegovina and Dubrovnik, Vojvodina and central Hungary, its western part with the centre of the old Austro-Hungarian Empire – Vienna, all of Bulgaria in its breadth, the former capital of the Ottoman Empire – Edirne, and then to the heart – both ancient and modern – Byzantium/Constantinople/Stambol/Istanbul, and all the seas in the area (the Adriatic, the Black Sea, the Sea of Marmara, the Aegean Sea). I finished my search in south-western Turkey and, at the very end, in the Princes' Islands. I covered it all several times. Persia was the only part to remain outside of my reach, as I was hindered by the wars in the Turkish surroundings – today non-existent Persia. Before that, the wars around Serbia, in today's non-existent Yugoslavia, hindered me from seeing things in my own backyard. (Belgrade, which was so vital to me, was presupposed also as a toponym. In any case, the whole thing started there and, in principle, soon everything will end there as well.)

In parallel, I also visited the architectural wonders of Mimar Koca Sinan, a contemporary of Mehmed Pasha and the second character in the forthcoming book. I also visited a man named Orhan Pamuk, and a certain V.B. These two latter became the second couple of the parallel action of the planned novel.

These four people became characters in the same book (placed, in fact, on opposing pages), which recruited all of them in a conspiracy against history as I knew it.

BEFORE THE VERY END

Before his death, of course, there was a life. A long and rich one. Powerful, but also insecure. As much his own as someone else's. From time to time, the ownership of his own life slipped away from him. If it had only been a matter of God himself – the Lord of lords or God's emissary, the choice would have been simple: Mohammed or Christ. Or both of them at the same time. However, someone, or more likely *something*, took over his life occasionally and left him without the essential possibility of choosing for himself to what or to whom he belonged.

Perhaps this in itself would not have been such an enigma if it had not kept imposing itself so often and so persistently, and with increasing intensity as he grew older. Even to the point of exasperation. Since he was unable to find logical reasons for it, he was also unable to solve the problem. And when the Secret was heaped onto the burden of so many years, life became a nightmare. It is possible that his approaching death (or, more likely, his wish for it) had an effect; the smell of its proximity could change his view of the world – accepted and proven a thousand times over – to turn it inside out into its own opposite and transform it into a completely repulsive truth. And yet, he could not reach even such a truth! So he thought that it would be easier to accept even the worst of truths, driven by his inability to capture *any* of them.

In no way could he take two possible explanations into consideration.

The first was understood: It was Allah's will! One dared not and could not contradict him publicly. In any case, since this was a conversation he kept within himself, the public had nothing to do with it, nor did Allah.

The second explanation did not lead far away from the Almighty. It could be said that it was moulded for him: it was his Destiny. This he could not accept because it was an invention of the powerless to justify their weakness.

He experienced the truth – oh the irony of it! – as the blade of the knife buried itself in his chest: he was the lord of his life only *halfway*. The *other half* was ruled by the other half of his personality: the first part of his personality, the one that belonged to Serbia and Bosnia.

He was both a Turk and a Serb. Both a Serb and a Turk.

What a relief.

To die.

AFTER THE BEGINNING

Planning the structure of a novel presupposes the existence of two beginnings and two endings, or two sorts of beginning and ending. One of the beginnings and endings has to do with action: how and when it will begin and how and when it will end. This is perhaps the most important secret of the book to the reader. To the author, another secret may be of more importance, the secret of the beginning and end of the ideas that stimulate him; that question or problem that actually inspired the author to come up with the book to begin to write, and that desirable, ultimate idea that could bring the book to its end.

While the structure of this book was still rather abstract and quite foggy, I knew that its protagonists offered the possibility of a profound story which explored the ideas of identity and change. That was the so-called starting point, while the ultimate goal could already be guessed: what is it that occurs to human beings, and around them as well, who happen to have a double identity?

The driving force of this novel, Mehmed pasha Sokollu (in Serbian he is known as Mehmed-paša Sokolović) made the decision for me about the *cause* and *reason* for me to write. (I recall how they prepared us in elementary school for the subject of logic, and the preparations for war, by teaching us to differentiate cause from reason. Most of us did not get it, and if we did, it was with great difficulty. Still, I managed, after great effort, to fathom it once and for all: the cause was long and carefully prepared, and the reason was a distraction and could also be given ad hoc, because it was simply a cog in a long-existing plan. The example they liked to use the most was the First World War – the lineage of the Austro-Hungarian monarchy, Serbia, Bosnia, Sarajevo, the group known as 'the Black Hand', and the assassin/patriot Gavrilo Princip).

In this case, the *cause* for me to work on Bajica Sokolović was the discovery that he was already eighteen years old when taken to Turkey as part of the infamous *devshirme* ('blood tribute'), and not as a small child who would hardly be able to remember where he came from. I wondered why he was chosen to become a janissary when he was already so old? While training them for the army, the Turks did not forbid the chosen boys to be conscious of their roots, but they rightly calculated that the fewer memories one has of one's homeland means that one will be less emotionally connected to it.

And ultimately, this was *my* real *reason* and the ultimate motive to start writing about Sokollu Mehmed Pasha: when I had studied everything I could find about the life and times of this interesting man, and all of that was still not enough to convince me to start writing (those other two possible books were still in play), one thing made the essential difference. I had found undeniable evidence (manuscripts and drawings, comments and descriptions from several sources) that around 1575 Mehmed-pasha had built in Belgrade, among other things, a famous caravansary and market place *right under the foundations of the building where I was living then, in 2005, and where I live to this very day!* Of all places, right in that very spot. A coincidence? When I say 'built' I mean that it was built according to his wishes and orders, and that he was the one who financed the project: the patron. The construction work was carried out by an architect-builder, in this case probably a man named Sinan.

After this discovery, whether I wanted to or not, whether it was pretentious or not, I felt the call to write something about these two people in one body. The question of double identity attracted me at the beginning exclusively as a problem of the dual national identity and religion of an individual. And with the entrance of Sinan the builder into Mehmed Pasha's life, there was the possibility of a double identity in *two men*. Thus, the double identity of *two people in one body* at once could have multiple meanings: it was even possible to divide the separate individuals into two personalities, but it was also possible that the complete (or even partial) similarity between two people led them to melt into one!

Now, back to my address. The foundations of this building in the Dorćol district of Belgrade, were laid beginning in 1914 (again, the First World War!) according to the design of Petar Bajalović, and the building was completed in 1924 in the so-called Serbian-Byzantine style with elements of the Wiener Secession, which is a rarely used combination in the architecture of Belgrade. It could be called *the place from which*

I speak, both in the literal and in the symbolic sense. If I would add to that the sense of writing, liberated, and here and there my own impudent attitude, then I could add something else as well. The historical heritage of Ottoman-Islamic architecture left behind by Sinan is not the only connection between the past and present. There are others: for example, the *wordplay* of the Serbian names Bajo/Bajica – a future vizier of Turkey, the most powerful empire at the peak of its might while he was alive – with the surnames of the Serbian architect of my building, Bajalović, and the author of this book – V. B. (whose surname, after its Germanisation by Maria Theresa in Vojvodina long ago, was closer to Bajalović's surname than to Bajica's name). Then, the fact that my home rests on the remains of that 'enemy' culture of the time, with its modern address being the 'Street of Emperor Dušan', named after a Serbian ruler from the 14th century, called 'the *Great*', who made Serbia the greatest it had been in its history, not only territorially speaking, just as Suleiman the *Magnificent* did for Turkey with the zealous aid of Bajica/Sokollu Mehmed Pasha two centuries later. Thus, that is *the building from which I speak*, whose square tower at the very top carries an inscription, in large letters, saying that it belongs/belonged to the Society of St. Sava (the *greatest* of Serbian Saints, and also the most important secular figure).

History especially favours the *greatest*, the *strongest*, the *most powerful* and all the other 'mosts'. This book, however, has a different purpose: to ask, for instance, whether any of these 'mosts' from the preceding paragraph ever came into conflict here, did they meet? And why? If the answer to any of those is 'yes', then the book asks how, and what happened before that, and after that, then again how, and perhaps even why... In this case, even the *name* of the place where these thoughts occur to me, the Dorćol district of Belgrade, is of Turkish origins (*Dort-jol*), suggesting even linguistically and literally that this is (was) a place of meeting, of gathering and remaining, because in Turkish it marks *four roads* or, if you will, the *crossroads*.

In summary: this *book* deals with gathering the probable and certainly the ephemeral.

Meanwhile, *history* still stands steady as a monument.

BEFORE THE END

By moving his family from the small town to his brother's place in the village, his father thought that they were saved from the Turkish menace; that gathering up of small Serbian children to send to various parts of Turkey, and even to the court, in order to make elite soldiers of the Empire out of them. However, he did not know that the Herzegovinian, Sandžakbey Skender Ornosović, had been given orders from Constantinople that every few years he was to trawl Bosnia and Herzegovina and 'to collect a *thousand* children in the 'blood tribute' and take them to the palaces…'[1] And that had meant an additional problem: in order to fulfil such a high quota of specially gifted children, which had been increased after the capture of Belgrade in 1521 due to heavy losses in the siege, the bey had to gather up older children as well, which had not been usual practice before that time. Just how strictly this duty was being enforced could be seen by the persistence with which, this time, he did not pardon the parents who hid their children in the forests, or even those who intentionally maimed their offspring because they thought that the Empire would not need them that way. Even in these drastic cases, the agas did not desist. They even visited the monasteries and took young men who were preparing for monkhood away from their books. Among them was Bajo Sokolović, taken by force back to the village of Sokolovići from the monastery of Mileševa; an Orthodox theologian far from being a child, a tall young man almost eighteen years old. In addition to his learnedness, there was a single factor that also went in his favour: he came from a noble family and therefore especially desirable for the tribute in blood. The fact that he had studied the Christian word of God was also not a barrier for the Ottomans. At one moment his Father Dimitrije found out just how special his case was: the head captain, Mehmed-bey, admitted that a special order had been given so that his Bajica would be taken by the tribute to the capital of the empire. Comforting him by saying that his son was destined for an important place and even more important works, he told him that the proof of that was that Bajica had been asked for by a certain Sokolović who had been taken away in an Imperial caravan some twenty years before. That man's name was now Deli Husrev-pasha. His younger brother had also gone not long ago, and was now called Mustafa. Husrev had advanced very quickly at the sultan's court, arriving at a position where, as a pasha, he could make important decisions as well.

All of these were additional reasons why his father and his cousin – a monk of Mileševo – together with the leader of that monastery, Božidar Goraždanin, could convince none of the agas not to take Bajica away, not even with their pleas or their money. In the end, he had to comfort himself as a parent with the fact that they left his two younger sons with him: the Turks kept firmly to their own rule that only one male child could be taken from a given home.

Though nothing, of course, could lessen the pain of their parting, it might be said that it was hardest for Bajica. He was the only one *leaving*, everyone dear to him was *remaining* together, so that they were at least partially protected from the heavy weight of loneliness that he was carrying as they said their good-byes. In addition, being forced to leave his home, he was driven into the *unknown* while his entire family remained *where they belonged*.

On the long journey through Serbia and Bulgaria, he was only able to think about all that he was leaving behind, and of all the things that yet awaited him. The first drove him to tears, the second caused him to be afraid.

Completely exhausted by his continual crying that occasionally broke into wailing, and then into sighs, deep and loud, at one point he finally ran out of tears – there simply were no more. He could go on crying only within himself.

If he only knew then what a huge part of his life he would actually spend like that – within himself – perhaps it would have comforted him. If he had perchance said publicly and out loud *at the end* of his life that he had spent the largest part of his life within himself – no one would have believed him. And why would they? His life was an example of living to a ripe old age, despite being cut short. At the same time, his life was so public and important that any other life, or anyone else's life, could not even draw close in comparison.

The ruler's every move was so highly visible to the general public and to every individual in the empire that the regularity of making public decrees, acts and appearances, the making of proclamations, travelling, going to war, receiving high dignitaries, punishing the disobedient, frequent hunting trips and Lord knows what else, all made it seem that the great vizier had no time to do anything for himself, much the less to have a private life. Yet, of course, he had more than enough time to be his own person. The frequency of his public duties (of which, in truth, a large part was done by the servile apparatus of the empire, and not by him personally), and especially the constant linking of his name to everyone and everything, made it seem that each time his name was mentioned he was actually physically present there as well and built the illusion that he was omnipresent. If such a thing were allowed, probably some of his loyal subjects would even have felt sorry for him. Yet this omnipresence fuelled stories about the ruler's doubles: the high visibility of a single person could only be created by replicating him, and since that was not possible, stories were invented that the ruler had doubles. Later, the reasons for the ruler's simultaneous appearance in several places at once were expanded to include his avoidance of assassination.

Yet on his journey, the pack train of horses and people that drew out in front and behind him to the horizon helped him to begin to gather his thoughts. In the first place, it was clear that he could never return again. Escape was hardly feasible, and even if he managed, he wondered what he would do with that kind of freedom. The new masters of his fate knew who he was; he had not reached this place as a child found by accident, but rather as a carefully selected young man, with a name, a surname and a pedigree. His departure for the Turkish Empire was actually decreed. He was indeed taken abroad, not to *vanish* but rather to *vanquish*. He needed to be smart and practical. His own father had advised him to make the best of the whole situation, and to even try to profit from it.

He prayed that God would not forsake him. He prayed that his memory would not betray him. At this moment, 'being his own man' meant 'remember everything'. As time went by, his memories slipped from his conscious into his physical self and thus built the organic memory that makes one what one actually is – in truth, the stuff one is made of. He had to be afraid of *forgetting*. He thought that if he forgot, he would cease to exist. He did not know that the body is able to read like the mind does: at that moment, in order to defend him from the new, it was actually reading through his entire childhood, his language, his faith, his parents, his brothers and sisters, his time in the monastery cell, and storing all of that in the farthest reaches of his body, preparing the messages of that language for a kind of hibernation, however long it might take. In that way, his memory could *last* with certainty.

It was only with the passing of time that he began to understand why his new hosts, at the same time masters and owners – did not have to worry about how much he and the other children with him would forget or not forget of what they had left behind. The tempo of events that followed and the sheer volume of new commitments would resolve that problem all by themselves.

CHAPTER I

When writing a book with at least a partial background of historical facts, it is almost impossible to avoid mystification, accidental though it might be. For example, when I thought through about all the coincidences that occurred as I wrote this book, it turned out that I started writing my novel about Mehmed-pasha Sokollu at the precise moment marking five-hundred years since the birth of his 'first half', that is Bajica Sokolović, in 1505. I thought to myself, well alright, I will incidentally be the single individual who will celebrate such an important anniversary, which passed with only the minimum of public interest.

Visiting for a while in Turkey in that jubilee year, I also did not notice that anyone paid any particular attention to the anniversary, either. It was as if this unique opportunity was given to me to subtly mark the occasion by writing about it, at first for myself, and later for the general public. Because, by the time this book is published, the anniversary will no longer be timely, in fact it won't even exist. Why, indeed, even as I write this, the time has (already!) run out. Thus, a celebratory mood ought to be kept under control or should at least be hidden by coincidence – a fortunate turn of events that it was overshadowed by another celebration – the coming of the New Year.

A party turned into a commemoration.

An anniversary replaced by New Year.

Mehmed-pasha disguised as Santa Claus!

A true possibility that seems like a joke. Cynical humour created by circumstances rather than the writer's talent. Like when a writer works without an outline and yet ends up with *a novel without substance*.

The big question is: what is coincidence in writing? The writer loves to displace, invent, augment, to multiply and then divide, organise, borrow... but above all he loves to intertwine. And when he does, then everything is possible. That is why his possible guilt for incidental (mis)deeds of which he is not even aware can be forgiven like the transgressions of a child. First of all, because those (mis)deeds occur accidentally and incidentally; they were not the goal but are simply there without forethought. Secondly, because their consequences can hardly be so dramatic that they are irreparable. And even if they are irreparable, they are not far-reaching. Thirdly, because the basic idea still remains as the centre of attention – the misdeeds are concomitant. Finally, does any one really take a writer seriously and at his word? That is another additional reason, if not also a justification, for why he is allowed to intertwine things so easily. And not to be held responsible.

Here is an example of such a (mis)deed: in the chapters that are supposed to be dealing with the present (like this one), at least for now, I keep having conversations with myself! Is that good or bad? Perhaps in the end I will realise that it is, after all, good for the book, although I doubt it at the moment. Why don't I allow the heroes to head down their paths, to – as they say – develop? Well, perhaps it is not their time. And on the other hand... it so happens that I am one of those heroes (the one with the initials V.B.). Am I not developing as a character through this very same dialogue with myself? Hasn't the reader begun quite clearly to make certain conclusions about him (me)? I mean, the reader should be drawing certain conclusions. If they don't draw them, who will?

CHAPTER 1

They stopped in Jedrene, or Edirne in Turkish, the famous imperial winter residence and former capital city.

After a rest, the caravan with its large number of children continued on toward the interior of the country. Bajica, along with a small group of a hundred or so, was detained at Edirne. The beauty of the place and the sheer luxury of the exterior of the caravansary occupied their attention and their thoughts. They almost forgot all the difficulties and the length of the journey they had just made. Before them lay their first life challenge, which they could not be aware of, nor could they clearly place it for themselves; they were merely comparing where they came from to where they had arrived, and as of yet they still had not even had the chance to see the second courtyard, much the less the third courtyard inside the caravansary.

Their senses were already overwhelmed, and no one had even offered them anything.

They were sent to the soldiers' barracks, which lay next to the room belonging to the Sultan's guard. A few guards were assigned to them – keepers who spoke Serbian, but who addressed them in it only insofar as their service demanded: they were not allowed to say anything privately, much less to offer any sort of explanation. Each of the future courtiers was supposed to understand by himself however much he was able to.

In the census books, in addition to the existing facts brought from Bosnia and Serbia, their new Turkish names were entered. Bajo Sokolović became Mehmed Sokollu. They were ordered to respond only to their new names from then on. They began learning Turkish immediately. Their lessons were based on the gradual learning of the basics of communication, but they also included concepts that they had to learn by rote, with the explanation that these things would be clarified later, when they began to study the Qur'an. Their language classes went on all day, interrupted only by physical exercise and scanty meals. Before falling asleep, Baja still called himself Bajica, but this would not last long: completely exhausted like all the others, he would go to sleep instantly.

The first months went by like a whirlwind. As soon as they had mastered their new language enough to communicate without difficulty (while in the presence of their teachers and supervisors, they also had to speak it among themselves), they began to read and write intensively. And even though it existed from early on, a clearly visible selection was now conceived: those who proved to be among the best were chosen to study various fields of scholarship and to enter them quickly, broadly and profoundly. Then they were immediately tested on the things they had learned and sorted into groups according to ability. One thing was common and clear to all of them; that their training was subjugated to the one and the same goal – that they were all to serve one master and him alone. Within that framework they were fit into various positions, but those were only nuances in relation to the unifying submissiveness and to the resulting blind and united fealty.

The Imam of Edirne converted them to Islam in a ritual, a humble and highly simplified ceremony. They were also circumcised. Only then were they able to attain true religious and spiritual knowledge, along with vigorous and varied military training. Before long the breadth and length of their combat exercises was completely matched by the time spent in lectures on Islam, in the study of the Holy Qur'an and in their community prayers. Bajica felt like they were making a super-man of him, capable and competent for all sorts of exploits of the body, mind and soul. He did not waste his strength on resistance; it was clear to him that through opposition he would not manage to ward off the inevitable. In that way, he at least had the comfort (or the illusion) that he was participating in the decision making process of his acceptance, without knowing if it was it forced or voluntary?

It was as if he was thinking in Turkish, but dreaming Serbian. Thus translating himself from one language into the other and vice-versa, it seemed that he was preparing his very essence to be the eternal guardian of the boundary between dreams and reality. Maintaining his balance on such a sharp edge, as time went by, it began to remind him of the skill of the tightrope walker at the bazaar. As the height increased, the danger of the fall grew as well, and of its consequences, but the profit from his possible success also rose. Actually these contradictions were the essence of his present, and also future – and therefore entire – life, were they not?

The choice was completely limited: he could allow the mainstream to carry him, or he could attempt to step out of it while yet knowing that there was no salvation in it; giving up would not send him home. He would only be forced into the worst possible life conditions as a common slave, all opportunities for change removed, much less for advancement or success. By obeying others' decisions about his life, he ensured for himself some kind of possibility that, somewhere in the future he would take over responsibility for decisions about that same life. His life.

CHAPTER II

The time of wars made in the territory of my former homeland has passed, hopefully, never to return. But not enough time has passed to wash away the consequences. One of them, naive only at first glance, consists of a new and persistent phenomenon of the vulgar exchange of quality for quantity, for example – turning literature into mathematics. Let me explain. Since the transition period of society among the uneducated is also taken as the attempt to express everything in numbers, then as a by-product of 'the establishment of primary capital' as it is called by those who rob the people and the government, it shows up as the need to give everything a rank. Of course, ranking is done – with numbers. For the money addicts, the only measures of value are (and always were) numbers. So, top-lists of everything existing have been made. Whatever subject you chose, you could express it in terms of the comparison of its ranking to *whatever else* you might have chosen.

Even in publishing and literature, numbers of all kinds began to show up: even numbers that expressed the numbers of copies of a printed book and the number of editions for a particular title. Such totals have always been around but, while they are quite important for publishing, they were never decisive, unchallengeable or divine. They were simply there, as a normal part of a whole make-up of various elements, including numbers as well, that constitutes a book and its life.

However, these other numbers that appeared after the fact in the transition, were excessive: for example, the number that marks the place a book *took* on the top-list of the most popular, most sold, most read, most modern and so forth... On the surface, *winning* a place through the democratic method. But, this was an illusion. The feeling is irresistible: the transition is being constructed through the use of numbers, by the *theft* of places.

And the measurements went on and on: how many weeks a book

was on the top-list, how many editions as a hardcover, as a paperback, as re-bound, in gold-leaf covers, absurd covers, ending in covering the eyes of the reader. And then, which place it held the week before, for how many weeks, how many votes it received, and if the voting was done electronically – how many 'hits' there had been on the voting website. Then the comparisons: all of the data about a book translated from a foreign language compared with the numbers in other countries. Then, the whole thing one more time.

There are also hidden numbers that never reach the public: agreements, binding contracts, the deadline for a writer to hand in her or his manuscript, how many pages she or he can or must write (not more, not less), percentages of possible profits in all possible situations for every party in the contract, and that means more than just the writer and publisher. Even what will happen in unforeseen circumstances is foreseen.

Non-fulfilment of the binding elements of such contracts can also be expressed in numbers: from punitive points to percentage losses. This kind of mathematics is even stronger than death. Seventy years after the author's death, the calculation remains the same: everything continues to be calculated, added, subtracted, multiplied and divided. It is fortunate that books outlive their authors, but the calculations never give up: they follow the author into the other world and do not allow him to rescind his rights. That *post-mortem* portion of time is called *happy mathematics*.

The arguments have still not come to a head – *for* and *against* this marriage and all like it, between literature and mathematics. The reason is simple, though it is not visible. Namely, in the transition, intellectuals lost their social and also cultural significance, which caught them off guard, then confused them, degraded them and pretty well marginalised them. To all of that change of status of their former significance was also added a new and cruel poverty. In such a pre-depressive state, some of the people in the world of literature and publishing became morally and materially corruptible. Popularly, they were called 'mathematicians'.

Yet, perhaps all of that would not have been so tragic had it not also caused a change in certain features and parts of their character. In combination with the question of nation, ethnic belonging, language issues, newfound independence and so on, the intellectual ultimately arrived at the problem of identity. And when it arrived at that point, the destruction and construction, construction and destruction started. Of identity. And of everything else.

CHAPTER 2

Martial arts could also be a mask for many of the other things they were subjected to: in what appeared to be a simple and quite cruel school of physical confrontation, they learned many spiritual skills. For example, in order to accept courage as part of his character, he first had to interpret cowardice; it was only after he had mastered that consciously that he could begin learning how to liberate himself of it. Then he could dare to call that new state of mind part of his personality.

Generally speaking, the crucial moment of the entire training was this very understanding between body and soul. Once he realised the connection, he was able to establish values much more easily and quickly. It was a natural consequence. The interrelationship of cowardice and courage, for example, resulted in the understanding of subordination and super-ordination. Fear retreated in the face of challenge, yet their teachers then raised them to a higher phase of penetrating the psychological barrier: they claimed that fear could also produce courage. And that it might be even more fierce than usual! They went so far as to enter those processes and prove the veracity of such teaching by their own examples.

These were the ways to understand the goal more correctly: they were not trying to make a superhuman of him (as he first thought) by implanting something foreign in him, but rather to bring to the surface the maximum that he had inside himself and to use it as efficiently and exhaustively as possible. It was as if they wanted to re-shape him into a whole person.

In truth, the latter was only true for Bajica and a few other young men from the group. No one else had to tell them that they were predestined for special assignments; they attended many of the lessons without the other boys. However, as a consequence of this separation and of so much time spent together, and probably also because of the stronger feeling of security in community, several of them began to develop a strange, perhaps also redemptive, newly found friendship; indeed, clandestinely so because they did not dare to show it openly. Up until one particular moment.

Even after several years of residence in the caravansary at Edirne, Bajica had never once managed to see his master. The Sultan was occupied with other business in other places. Even when he came to Edirne, however, the ruler would never see them at all, because as he drew near to the caravansary all the boys would be closed up in the training rooms and kept under strict control so that no one outside would ever see them as long as the ruler was staying there. The Sultan, they were told, was regularly informed about the advancement of the future keepers of the empire, because he was quite seriously and constantly interested in their destiny. Proof of this was the sudden appearance in the court of his emissary, Deli Husrev-pasha, one day. His was a face they were allowed to see.

For that guest and host in one, the public display of some of the skills and knowledge of the young students of the empire was immediately organised, according to official protocol and with the wearing of formal clothing, as part of an entire ceremony. They amazed him with their knowledge of Persian and Arabic, of history, and by the number of learned and recited sutras from God's revelation to Mohammed.

The pasha gave them a speech at the end, as they were assembled in front of him. And then, dismissing the others, he invited the ten of them who were special in every way to come into the inner court of the caravansary, telling them that they deserved to see some of the sultan's rooms. When they stopped in one of them, seemingly important because of its lack of furniture and decoration, the pasha told them,

"When our master gathers the viziers at Edirne, this is where the imperial Dīvān meets to decide about important matters of state. And up there, near the top of this wall, right next to the ceiling where you see that small screened window, behind its curtain sits the Sultan, listening from above to the work of his viziers."

"Just as Allah watches all of us from above," Bajica blurted out, at which most of his comrades looked at him in amazement: some with annoyance, some with approval.

However, the real amazement came when Deli Husrev-pasha dismissed his escorts and the boys' guardians, and led them to the outer court, where he spoke to the boys in Serbian!

"You have proven to be good students of the empire. When I report that I am satisfied to our ruler, that will mean that you all will soon begin to head off in different directions, based on the detailed information given about each of you by your teachers and supervisors. You will be assigned to various jobs in different parts of the world."

There was a pause.

Then he approached one of Bajica's companions, now known as Mustafa, and suddenly hugged him and said to him gently,

"My brother."

The boy was confused, not comprehending what was happening, afraid that he had perhaps not heard the pasha correctly. The pasha then whispered something for several moments to him, and then he put his arm around Bajica's shoulder and whispered to him,

"He's my brother, but he's also your cousin."

Then he once again addressed the group,

"It is clear to you that I am also one of your people. I was brought here just like you. From Herzegovina a full twenty years ago. I am of the Sokolović family, and I requested some of you be brought here. I'm now seeing my younger brother for the first time since he was born. Isn't that wild and wonderful?"

Mustafa looked at him, his eyes and mouth wide open. Bajica observed him in no less amazement. To hear, from these lips, after all this time, their own surname, not quite forgotten but completely suppressed!

The pasha's whole story, they understood, was aimed at encouraging them to not back out on the chance they were given to get as good an education as possible, to use what they were offered to the greatest possible extent and, when the time came, to utilise all of that to meet their own goals – whatever they might be and whenever they might become known. He showed a measure of intimacy, touched by their presence and overwhelmed with feelings. He tried to be clear, but he was careful not to reveal too much. And each of them understood, without being told, that they should help and support each other as much as possible, using every opportunity offered to them. That they should never forget where they came from, but they should also never shy from what was awaiting them. If they were already destined to have a given past, but a different future, they were to create and retain something from it that would, either in secret or visibly, make them different from all the others. Only in that way would they be able to maintain peace in themselves and with themselves. He emphasised that, if they were not conscious of the duality into which they had been cast, they would never be able to withstand even one of the trials awaiting them.

"Whoever among you manages to rise above his own duality will turn misfortune into an advantage. To not have either of your parents is a real tragedy. To have both is great happiness, but it should be remembered each and every day. Perhaps it seems to you now that you have no parents, but very soon you will see that you have both of them."

The pasha's speech helped Bajica to come up with his first, youthful piece of wisdom: if something cannot be avoided, then it must be confronted.

One strange consequence of Deli Husrev-pasha's was that after his departure, this handful of chosen lads began to openly speak Serbian among themselves, respecting their own unspoken rule that they did so only outside of their training, but no longer trying to hide it. And just imagine – no one objected, and certainly no one tried any longer to forbid it! Why would they? The time was inevitably coming, and they knew this very well, when they would be disbanded and there would be nobody to speak Serbian with.

CHAPTER III

From its over-use during schooling, I have an aversion to the definition of anything. Yet, continuing with the topic of the melding of literature and maths (another school word that introduced children into the sphere of operations with numbers), I developed an irresistible urge to define money. And this is the conclusion I came to: money is a value expressed in numbers. It may seem that such a conclusion does not require a lot of intelligence. Couldn't we say the same thing about, for instance, time: years are a value expressed in numbers. Ha! Precisely, just as many other things could be expressed with the exact same definition. But that's not the point. If it is true that this 'wisdom' can be applied to many other concepts and phenomena, that does not mean that the original definition is not correct nor does it annul the existence of things.

What do I want to say? Well, that value cannot be equated with quality. Therefore, there is a different meaning in the claim 'money is a value expressed in numbers' and 'money is quality expressed in numbers'. Now we are getting to the so-called crux of the matter: imagine when certain writers give in and equate the system of value expressed in numbers (the place held by their book on the top-list, let's say) with the quality of their book. You do not know which is harder to forgive: the vanity of the writer or the creators of those monstrous apparatuses – the top-lists.

Yet such phenomena would not be worrisome if they remained at the level of phenomena. However, they move on to becoming the focus, with the aim of becoming the rule and the natural order of things. No longer incidental or ephemeral, their goal is to become, and remain, a lasting value: quantity is equal to quality.

But how does this look in practice? Recently I was invited to a presentation by a popular authoress defending numbers. In order to prove that her first-place ranking on the list of most read books was unquestionable in every way, she compared herself with the most highly regarded writers of the century! Of course, in her ego-research she did not seek or find any corresponding numbers like, for example, the places held by the books of those respected writers in the top-lists of the time. True, she could not find them because at that time such lists did not even exist, because they were also not necessary. Writers then held their positions based on merit, and they did not mark them numerically. I guess my message is clear. Our writer was offended because earlier someone had publicly dared to challenge her claim that the first place is also the place of the best. She confused this formula with another, rather enticing one: that the first place is also the best one.

And let there be no mistake: the first place may be the best place, but that does not in any way mean that it is the place of the best.

CHAPTER 3

Several months later, the greatest and most important consequence of the pasha's visit (it turned out he had been spying on them) was the arrival of His Majesty in person among the boys of the blood tribute. Perhaps it would be more correct to say that, this time, they were allowed to stand before the great sultan. His generosity amounted to having the patience to look the group up and down once, to wave his hand indicating that they were to be at ease, and to sit on the couch and allow the ten of them to be introduced individually. This was done by their teacher-aga, as was his right, and Deli Husrev-pasha as a man from the ruler's escort, and therefore a man of special trust.

The pasha spoke with unfathomable self-confidence about each of the boys individually: from where he was brought, from what kind of family, the things he had shown special talent for during his studies and where, in the pasha's opinion, he should continue his schooling and his service. Thus, it was in front of the Sultan that Bajica found out that his destiny was planned to be closely connected to the supreme ruler: the imperial caravansary in Istanbul!

For one brief moment he had the chance to glimpse the Sultan's looking at him; and it made his blood run cold. In the Sultan he saw an odd combination of lethargy and interest, but above all, an icy coldness born from the ubiquity of his power: from questions concerning the tiny destinies of individuals to the shaping of the future of entire tribes or states. On the other hand, the soldier in him was not so sleepy that he did not show interest in these educated slaves upon whom, tomorrow, his life might depend. Bajica was taught that all the children brought here, from Janissary soldier to future high councillors to the emperor, were assigned an equally deserved, identical role with regard to the Sultan. In time, the Sultan, depending on how and when he got close to them, would have more trust in them than in any other military formation. His very life would depend on their loyalty, both individual and collective. But so would their own lives. They would be a shield against all others, both outside and inside the empire. And he would be theirs.

Bajica thought through all of that in the days that followed. After he had sifted through all the other impressions, the one thing that remained most important was that he, Bajica, was no longer hidden from the emperor! Now knew that he meant something to them. Perhaps this was the recognition he received for his acceptance of the foreign. In exchange for that acceptance, he would be given privileges and not be condemned to a slave's life; though no one would ever be able to free him from his slave status, not even the Sultan himself.

What he had now been offered, was the chance to be the perfect slave.

CHAPTER IV

Numbers applied to literature and books sometimes take on humorous characteristics and bring about absurd consequences. At a recently held local book fair, the organiser published a ranking of all the participants in the national press. There were a lot of things written in that missive, but the only thing that was not were the criteria used to rank the publishers: they were the 'best' of something, but no one knew at what. And then, after serious analysis and search for the reasons for not citing the essential criterion, it became clear that this detail was not even important as long as they were the 'best'.

The time has come, or the place has been reached, for me to quote myself from the beginning of this book: 'history loves the *largest*, the *strongest*, the *most powerful* and everything *the most*. This book, however, has a different purpose…'

That is why this book remains in the margins, on a side-track, while history allows the eternal values of popular ranking to be set alongside its stolid and dignified monuments. The popular stage[2] is sly, it uses the weakness of history to reward all sorts of victors (even toward the fake, insignificant, grotesque…), and thus easily snuggles up to it. It whispers compliments to history that skilfully help win its heart. And charm is part of *the place from where one speaks*: in the so-called popular entertainment business, that place is called a podium, and in political activities – the stage.

It was only the social and economic transition process of individual European states that finally showed the dangerous similarity between politics (as future history) and popular entertainment skills (as the eternal now). That similarity, tried, tested and carried to the level of perfect impudence, or impudent perfection, proved to be the ideal union of forces joined against the book. Catchwords were quickly created, along with the interfacing of populism and elitism. And since it was selectively intended for a small number of people, it worked against democracy which is, it goes without saying, intended for a large number of people, if not for everyone. There you have it – transitional dialectics!

The fact that, included in world heritage, there are books that arrive in the present from the past which are certain to survive in the immediate and perhaps distant future, only solidified the positioning of the attacker and the argument for the long-lasting.

The battle between the day-long and even slightly longer turned into the battle of the loud against the quiet (the latter being that way because of proper upbringing and not because of fear), the voice of secrecy against the *vox populi*, of insult versus tolerance, of the aggressive against the customary, of war against peace.

Who will achieve victory? Well, the victors.

Hopefully we've learned that much.

CHAPTER 4

After the Sultan's departure from Edirne, Bajica began to think again about Husrev-pasha's previous visit. He was attracted by the pasha's careful preparation for a successful welcome; setting the stage for the Sultan's arrival. Everything had been done so that nothing would surprise the ruler, inconvenience him, or even disappoint him; but rather that each detail would await him as something expected, familiar and certain, in order to convince him that everything that happened was under control. Bajica realised that all this happened according to a *plan* made by the pasha. Furthermore, he concluded that the ability to foresee events was of exceptional importance for those in power: if one could only foresee all the possibilities, whether national or personal, and then make decisions that matched the possibilities and goals with the needs of a situation, then one could also determine the path to achieving those goals. This could, therefore, be called planning. Or politics.

In precisely the same way, one could avoid all the undesirable consequences of future actions. By choosing what he anticipates, a man can avoid making mistakes, unnecessarily wasting time, and thereby – if a decision of state is at stake – losing too much money, too many human lives or even too much territory. This same approach, if used without explanation in front of people who were not aware of the background, could seem like prophesying:

If one knows *what* will happen, one also knows *what attitude to take* toward the event.

What he now termed as Deli Husrev-pasha's 'spying' visit, could be divided into two subcategories. The capacity for planning was one of them, and publicly showed the ruler's power over events. It perhaps even reflected the wisdom with which all human relationships can be resolved, from incidental encounters at the bazaar to those among rulers and entire countries.

The second category was perhaps less transparent and was certainly not for the public. It had the intention of revealing faults rather than qualities, looking for the mistakes made during the visit rather than the successes. It looked for the vulnerable places so that, if it ever became necessary, they could be used. Like a sabre hanging above a victim's head that, at any moment and for any reason, could suddenly drop. It would be like an enduring document written in indelible ink, stored in an invisible place from where it could be made public easily, quickly and at any time.

This must be the path toward the creation of the superior individual and a noble empire. He decided, whenever it was possible, to attempt to 'spy' on himself. Both secretly and in public.

It was only much later, when the remarkably more subtly veiled knowledge about ruling a country became available to him, that he realised just how correctly he had sensed the importance of this kind of spying; recognised for the first time, with the seemingly accidental intertwining of events and the destiny of individuals and entire peoples.

CHAPTER V

What would it be like if certain words, expressions or phrases from the current political glossary were applied to literary language? Here is one of my favourite words: *sustainable*, to which is added the necessary element, in truth, something to do with the future. Now, just imagine what kind of tomfoolery comes about when this sort of sustainability is used to augment the word 'history'.

It is very important for us to know, according to the interpretations of European political institutions, what accompanying instrumentation goes along with such an artificial phrase. Along with them, most often a sort of intimidation occurs: if you do *a* and *b*, you will receive *y* and *z*, in which case your project is *sustainable*. That is the essential meaning. Certainly none of the authors of this explanation would ever admit this, but would rather talk about fulfilling various long-term conditions, not because they are blackmailing you, but rather because of the very success of the project. More succinctly, they would explain to you that, when deciding to support a program, they create a projection about its realistic future, about its ability to last and its most certain survival. Where is the truth in all that? It could be said – most likely somewhere in between the two explanations. However, it is not. It is actually closer to blackmail because, for the negation of this extortion, there is this exceptionally logical explanation which is not only partially true, but is also ideal for manipulation. It is not bogus in itself, but it simply begs to be augmented.

I would like to cite an example from one of the most authoritative (French) books on the Ottoman Empire, an anthology of texts by about twenty world famous experts, specialists not only for certain periods but also for given topics from this field, all under the direction of a man of indubitable authority, one can find a manipulation of facts in the section entitled 'Administering the Empire' with its extension in the chapter 'The Levers of Power':

'The system was characterised by the exceptionally ethnic variegation of the ruling class in the Empire. Among forty-seven grand viziers (during the reign of eleven sultans – *note V.B.*) who ruled between 1453 and 1623, only five were of Turkish origins.'

Few people know of this shocking, mathematical puzzle (this time buried in history, and only later in literature): that the strongest empire for centuries on the soil of Asia and a good part Europe and Africa could so easily and consistently put the greatest power in the hands of people who *were not* even of its ethnic background, and most often not even (originally) of its religion! If nothing else, this fact in and of itself demands that we stop to give pause in the quotation, doesn't it? Then the fire gets turned up:

'Among others there were eleven Albanians, six Greeks, one Circassian, an Armenian, a Georgian and an Italian, while ten of them were of unknown origins.'

After some quick addition it is clear that this is far less than the sum of forty-seven grand viziers. So where are the other eleven? What was their background if they were not among the Turks or *any of the other* ethnic groups cited, or even among those 'ten of unknown origins'?

Reading on in the same passage, there's another infuriating anomaly: 'The grand vizier Mehmed-pasha Sokolović, the Sultan's own *kul*,[3] a Serb from Bosnia, proved to be loyal to his roots when he built religious endowments in his home country or when he made the renovation possible of the Serbian Patriarchate in Peć in 1557.'

Here we have one more grand vizier, non-existent in the previous calculations! Now we are only missing ten! But I would like to suggest that the authors of the study did know who those viziers were as well. We just do not know whether this one that we discovered belongs to the 'ten of unknown origins' or to the other ten that are missing from the total. Obviously, the authors know everything they need to about Sokolović, yet they first denied his existence as a grand vizier, and then already *in the very next paragraph* of the same book, wrote him in. This leads one to believe they also know about the others, and to question why they have also left them out.

I, for example, know about at least one more of those 'non-existent' viziers, because that vizier was also a Serb by background. His name was Rüstem-pasha Opuković. He was born in 1500 in Bosnia, not far from Sarajevo and held the position of grand vizier *twice*: from 1544 to 1553 and from 1555 to his death in 1561. Twice – unusual and rare, and especially easy to remember. He was invested as the grand vizier of the empire personally by Suleiman the Magnificent after a conflict between the Grand Vizier Hadim Suleiman-pasha (the namesake of the Sultan) and another vizier, Deli Husrev-pasha (who was, as we already know, also a Serb by origins). The Sultan punished both of them by divesting them and expelling them from the capital. Thus, the authors of the study pass right over one of the grand viziers from the time of the most powerful sultan of the Ottoman Empire, who was at the very height of his imperial strength from the very beginning. The man to whom as a wife the Sultan gave his own favourite daughter Mihrimah, born out of his happy and everlasting love with Hürrem (formerly a slave-girl named Roxelana, the daughter of a Russian Orthodox priest!).

We could perhaps put these omissions down to forgetfulness, lack of knowledge, or coincidence, but if I were a believer in conspiracy theories, I would claim, or leave room for the possibility, that the remaining grand viziers erased in the anthology were Serbs – each and every one!

So, there is some homework for those with nothing better to do.

The missing viziers could also be of any one of the other ethnic backgrounds, as long as they exist!

And again it seems that mathematics in history can be almost as successful as it is in literature. Yet we remain with the question: what shall we do with sustainable lies?

CHAPTER 5

In spite of the quite visible outward sameness in their studies and behaviour, Bajica could clearly see differences in the way the boys around him accepted the teachings of Islam. The first to stand out was a group who had arrived in Edirne a few years earlier. Among them was Mustafa, Deli Husrev-pasha's brother. These boys were very careful that their revolt against Islam did not surface in front of their teachers and guardians, but they did not hide it whatsoever in front of the other students. They said that they could never reject the Christian faith, and they especially liked telling this to Bajica. They felt safe because he was the only one among them to have studied to be an Orthodox monk before being brought here, and indeed he had been brought to Edirne literally from the monastery.

Yet, they were surprised by his reserve, and by his counsel as well. They were probably expecting not only that he would openly and directly support them, but that he would indeed most likely decide to be their leader. To be honest, they were not sure their leader in what; although their inclinations were probably towards rebellion. Surely not in an open one, but rather in a conceptual, clandestine one. Bajica, for his part, confronted them with the fact that they had already changed their faith through their conversion in every possible way: in their pledge – in their words and body, their clothing, food, language and prayers. He supported them in their right to go on believing whatever they wanted, even in the Father, Son and Holy Spirit, but deep within themselves. That right and that secret, he kept telling them, could never be taken away from them by anyone. All other protest against faith in Allah, even if it were only slightly visible in public, would end in the violent loss of their life. Between the two extremes offered – life with Allah and death without him – there were no other possibilities. Only one of those two could be chosen. Of course, they could go on like this, half in secret and half publicly, rejecting faith in the Prophet Mohammed, but in doing so they were, he warned them, each day increasing the danger of betrayal that would come most likely from among their own ranks.

After several discussions, they settled down. They did not accept the foreign faith with their hearts and souls, but they understood that they had no other choice outside that intimate truth, unless they chose to go to their deaths, either by their own hand or someone else's.

It was good that they did not take his words as a defeat, especially when he spoke to them about the feasible duality of belief. He told them that no one could erase his memories either. Even if he wished to erase them himself, how could that be possible? One cannot extinguish a part of one's life by making a *decision*; only life up till now. Nor can life begin on a day of one's choice. It could be seen that they were surprised by these words, but they realised that they were spoken by the wisest among them.

Only then did Bajica figure out that, of all those in this conservative group, Mustafa, Husrev-pasha's younger brother, was set apart for higher education, and that he was the only one among them who was destined to service in the ruler's proximity. Later, he even reminded Mustafa of this, telling him in confidence that they would soon all go their separate ways, and that he alone would remain without anyone else from the rebel group; while some of them might stay together, others might not. He counselled him to be patient and wait for the events that were certain to come and bring change.

He also reminded him that they were related.

CHAPTER VI

When Lord Byron published *The Corsair* in 1814, in just one day of sales, the first day, it sold ten thousand copies. But, since he *did not wish* to capitalise on his writing, in accord with his aristocratic constancy, it was not he who sold the books but *booksellers*. He was of *sustainable* character and did not wish to sell himself. Thus, others got rich off his work, and he continued to get into ever greater debt 'as was fit to his name and reputation', as the charming interpreter of Byron's work, Zoran Paunović, would say.

I would add that this is indeed a case of the sustainable transformation of mathematics into literature. It should be noticed that this is one of the rare examples of that transformation that runs opposite to the normal way.

Oh, yes! I almost forgot (like those famous historians): at approximately the same time as the loss of the above-mentioned money in England, in the Balkans, the Serbs and Turks were losing their lives. The Second Serbian Uprising was being prepared, which is referred to in the west as the 'Second Serbian Revolution'. Dead capital in the west, dead people in the east. Some people were buying the freedom to read with money, and others the freedom to live – with their lives.

Good old Europe, in both cases, was liberating some from slavery and turning others into slaves.

All of this melding of mathematics into history, the overflow of calculations into literature, is actually a preparation for observing the life strategy of nations and states that also see their temporal survival through the prism of attack and defence. It is likewise an introduction to the topic of turning defeat into victory.

I was completely sure that using certain Turkish-Serbian examples from the history of the two peoples, the two states, the two empires – Orhan Pamuk and I could reach some kind of possible truth. And if not a truth, then at least a few new claims or a justifiable presupposition. I felt an irresistible desire for that.

Pamuk won my heart with a sentence that begins rather light-heartedly, but becomes very serious,

"You are persistent with these numbers and the art of writing. I will give you an example, in truth someone else's, of how literature is turned into history, how fiction turns into fact."

Then he quoted Voltaire who, on the occasion of the famous naval battle at Lepanto/Inebahta in 1571 between the Ottoman armada and the united Christian navy, wrote the following sentence which is a prime example of the absurdity of the relationship between truth and its background: "It seemed that the *Turks* were those who *won* the battle of Lepanto." (emphasis mine)

I admit, this quotation was doubly important to me in terms of the credibility of the event, because it entailed one of the rare and undoubtedly drastic military *defeats* of the Ottoman Empire, and at a time when it was at the peak of its power.

I asked Pamuk what he found wrong with this defeat.

"Usually you'd say, one defeat or another, what's the difference? But, in this case, the defeat was not unavoidable. It was stupid to let it happen and, of course, it was absolutely unnecessary. However, the scale was tipped by Ottoman imperial conceit and exaggerated certainty based on previous victories, based especially on the conquering of Cyprus."

"Meaning that the decision-makers were not in agreement."

"That's right. There were careful, wise and experienced men there who opposed an impetuous entry into open battle."

"Who took which side?" I asked.

"The Supreme Commander of the Sultan's navy, Ali-pasha Muezzinzade, managed to get the assent of almost all the members of the viziers' council for the attack, by enthusiastically inflating the greatness and strength of the previous conquests. In addition to all that, he had the support of the Grand Mufti."

"Who was *careful*, who was *wise* and who was *experienced*?" I insisted, knowing very well how adroit Pamuk is in the use of epithets.

"The second vizier of the empire, Pertev Mehmed-pasha, who held the position of senior strategic advisor in the army, was not sure about the information on the strength of the enemy army, especially when united in such a diverse corps. The union was put together in 1571 by the Christian leader Pope Pious V (this time successfully) and it united the Venetian Republic, Spain, Malta and the Italian cities. But Ali-pasha was certain that the infidels would once again be disunited as they had several times before, becoming individually weak, and he did not give in to the *caution* of Pertev pasha. Grand Vizier Mehmed-pasha Sokolović tried to get the battle put off for a year. *Wisdom* urged him to wait until the fleet was better equipped. He had experience with such situations: he was the one who, once upon a time, replaced the legendary Hayreddin Barbarossa in 1546 as the admiral of the Ottoman fleet. Primarily because the man had died, otherwise he never would have dared to even try to be his replacement. However, Sultan Suleiman the Legislator[4] published a decree that was not to be contested. And once he had given in, then he emulated the deeds or pronouncements of his great predecessor in the reasonable rethinking of each of his own decisions. One of them was: never rush, not even into victory!"

"And experienced, who was experienced?" I enticed him further.

"Uluj Ali, the famous pirate, to whom the Sultan had entrusted command over parts of the navy on the basis of his slavish loyalty that had lasted for over fifty years. This brave man had destroyed European vessels for decades in the Mediterranean with exceptional success. But he had two bad sides. One was his strong language (which was sometimes forgiven in the light of his profound *experience*). This time he said the following (overly) poisonous sentences to Ali-pasha Muezzinzade, and that at the moment when he realised that the latter was not backing away from his ill-fated decision: 'Istanbul Turks cannot even begin to imagine the strength of the Christian fleet. To such sheep (let there be no confusion, that's what he called them – the Turks of the capital, not the Europeans! – Pamuk said aside) you have to embellish the news about the numbers and strength of our European enemy so that the truth will get into their heads at least that way!'

"Muezzinzade Ali-pasha, a proud and brave man, was offended by these words and he retorted in kind: 'You want to save the Christians because you were one in your youth! You want to save your Italian homeland!'

"This insult in return had an effect: Uluj Ali fell silent, not wanting his loyalty and courage to fall in to doubt. (His Christian background, besides his sharp tongue, was his other bad side)."

I thought about how clever Ali-pasha was. With these words he insulted both the Grand Vizier and the second vizier at the same time, and in a situation like this one, it seems that this could go unchallenged.

Neither Mehmed-pasha Sokolović nor Pertev Mehmed-pasha reacted to this comment, out of sheer precaution. Had they done so, Serbs by background, together with the already challenged Uluj Ali, they would have seemed like undeniable defenders of their former Christian faith. Ali-pasha was thus shrewd to the point of impudence, depending precisely on such a reaction. As Pamuk went on, this was only confirmed.

"With their silence Sultan Selim made his decision, removing the turban from his head and saying: 'If this turban can cover three heads, then too shall the infidels join forces against me...'"

Pamuk's quote from the Sultan himself made me think about how his charming but comfortable eloquence would cost the empire greatly. The fact that the decision was not made unanimously or easily is hardly any comfort. Although it does, after all, say something about the existence of quite reasonable, stable people at the top of government who preferred all-encompassing forethought.

Unfortunately, and to the detriment of the Ottoman Empire, 'the infidels joined forces'. Going into battle at the Bay of Lepanto, where the Turkish armada had taken refuge to await the enemy, with an incidental plundering of Corfu, Ali-pasha got an additional moral wind under his wings, though just before the beginning of the clash of the two armies, the real wind turned in favour of the Christians.

Pamuk laid out the pre-battle troop-strengths for me:

"Ali-pasha Muezzinzade led a flotilla of 210 galleys, 66 galliots,[5] with about 50,000 oarsmen and sailors, and some 25,000 troops on board. Don Juan de Austria entered the battle with a fleet of 236 galleys and 6 galleasses.[6] On board there were 44,000 oarsmen and sailors, and about 28,000 soldiers. Although they had smaller numbers of vessels and combatants, the Christian army was twice as well armed, both with heavy cannons and with all other sorts of firearms. That's what decided the battle."

"Now tell me about the numbers *after* the battle."

"All right. But I will skip the strategy of the battle. Mind you, it is studied in every detail even today in military schools as an example of the greatest naval battle in history up to that time. So, Ali-pasha's armada lost over 200 ships, of which more than 80 were sunk and 117 were seized. About 25,000 Turkish soldiers and sailors were killed, and 3,500 were captured. From the captured ships, 12,000 Christian slaves were liberated who had been serving as galley slaves.[7] In contrast, the fleet of the Holy League lost only some 15 galleys and had 8,000 dead and 2,500 wounded. Therefore, the Turkish defeat was terrible and complete."

"I reckon that you're quoting me all these numbers to make a point," I beat him to it. "I suppose that the *consequences* of the defeat are the most important?"

"Oh, yes. The shock among the Ottomans was indescribable. Lulled and constantly primed in the self-loving delirium of power, they could not accept even the theoretical possibility of the existence of defeat, much less the fact that it had happened! The news reached the Grand Vizier Sokollu from Pertev-pasha who managed to save his own life by reaching shore. He reported that kaptan derya[8] Ali-pasha Muezzinzade died in the battle and that both of his sons were captured. This letter caught up with Mehmed-pasha at Edirne, where he was accompanying the Sultan and the entire entourage in the autumn hunt. Witnesses say that he pulled out patches of his beard, and that he gave the news to Sultan Selim at the moment when the latter was talking with a dragoman[9] from Dubrovnik. This man reported that, upon receiving the news, the Sultan was left shocked, and then began to show great fear that the victors might turn toward Constantinople. He thus ordered that the Dardanelles be closed off immediately in the best possible way, and that the capital be protected from all possible attack."

"I read that this news caused great disturbance and fear all over Turkey," I told Pamuk. "The people actually experienced – what we would call today – collective stress. Here, I'll actually quote for you the witness in front of whom the Sultan was told the news, the emissary from Dubrovnik who you just mentioned. Because of his being present and having the advantage of speaking the same language as the Grand Vizier Mehmed-pasha, he was able to note down the reaction of the public and people in the greatest of detail: 'The crying and wailing was incredible, as was the immeasurable cowardice that those people suddenly showed. At one moment ready to speak of the Christian forces with scorn and contempt, they cried like women as soon as their Turkish conceit and arrogance was deflated. They were only thinking of how to avoid the approaching danger and how to avoid saying the very word "war".'

Pamuk picked up on the theme.

"And objectively seen, that fear was not unjustified. For example, one consequence of this defeat were the many uprisings that began among the momentarily encouraged Christians who were under Ottoman authority. In the western world the Christian victory resounded remarkably loud and encouraged Europe with the thought that, after two centuries of continuous defeats and constant fear, it was possible for something different to happen as well. After many years, the existing balance of power was being seriously shaken."

"I also read," I continued, "that the real problems came about when the Grand Vizier Mehmed-pasha Sokolović, who seems to be the only one who didn't lose his head, or at least was the first to come to his senses, managed to convince the Sultan to shift to a kind of offensive action. Not warring, but through action to surpass the passivity that had completely disarmed the entire state. So, soon thereafter, fermans[10] were issued on the renewed recruitment of soldiers and the renewal of the navy. But it seems that the real problems began then! The Sultan's followers, as the records say, 'would no longer even hear of war', and it even happened that the entire population of 'three hundred Anatolian villages fled to Persian soil out of fear that their men would again be forced onto the galleys.'"

Pamuk added further to my citations.

"There was even more. A large number of dignitaries began to renounce their titles and incomes because, without them, they were not liable to answer to the tax and (pre)war duties of the Porte. In turn, the Sultan had many of the spahis impaled, so as to instil fear in the others. However, those were just moves of desperation.

"Disconsolate, Selim II returned to Constantinople and tried to uncover the reasons for the defeat. He held insufferably long sessions of the Dīvān, interrogating everyone around him, debating with the Grand Vizier until deep into the night about the causes and consequences of the loss, he talked to everyone who was considered to be wise and experienced, he questioned soothsayers, he confronted prophets, and everywhere and to everyone he repeated that 'such a misfortune had never ever occurred to the Turkish empire before.' He did not try to conceal his perturbation in the least."

I continued to support this rare historical illustration of panic with facts from the chronicles of contemporaries.

"The Sultan in this frenzy of fear made several consistently irrational moves: of those people who directly participated in the battle at Lepanto, he punished some without reason, and he rewarded others undeservedly. The second vizier, old Pertev Mehmed-pasha, who had been against the conflict but still fought courageously in it – the Sultan removed his title as vizier and did not allow him to even try to justify the faults of others (because he had none himself). At the same time he rewarded the Algerian pirate, bey Uluj Ali (who had also been against going to battle!), because he regarded him to be a hero. In fact, when Uluj Ali realised that events were not unfolding favourably for the Turks, he retreated from the battle in good time, or even better said, too early. He snuck away from the Preveza harbour, gathering up the remains of the flotilla along the way. He managed to gather eighty-odd ships, some intact and others damaged, and flying a banner he had stolen from the Maltese knights, he sailed into the harbour at Constantinople, practically like a victor. In return for this bravery, he was awarded the position as the new admiral of the Ottoman fleet. (Or perhaps the Sultan, actually, was clever enough to fill the position of the killed kaptan derya Muezzinzade in the least troublesome way.)"

Of course, Pamuk knew more about this than I did. He added:

"About the Sultan's psychological state, I gathered most from his behaviour toward his favourite and oldest friend Jelal Celebi, with whom for years he had been drinking and carousing, sharing all his secrets with him. He renounced him and ostracised him from the court, just because the Grand Mufti Ebusuud Efendi marked him as one of those guilty of the defeat (even though down to this very day it is difficult to connect any of his roles with the battle or the decisions made about it).

"It should be said that both the Sultan and the Grand Vizier, in terms of their relationship, kept their wits about them and they did not turn on each other. Most likely they both realised that it would just make things much worse, and that, in such a situation, it would be hard for either of them without the other.

"Both of them made gestures worthy of praise: Mehmed-pasha did not ever even refer to his timely opposition to starting the battle of Lepanto, nor did he ever repeat it again, and he did not use the opportunity to blame it all on someone else – which he easily could have. The Sultan did not show even the slightest signs of anger toward the Grand Vizier, and rage was out of the question. He let him know, in various ways, that he was aware that Mehmed-pasha Sokollu had been right. But he never said it out loud."

I asked Pamuk, "What do you think: when the Sultan was deciding whether to go to battle with the European fleet or not, did he take into account the Christian background of his first and second vizier, and that of the pirate bey? Did he think about those things like the admiral of the fleet did?"

"I'm sure he did not. Whatever kind of person any of the Sultans in power were, each of them had hundreds of chances to test the loyalty of their subjects. Think about it. Why were there so many steps in front of each of them to advance in their careers? And why did every promotion take so long? Because, even the smallest step taken was a test of the marriage between ambition and loyalty! The Sultan did not need to lower himself to the level of insulting his subjects like Muezzinzade did. If the Sultan had any doubt, someone lost their head."

CHAPTER 6

Although Bajica's age seemed to be a constant problem for his advancement at the beginning, after a time it became a desirable addition to the talent, dedication and focus he showed in his studies. He was sought after not only by those boys who did not in the least like being subjugated to a foreign faith or to others' wishes, but he was also quite often consulted by his teachers and by officers in various services of the Sultan. He was noticed by everyone and thus, with a dozen or so other young men who had also stood out, he was destined for an education at an accelerated pace.

It was only three years into his stay at the Edirne caravansary, together with the other gifted young men, that the experience of fighting a war was forced into his life. Five years after the capture of Belgrade, in April of 1526, Sultan Suleiman set off on a new campaign against Hungary. His favourite, Grand Vizier Ibrahim-pasha, by background a Greek from Parga, demanded that the mature boys from the caravansary accompany the ruler so that they would become war-hardened as quickly as possible, ready to become officers. Thereby, Deli Husrev-pasha, as the one who carried out secret and important missions, once again determined the path to success for the young men. He left his brother Mustafa, as being too young, at the court in Edirne (even though he had arrived at the caravansary before Bajica/Mehmed and was thereby 'older' than him).

In his first life as Bajo Sokolović, Bajica had thought of Belgrade mostly as a capital city in which he, in fact, had never set foot. News from that gorgeous fortification had reached him, like it did to others, from merchants who often visited unfamiliar places. Even when he discounted part of their stories as the normal exaggeration of facts, even then the remainder indicated that it was undoubtedly a proper, seriously fortified city. He had thought about the city often, but had no desire to go there. Because nearby he had the River Drina which, he reflected, could not be much different from the Sava or Danube; and in other places he had seen several smaller fortified towns, and he could therefore imagine what a capital might look like. Travellers told that, except for its size, it was not much different from the town previously built in 1404 under the Serbian despot, Stefan Lazarević.

Since he had become Mehmed Sokollu, however, his thoughts about Belgrade had gone further. For five years now, since the town had been taken by Sultan Suleiman, it had become primarily *Ottoman*, and then the most important Ottoman *point of departure* (and therefore of resistance) toward Central Europe and the starting point of the old dream to conquer, after Hungary, the Austrian empire and, of course, to get to the gates of Vienna. Bajica now saw the place also as an Ottoman who had mastered strategy, planning and military strength, but who also possessed an imposed belief in invincibility. At the same time, a new *emotion* began to recur that he recognised in amazement because it rose *in anticipation* in him about a city that he had never seen. The only answer he could offer himself in this questioning was found in the probability that this was part of the resistance of the still crude duality of which he was made. And when he did *see* the city, he realised that *he had to fall in love* with it as he had – ahead of time and in his head. Looking at the gates, the towers, the ramparts and the buildings within this Fiçir bayir,[11] and its European style houses next to Kalemegdan[12] connected by cobblestone streets and alleys, the old Orthodox churches and the mosques being built, with a fountain here and there and an outer city gate; seeing all that, he understood why he had had to fall in love with it. Belgrade was like him: a half-breed with clear signs of the addition of a new life on the existing one, quite different from the previous one. Still, in the city he saw both Serbs and Turks. They were right next to each other; whether they liked each other, put up with each other or simply stomached each other, he could not tell. But it seemed that he could tell, unable to explain to himself why, that the future and destiny of this city could be like his own: *the Serbs would never renounce it, and the Turks would consider it their own!*

Seen in a broader context, this kind of thought was backed by several facts from their common past. The first Turkish attack and first successful defence had occurred in 1440. An entire fifteen-odd years later, and just three years after the conquest of Constantinople and its transformation into Istanbul, Sultan Mehmed II began an enormous new campaign against Belgrade in 1456. The short span in between indicated just how important Belgrade was in the political priorities of the Ottoman Empire. In the battles on Belgrade's rivers and their banks, the defenders showed incredible courage, especially the Serbian sailors among them. They managed to save the city. From that moment, Belgrade became the symbol of the overall defence of Europe and was given the title of the 'Ramparts of Christianity'.[13] But, it could not defend itself against Suleiman I the Legislator. This ruler gave the 'White City'[14] an Islamic name – Dar ul-Jihad,[15] and he was thereafter given the name 'the Magnificent' by his enemies.

The truth was as follows: to the Turkish Empire, this city was the perfect *springboard* for each new conquest toward the ultimate goal – Vienna, but to the European powers united against the Ottomans – it was a *much-needed borderline* peopled with victims who were not their citizens. The Serbs were in an ideal position for the interests of the two sides – both Moslem and Christian: a malleable mass compacted and stuck between a rock and a hard place.

That was the past. But what if the future said something in contradiction to what he had just been thinking: *the Serbs will reject him, and the Ottomans will never accept him as one of their own*? He did not dare to think more about that when the similarity or even sameness of the destiny of the city and his own appeared before him.

Bajica was finding out what the Emperor's highway was, the one the Serbs called the Constantinople highway, by which he had arrived in Belgrade. There was no way for him to know just how many times, usually following the river valley, he would travel back and forth on it. That road would become more than a symbol of his entire life.

The military commanders spared the boys from Edirne in only one way: they never sent them under any conditions among the fighters on the front line, nor did they send them into direct battle. They could not take the risk of losing their lives because they *still* had to prove to the sultan and the empire how capable they were, primarily in the defence of their own lives. Above all they had to stay alive. For the beginning, it was quite enough that they saw a lot of bloodshed close at hand; it was not necessary for them to bloody their own hands as well. This first encounter with massive death shocked Bajica and his comrades just enough that they managed to keep their wits about them and go on with the quite simple tasks the agas gave them. Their superiors, it could be seen, had a lot of experience with such situations and they never made a single excessive move. The large number of responsibilities that an attack demanded, especially of the commanders, proved welcome in justifying their 'lack of care' for the young men. In actual fact, this was all planned: the boys were allowed, on the surface, to harden themselves and realise what their future held. Of course, the agas were, carefully hidden, more careful than usual in looking after them and watching out for their safety. At first this semblance of being alone caused terrible fear in the boys, but after the job was done, they were rewarded with self-confidence.

By the very nature of the place where they were bivouacked, Bajica and his friends were among troops made up of fighters – assault troops, janissaries and units made up of local soldiers. Behind each assault soldier stood several regular soldiers and reservists, craftsmen, merchants, supply officers and others whose burden it was to ensure that each of them was able to do their jobs as well as possible. Whether a soldier at the head of the attack would die, when and to what end – it all depended on them. Or perhaps they would not die. It was then that Bajica understood the importance of strategy, of the organisation of a whole chain of jobs and tasks that made up the integral whole. If one link in this chain gets fractured somewhere, regardless of how insignificant that link may seem, the whole enterprise falls into danger. Seen from the outside, things looked quite different: those (individuals or events) at the forefront were visible, but the whole armada that made that visibility possible remained deep in the shadows. Using this example, he could apply the mechanisms of action to the entire empire as well. The fighters on the front lines (like the sultan and those close to him in the state) risked their lives more than anyone else (meaning that they carried the greatest responsibility in the state), sometimes even losing them, but they also, therefore, took on the greatest 'burden' of fame and fortune when there was a victory (meaning power and comfort in the state).

Killing, as the most visible tool of this campaign, did not interest him in the least, much less bring him delight. They had also taught him that skill at the caravansary. Now he saw the exercise of it in practice. He was certain that it could be reduced to a bare minimum. Force could not be, and did not have to be, practically the only measure of success to such an extent. Avoiding death interested him. He grew accustomed to death more easily than to killing.

He was more allured by the craftsmen and inventors. He was also drawn closer to them by the variety of languages they spoke. He was amazed by their faith in their own, still unmastered, *future* knowledge: they were obviously not satisfied by what they already knew. This was especially evident when the sultan or a grand vizier would give them a sudden, new and seemingly impossible task. Their faith in the *possible* completely enchanted Bajica. They approached the solving of every problem, even the smallest one, with such dedication that it seemed the destiny of the world depended on it.

Among the builders and craftsmen, he noticed a man who must have been more than ten years older than himself, but who had so much energy that he differed from the others and seemed to be as young as Bajica. And Ibrahim-pasha actually sought him out on several occasions!

One time they were close enough for Bajica to *hear* them talking to each other in Greek. He knew that the Grand Vizier was Greek by background, and now he knew that this young man, like Bajica himself, was brought here in the *devshirma* to serve the Ottoman Empire. Ibrahim-pasha was telling him to draw attention to himself with his ideas so that he could advance in the service more quickly.

Bajica was overjoyed with his eavesdropping and with his knowledge of Greek, learned with such enthusiasm at the monastery – now he would have one more partner with whom he could come to an understanding in several ways.

Just as these thoughts crossed his mind, the Grand Vizier noticed his unhidden interest in their conversation. The pasha obviously knew very well who Bajica was, because he addressed him in Greek and offered to introduce the two young men.

"You will not just get to know each other," the vizier made the introduction, "but you will also get to know what the other one knows.

"This is Sinan. He's studying to be a high-ranking officer, but he's also interested in engineering. When I start looking for him, I usually find him among the engineers and not among the soldiers. Since he is a member of the sultan's bodyguard, the ruler remembers him and occasionally asks about him. Lutfi-pasha, the guard commander, and I often have to make excuses for his absence. Though, to be frank, he has proven to be more useful to the sultan with the ideas in his head than with a sabre in his hand."

Bajica was surprised by the intimate tone of the Grand Vizier toward a former victim of the blood tribute.[16] But Ibrahim-pasha was already giving an explanation,

"From the first days of 1511, when he was brought from the Anatolian province of Kayseri to the heart of the empire, he was just about to turn nineteen, and Sinan Jusuf was appointed to my court. In that way you are alike: you were also brought at that age from Bosnia, although at a later date. You are both Orthodox Christians by background, and you, Mehmed, almost became a monk. Sinan proved to be a brave and excellent warrior five years ago during the conquest of Belgrade, but he also revealed some of his other sides of which the empire could make great use of: he is interested in building, so he has been allowed to study that craft. This is an ideal chance for you also to learn the connection between destruction and construction."

Bajica, on hearing this last sentence, looked at him oddly and blankly, so the pasha explained it to him, smiling in self-satisfaction all the while.

"I see you are wondering how to learn about *building in the middle of a war* that actually serves the opposite forces, with the intention to destroy things! Did you ever think about what the army must do *before and after* the destruction?"

Well, really. This had never crossed his mind.

"You see, the engineers often go ahead of the army before the attack and build roads, bridges, dikes, and ramparts. After the battle, it often happens that they find what they built in ruins, and so they have to fix it. It could be that the enemy destroys all of that, and they have to rebuild it, while we mainly destroy things, because we are conquering cities and fortifications. Most often, not much is left of them after we finish, but things have to be brought back into order for us to leave our soldiers and outposts in those fortifications once we move on or head back. We defend those fortifications from others. In truth, the engineers have nicer work in peace time: then they can build mosques, caravansaries, covered markets, fountains, minarets, hospitals and schools. And in wartime and in peacetime, they have to build graveyards."

Then Ibrahim-pasha realised that he had got carried away, and so he let the two of them left them alone to continue the conversation.

Having met at that moment, Sinan and Mehmed did not part for a long time afterward.

CHAPTER VII

Orhan Pamuk and I both came to our next session fully equipped: with chronicles, travelogues, notes, peripheral notes from German, French, Venetian, Hungarian, Serbian, Polish, and Turkish travellers, those from Dubrovnik as well, but also civil servants, explorers, emissaries, spies, educated slaves, merchants and all kinds of other people who found it worthwhile to leave behind a trace of their view on events in the Ottoman Empire.

We seemed amusing even to ourselves: like kids trading football cards, we almost began to taunt each other about who had the better collection! Pamuk first offered his own thoughts about Sokollu.

"At the critical moment, Sultan Selim figured out two important facts about his Grand Vizier, in this particular order. First, Mehmed-pasha showed exceptionally high moral standards, thereby looming over all the others around him, because he never referred again to his warning before entering the war and thereby not exploiting the chance to entice the (vulnerable and gullible) Sultan to expose the pasha's opponents to punishment."

I interjected, "There was a reason why they called him 'the Tall one'".[17]

"Well, that's true. You know that the women at the court first noticed his physical appearance. Everyone spoke of his posture, saying that they had never seen such dignified carriage," Pamuk added.

"It's fortunate that he was also handsome, or as they would say back then – pleasing to the eye," I tried to go on light-heartedly. But Pamuk became serious again,

"Second, without a moment's hesitation, the vizier showed a steadiness, decisiveness and certainty in his proposals that they must take action immediately. The Sultan could not have wished for anything of greater use to the empire in the dangerous state of his own cowardice, and the general cowardice that prevailed. With his idea to build a new fleet immediately, the pasha did not mean to say that they should go straight back to war, but rather to make their enemies *think twice* about doing further battle. Above all, the message meant: the Ottoman Empire will not bow down!"

I had a commentary of my own.

"They also had a bit of luck. The Europeans, for their part, were ecstatic with their unexpected victory, and because of their similar feelings of unwarranted or overindulged security, they sent their ships back to their home ports, counting on finishing up the job the next year. In fact, it must be admitted, the winter had already set in, and all acts of war at sea were becoming harder and harder to carry out."

"Yes. You're right. Perhaps Mehmed-pasha, foreseeing such a course of action or knowing that it was certain, was actually able to insist on renovating the fleet. Although it became clear very quickly that their enemies would not attack the capital, the Grand Vizier rushed to put his ideas into action: it was necessary to show everyone, both at home and abroad, that the great power had once again become the centre of the world."

It was true. History records that, through the exceptional organisation of the task, the Grand Vizier re-built the Ottoman fleet in just a few months! Mehmed-pasha first had several shipyards built which then proceeded to build a fleet of new ships, one hundred and fifty strong! All in the period from the end of 1571 to the beginning of 1572. In addition, when the Sultan wanted to praise and reward him personally, Sokolović said that they should not believe in him, but in the strength of the empire. What sultan would not want to have such a man beside him?

Truth be told, a part of his internal self-confidence (which he did not allow to surface in the presence of others often) actually came from the vizier's earlier experience, when a quarter of a century before, as the high commander of the Ottoman navy, he had hundreds of new ships built. He was better at that task than at going to war at sea. That was why he let those with greater skill than his own lead the naval battles. During that same period, he built new arsenals for shipbuilding, all together forming a terribly powerful shipbuilding industry. At the same time, he executed a fundamental reform of the navy and made plans for the future conquests of territories in the Indian Ocean, north Africa, and the European parts of the Mediterranean. With his knowledge, his diplomatic skill, his sense of order, discipline and hierarchy, and with his realistic visions, he completely prepared the field for his commanders to turn his plans into their actions.

In the revival of the fleet after the defeat, Mehmed-pasha activated the entire country: there was not a class or a strategic entity that did not have to respond to the decrees in its own way. The vizier intentionally made such a far-reaching noise about it in order to motivate the demoralised citizens across the country by the breadth of the action, and to warn those outside the country that the Turkish Empire was indeed still to be reckoned with.

The vizier knew what he was doing. Immediately after the defeat, he was visited by the Venetian diplomat Mark-Antonio Barbaro, who had not left the Ottoman capital despite the war, so that he could somehow determine the further intentions of the empire. Mehmed-pasha, as an experienced politician, received him in a friendly but cynical atmosphere, "You've come to see if we've lost our courage after the defeat." Then he surprised the diplomat with a comparison, "There's a huge difference between your loss and ours. By snatching the Kingdom of Cyprus, we have cut off your hand; by battering our fleet, you have set our beard on fire. A hand cut off will never grow back, but a singed beard will grow back even thicker."

He was right.

"But the Grand Vizier treated his own people the same," I said to Pamuk when he told me these facts. "When the newly-appointed *kapudan-derya*, who was his most direct helper in the job of rebuilding the fleet, and who longed in every imaginable way to have a strong armada, began to doubt that the vizier's plans and decrees would succeed, the crucial part of their conversation went like this, or so a chronicler says:

Kilij Ali: 'It's easy to build ships, but in such a short time it is impossible to obtain enough anchors, ropes and other equipment.'

Mehmed-pasha: 'The power and wealth of the High Porta is such that, if necessary, it is possible to make anchors of silver, ropes of silk scarves, and sails of satin and velvet. Ask me for whatever is missing on any of the ships, and you will get it.'

At these words, says the chronicler, the admiral fell on his knees before the vizier, his hand outstretched, he touched his forehead and palms to the ground and said, 'I knew that you were the only one who could build the new navy.'

Both Pamuk and I concluded together that this is a real example of a story with a moral to it. Both sides in the conflict allowed their vanity to overwhelm them: the Turks *before* the battle, and the Europeans *after* it. And both sides, each in their own way, paid with historical consequences for that weakness. No matter how skilfully and quickly they diluted, diminished and hid those consequences – and however praiseworthy their efforts – they still had to pay the price.

CHAPTER 7

As the Ottoman army's conquest went forward, the words of the Grand Vizier proved to be absolutely correct. The business of war in that insignificant Auxiliary Unit turned out to be not only quite important, but so much so that the army would not have succeeded without it. There were so many places where they had to get through swamplands or to bridge rivers, reinforce levees, build non-existent ramparts or strengthen existing ones, along with trenches to be dug or filled in. Without the various inventions and quick-thinking of the members of this unit, it was not possible to conquer high barriers or knock down walls. There were all sorts and sizes of apparatuses, tools, ladders, platforms, cannons, self-winding weapons with ammunition of stone, metal balls and incendiary materials, strange carts and battering rams for knocking fortress doors down and myriad other weapons of which Bajica had never heard, much less did he know what they were used for. Yet, above all, it turned out that the soldiers in these units actually showed exceptional courage as well, because they were often sent ahead of the battle troops, and sometimes covered the rear during retreats. They were never left by themselves, of course; they were protected by the other units, but these 'thinkers' went after the enemy with equal fervour and bravery.

This was also Bajica's first impression of Sinan, who constantly gathered information from the other apprentices and craftsmen, giving ideas and applying them immediately if possible, and at the same time going into battle at times, more to defend his companions or their inventions than to attack. When it was necessary, he was quick in offering his thoughts and quick to act, but he was mellow and peaceable when at rest and in conversation with Mehmed. Mehmed in turn, questioned him about his memories of Belgrade from five years ago, about his plans, about his hometown, his family and his background. Sinan's stability pleased him because it was a quality he lacked (and not just because he was so much younger). And Sinan had an explanation for this certainty of his., since he had been brought up in a village inhabited by purely Greek Orthodox Christians, but which was set in the middle of an Anatolian region with an Ottoman population. Even though he was born on that soil, it did not free him from the destiny that also happened to Bajica, who had been brought in from a *conquered* land. Even though he belonged to the Ottomans by the very fact that he lived *within* the empire, he was taken from home by force, just like one of the infidels. So judgment was passed on the background of his blood, not the land.

At one moment, Sinan thought that, as he was evaluating young Mehmed, he was using the same measure of blood and (former) religion, but he quickly changed his mind: of course this had some influence on a deeper consideration of a possible new friendship, but it was not the crucial thing. Above all, he liked the candour that Bajica showed toward him from the very beginning. Understandably, in the chaos of war the young man had come across someone who had experience in battle, in fear and sadness, but also in living with the issues of an unstable background of body and soul. It was thus natural that this insecure and confused young man should stick close by him. Then again, it was clear to Sinan that this confusion was caused by the chaos that the conquest brought with itself, and that it was not one of Mehmed's normal qualities. To a great degree war is, among other things, made up of sounds; from the reports of guns, the thunder of cannons, the chopping of trees and meat with sharp blades, battle cries, death wails, the clattering of horses' hooves, the pounding of drums, gentle pipe notes and brassy trumpet sounds, rarely those of a song, the barked orders of the commanders and the quiet prayers to the Almighty in solitude. Mixed in with this are the sounds of nature: rain pouring down or a thunderstorm, the popping of a campfire and the roar of wildfire, the babbling of brooks, the rumbling of bridges and ships on flooded rivers and the waves of the sea. Defeat shatters these sounds, and victory raises them into a harmonious melody.

Still, sounds could not be the deciding factor in a friendship.

The essence of attraction between people evaded clear explanation.

Finding himself more and more often near Sinan, Bajica began to take the difficulties of the conquest more easily. He met ever more people who had lived through his current fate before him, and who managed to survive its difficulties by carrying out their duties. Now they seemed to him to be quite at peace with themselves. On the march toward Osijek he saw hundreds if not thousands of *Cherahors* and *Armatoles*, and they had a calming effect on him. Government under the Cherahors seemed to be completely stable even though it was composed exclusively from military units formed of the local population from the frontier provinces of the Ottoman Empire. All of them Christians, most of them were craftsmen of all sorts: masons, carpenters, blacksmiths. They were the indispensable and the most important. All the others were in the support lines. But altogether, they actually *maintained* the army. In addition, work was also done by the inhabitants of the surrounding villages, but also by the Ottoman soldiers when it was necessary. Most of the work included the building and repair of fortifications, bridges and roads, but also logging, clearing swamps, digging trenches and the transportation of military supplies. The Cherahors were paid and given tax breaks, although they were brought in by command, almost by force. Bajica found it strange that he occasionally heard Serbian being spoken without any kind of reserve or attempt to hide it.

He was further comforted when he got to meet a few of the military commanders. Among them were those who had kept their Serbian names and religion, and all that went with those characteristics, and there were also others who had been converted.

One of the leaders of the Armatoles, Christian units that were mainly left behind to man conquered strategic places, was the river fleet commander Petar Ovčarević. With his attitude, courage and lack of hesitation, he left a powerful impression on Bajica. Bajica knew about his position in the defence of Belgrade from the Turks in 1521, his retreat when all hope had been lost, and that he had later received an invitation from his former enemy, the Sultan himself, to personally gather up the disbanded river fleet and to be their commander in service to Suleiman. Long before including him in this conquest five years later, the Sultan had honoured him by sending him the invitation and permission to move to Belgrade with his river fleet, and he had even named the part of town where they settled after him – the Ovčar-oglu mahala (district). Ovčarević explained to Bajica and Sinan without hesitation that he felt completely justified by the whole undertaking: he was hired for money and privileges, he was still a Serb by background, religion and name, and he was participating in, as he said, 'safeguarding Belgrade, *momentarily* besieged, but always Serbian'. Bajica interpreted his courage in saying this to be bravery on the sailor's part: the Sultan and the Grand Vizier might have laughed at his impudence, but they did not argue with his right to think that way. Above all, they admired his proven daily heroism, which was more important to them than his bravado. After all, thousands of Serbs who had placed themselves in the service of the Ottoman Empire listened to him. It made no difference if that was temporary, forced shrewdness or some other calculation. He was a man who maintained his oath to the Empire on his word alone. That is why they respected his other words as well.

It was also here that Bajica met the sons of the famous Jahja-pasha from the Jahjapašić family: Bali-bey, Ahmed-bey and Gazi Mehmed-pasha. All three of them were known as cruel warriors, like their forebears, who also like Ovčarević no longer questioned their background, yet wanted to suppress their old religion completely since they had converted to a new one. That is why Bajica had nothing to discuss with them. They were unruly conquerors who blindly followed *their* masters' orders, terrifying their opponents and taking over new territories with their insane bravery and brutality. They triumphed, unashamedly loving battle. And they were dangerous.

On the other hand, Bajica reflected, however different they were by background or not, in the approach to their own or others' lives, with their views of justice, their own conscience or whatever else, each and every one of them was involved in the same thing: in the service of spreading the Ottoman Empire! Here, all differences disappeared, and if they did reappear here and there, they were insignificant. There you have it, his thoughts from the school in Edirne were coming back. Everyone subordinated to the One!

That One, the Empire, with its true strength showed an exceptional power that, by itself alone, paralysed the enemy. Enemies who had still not been defeated were afraid, and the conquered peoples saw their repression to be eternal and unchanging. It seemed like it had always been that way, and that it would always be that way. It was impossible to imagine a force that could overcome such a power. Individuals saw only two possible paths before them: either make peace and blend into such a perfect world or to resist it in their minds, with their will and whatever inner strength they could muster. However, this latter did not bring liberation; on the contrary, it dulled everything because it did not offer even the possibility of change, but rather only dejection

73

and apathy. From such hopelessness, it was hard for an entire nation, much less the defeated individual, to find an exit.

However, listening to the various participants in this conquest, Bajica also caught a glimpse of the first, well hidden, crack in the walls of the invincible empire. The official reason for the Sultan's sending such a large army were the renewed and more frequent incidents with Hungary. But the secret reason was that there had been a janissary rebellion in Istanbul the year before. The Sultan and the Grand Vizier were, rightly so, afraid of their most loyal and elite troops. Understandably, the security of the empire depended on those soldiers being satisfied. Their courage and dedication made up the core of all things Ottoman. Together, in battle for the empire or in rebellion against it, they were exceptionally dangerous. If they were to rise up against their ruler, they had to be pacified as quickly as possible. Afterwards, as individuals, the leaders could be executed, but during the rebellion, no one dared to oppose them. In battle for the Sultan they were invincible, and thus for their great courage, in addition to the ruler's generosity to them, they were often rewarded with the permission to plunder. The Sultan's embarking on a new conquest was promise enough for them; it pacified the dissatisfied janissaries and their anger, and turned their fury and belligerence toward the enemy.

Bajica witnessed both his own and the overall confusion. He was relieved when he understood the terrible truth that the problem of duality was shared by the entire Serbian nation. On one hand, he saw the Serbian sailors on the Turkish side, and on the other hand he saw their compatriots fighting in the defence of Belgrade among the Hungarian army units. Not having their own defined state, and having a homeland which was constantly traversed, plundered and occupied, the Serbs survived by making their own individual or group decisions. That is how the senseless situation arose that they were split in loyalty and forced into a position of constant personal and collective instability. The Turkish and Hungarian rulers saw this as an obvious and serious problem, but they did not solve it because they were better suited by the divisions among the Serbs: it was easier to rule them that way. The only time they were careful was in wholeheartedly avoiding battles where 'their' Serbs might meet and, God forbid, come into conflict with the 'other' Serbs. Yet, they did even that if it was in their own interests.

CHAPTER VIII

It is strange how imagination can conjure up life!

Less than a full month before writing this sentence and only a dozen pages above this one, I compared the behaviour of Orhan Pamuk and myself with 'kids trading football cards' as we boasted about who possessed more detailed information about certain events from our mutual Turkish-Serbian past. At the time, that comparison seemed to be a good illustration because I instantly remembered how, at the end of the sixties, on the cobblestones of Belgrade, as children, one part of my one-half impoverished childhood (when Yugoslavia began to arise from the poverty of classical socialism and entered the phase of the unmatched leader of the Non-Aligned Movement and the blasphemous acceptance of the capitalistic standard) was spent in trading cards of famous football players that we collected for our albums of World Football Championships. In addition to the classic trades, we also played 'knockout' by which we, in a sporting, victorious way *captured* individual cards from our opponents in the game. This somehow got us even more involved in the whole story. We had the feeling that we had an influence on getting the prize with our abilities and that it was not just a question of luck. I also remember that no one sold cards to others and that money as a category in this case (regardless of the Leader who was taking us all toward the material world) was not even mentioned, and certainly not used. It was enough to send your completed album to the organisers of the lottery and try your luck at getting picked from the drum for winning the prize.

Why do I bring all of this up? Because coincidences arouse in me an odd sort of superstition that I otherwise do not remember or believe in. In this case, in the meantime, between writing the quoted words and these I am writing now, I was strolling with Pamuk around one of Belgrade's central squares called 'Terazije' (another Turkish word in Serbian). His boyish and never-ending curiosity, and admittedly mine drew us toward the Moskva Hotel and a crowd of about one hundred grown up men and schoolboys. When we drew close, we saw that they were trading football cards for their albums before the beginning of the World Football Championships in June of 2006 in Germany! I was surprised by my intuition, which had precisely described this phenomenon in the manuscript of an unfinished book only a few weeks before and in which, *on that occasion*, the protagonists were Pamuk and I. I told him about it. Instead of answering, he reacted even more surprisingly: he got noticeably involved with the people and their football cards. The whole situation overwhelmed him completely. I was hardly able to drag him away from there.

I bet that he went back there after I dropped him off, because of a sudden rain shower, at the restaurant of that hotel whose outer walls were all of glass, so he could sit and record his impressions, and draw in his blue notebook what he had seen in his mind's eye.

Then again, I went back there, too. I discovered that, in today's childhood as well (for children and adults alike) money has no place. The only difference was, I found out, that there were no prizes for finished albums. And that adults had gotten involved in the game too, apparently in a state of childhood regression. It would be nice if the reason for that were the introduction of a new naïveté in the game. The adults here were not accompanying little kids but were playing equally with them – like kids.

They had never heard of a 'knockout'.

Perhaps all of this was happening for a reason and not accidentally, right on the square named 'Terazije'.[18]

I am certain that, in Pamuk's notebook, something was recorded about this exchange of the naïve and the establishment of equilibrium (between the large and small participants, the excess and lack of cards). If I only had the least bit of talent for drawing (like Pamuk does), I am sure that I would be in a dilemma about this testimony of simplicity – is it better to write something down or should it be drawn?

It is quite obvious from this account that I have never been much of an expert or fan of football. Like with other phenomena, however, I was attracted by the oddity of its collateral consequences or connections. Not so long ago I watched the film *The Cup* by the director Khyentse Norbu. This is an incredible melding of Tibetan art and western European film technology (and most likely production money). Against a background of indescribable remoteness and distance from the modern world, we see Tibetan Buddhist priests, in addition to their thousand year-old chanted mantras, along with their completely childlike naïveté, organising their watching of the televised broadcast of the World Football Championships *within* the gates of their monastery and of their – not so football oriented – beliefs. The absurd connection of the un-connectable through the unbridled humour in this film, shows how *everything is human*, and especially that which seemingly could never be. In the film, the 'acting' is done by Tibetan disciples and teachers themselves, with names (and titles) like *Neten Chokling, Lama Godhi, Jamyang Lodro...* Thus, once again, local boys and grown men.

It so happens that, soon after my fascination with this film, a friend of mine showed up after just spending a year of his life with these 'football heroes' from the top of the world! And like a true kid, he told me, "They're just like in the film!"

CHAPTER 8

It now seemed to him that he might be able to better understand the extremes in the behaviour of those who had converted to the new faith and to reach a greater understanding toward the split character of those who had not done so.

The janissaries were prime representatives of the former. They were used mercilessly as if they had no roots, families or any reason of their own for living. Everything was expunged from their lives so that the drive to serve the sultan could be imprinted in its place. Well trained, they acted accordingly: regardless of the battle tactics of the commanders, as individuals, they penetrated all the boundaries of courage and literally rushed headlong into battle, and often to their deaths. On the other hand, this headlong rush often saved them; seeing them like that, the enemy frequently gave up in battle, often in tactical retreat, and sometimes even running for their lives. In this way Allah, or their former God (or both at the same time), actually saved them from their own madness. That is why they were uncontrollable in their victories. Using the far-reaching reputation of their intrepidness, they often plundered, raped, tortured and murdered at will. Unless the sultan or the grand vizier personally forbid them. Not only did they take delight in the role of proving their bloodthirstiness, they also showed their loyalty beyond all limits of good taste. And when something of the spoils did not fall into their hands, they also uncontrollably raised their voice against their commander and showed him that same unbridled impudence that was even able to upset the ruler. The ruler would in turn delegate the grand vizier to quiet them down. There were cases when, at such moments, they paid him no heed either and thus managed to overthrow him; even killing a few of the grand viziers along the way. However, when they were content with the booty, they would again become fanatically obedient to their lord, behaving as if nothing at all had happened.

Bajica interpreted such behaviour as a kind of madness, because it could not be explained with reasonable arguments. Their rebellions were violent, fast, heated and dangerous. As soon as their demands were fulfilled, and when the leaders had been punished, the uprising would die out with equal speed and determination. These abrupt changes in their disposition kept the rulers under a constant tension. Truth be told, in that tension there was a kind of justice; if unquestioning loyalty was wanted, then the rulers had to count on the occasional risks that such allegiance implied.

Although this behaviour among the janissaries was essentially caused by their proselytisation, it seemed to Bajica that it was not the fundamental reason. After all, these men became part of a living legend as time went by. That legend, primarily according to military standards, rightly made them into elite units that were unmatched either in the sultan's army or any other.

If the coals of their former faith glowed beneath the flame of their new one, this too could be seen among the agas, beys, pashas and other commander-converts. In order to advance as quickly, easily and indubitably as possible, many of them became greater subjects of Allah than most of the Ottomans. Much more complicated were those who remained divided in their loyalties.

It was easiest to die. Any infidel could afford himself that luxury just by immediately, clearly and completely showing that he did not want to convert to the new faith. Yet, even that was not enough to receive the death sentence. Namely, the Ottomans did not think they should be opposed in their ideas. To the contrary, they forced no one (except those chosen for the *devshirma*) to convert to their faith. Death came only if someone drew a weapon on them.

To a certain extent, it was harder to not accept Islam and remain a subject with one's own faith. But it was even more difficult to not forsake one's faith, and go into the service of another! To others, this certainly looked like cupidity. But what other choices were there? Had staying alive become something unnatural? Shameful? Should one die in order to exist? Extinguish an entire nation only to go on procreating? And how does one do that?

All of these questions were a burden on his soul. He had not yet met anyone who could even pose these questions clearly, much less answer them. The most he could do was to gather partial answers from those around him.

Thus, just as his whole nation was divided in two halves, neither of which could be naturally defended by a foreign entity, so it was that every individual was divided in half, yet did not have anything to say about it. Or, perhaps, for some of his compatriots that decision had not been made. But there was a trap in front of the decision: when making that decision, the only thing that was impossible was to remain true to oneself and oneself alone.

It was quite fortunate that such great questions without answer came up right in the middle of a military campaign, and Bajica was forced to end this sort of self-torture and go on with his participation in the events of the day.

The conflict on the swampy battle field at Mohacs between the two armies or, better said, the Hungarian heavily armoured, and therefore hardly manoeuvrable, cavalry against the Ottoman cannons, lasted for only two hours. The Hungarians were scattered by the artillery and did not even manage to engage the enemy cavalry or infantry. Bogged down in the mud, they were sitting ducks. King Lajos II himself was killed in battle. The road to Budapest lay open. On that road, Bajica saw all the abilities of his new friend. With marvellous ease, Sinan found new solutions when faced with new challenges. This he did quickly, without a lot of talk, moving past a job done as if it had never happened and finding a solution for the next problem. At one moment after the battle, he said to Bajica, "On the same date, August 29, I've witnessed two victories in the last five years: in 1521 at Belgrade, and *on the same day*, five years later, at Mohacs."

Both the Vizier and the Sultan assigned Sinan to independently lead operations. Not only did he prove to be agile in solving all sorts of technical problems, he also distinguished himself with his ability to communicate with the craftsmen and builders with a special kind of respect in his commands, so that he achieved incredible efficiency in those operations. Everyone gladly and whole-heartedly participated in all phases of the work. Altogether he possessed remarkable organisational skills: as an officer he knew how to evaluate a situation, giving timely, precise and correct orders; as an engineer he proved his knowledge, and as a supervisor he showed that he cared about those who worked under him. In the system run by the Grand Vizier and the Sultan, this path was unusual, but they allowed him to go down it because he was so useful to them. For example, since the settlement of Osijek was completely destroyed on their way to Budim, it was no problem for Sinan to immediately issue the order for its renovation and rebuilding. Departing from the place, he left behind only a couple of agas and craftsmen who quickly employed the inhabitants and immediately began construction according to his plans. Even the newly created vassals were impressed by the decisiveness and speed with which the conquered towns were re-built without delay. This simultaneously improved the image that the Ottomans left among the common folk and the subjugated nobles. On their account, Sinan created, if not respect, at least an alternative to the cruelty.

Bajica carefully observed the behaviour of Grand Vizier Ibrahim-pasha, too. He pretended that Sinan was pleasantly surprising him, even though it was clear that he had actually pushed Sinan into that 'surprise'. Allowing him unusual freedom, rarely given to an apprentice officer and future official engineer, the vizier kept all his commanders on edge by loosening or tightening his grip on the reins. They did not dare to let their guard down even after they had been freed by the example of Jusuf Sinan. The Grand Vizier obviously noticed the abilities of his protégé in good time and thus gained the right to protect him, making sure that Sinan constantly proved himself with his work, so that he would not cause unnecessary envy among the other officers. That envy, of course, could not be completely avoided but, through the skilful manipulation of Ibrahim-pasha, it was reduced to a benign level. Having married one of the Sultan's sisters just a year earlier, the Grand Vizier had felt the effects of jealousy himself. Using the Sultan's protection, he applied the skill of exchanging the cruelty of ruling with the nobility of forgiving, even to himself. However, he made sure that, from this behaviour, no conclusions were drawn by which rules and legalities could be recognised. Or, God forbid, weaknesses. Thus, he always remained ahead of the others and he could always surprise them with an unexpected decision, or even with an expected decision made at an unexpected moment.

Ten days after the Battle of Mohacs, the Sultan's army entered Budim, almost without resistance. The Sultan stayed there for a while, and then crossed over into Pest, from where he ordered the main body of the army to return to the Empire. He left behind the newly appointed Hungarian king, János Szapolyai, to rule Hungary as an Ottoman vassal. In fact, the Sultan already knew then that this decision would not be accepted by the followers of Ferdinand of Hapsburg, the brother of Charles V, nor by Mary of Hapsburg, the widow of Lajos II. Therefore, he would have to return to this region again. But that had been planned long before, even without the battle for the Hungarian throne, without the enemy's knowledge.

Passing by Belgrade, Bajica tried to figure out what it was that the Belgrade fortress reminded him of; its setting and surroundings. But he did not manage, something was confusing him. The water, probably. And then a wild idea crossed his mind: this magnificent view belonged in similarity to something he had not yet seen!

He parted with Sinan somewhere around there. The Sultan asked the trained and the future pages[19] stay with him, and the engineers to fall behind the army and reconstruct the destroyed buildings and to give a facelift to the empire as the army departed. Bajica returned to Edirne, and Sinan went on to Istanbul, as a newly appointed captain of the Sultan's victorious army, no more no less.

CHAPTER IX

For me, the ensuing conversation about the Battle of Lepanto brought up a kind of parallel and a comparison with the Battle of Kosovo, not because of similarities between them, but simply as a reflection on the consequences of the defeat.

However great the shock of Lepanto was for the Ottomans, it did not knock them to their knees before their opponent. It rather revealed to them that their empire was vulnerable, that they had to beware of arrogance, and that conceit often bore a price to pay. But the empire, no matter how shaken it was, was not in serious danger. Through the wise actions of those courageous enough, they quickly re-established their security. That strength was objective, as opposed to the feeling of weakness – which was subjective. Yet, often the un-objective factor, so abstract and based on a psychological impression and not on hard numbers and facts, was harder to overcome than the truth. Probably because it was more inclined to surrender than to fight; because the desperation of disbelief was stronger than making a new start.

It was most important that the Ottomans did not turn Lepanto into a martyrs' defeat.

In contrast to them, the Battle of Kosovo in 1389, which happened almost two hundred years earlier, was taken by the Serbs as a defeat in the name of martyrdom. To some extent understandably, because from that point forward they only fell deeper into slavery, losing their personal and collective freedom, empire and state. Short intervals of renewed empowerment and hope did not change their destiny as a whole. There was not much for them to depend upon: just their language, religion and the church. And the church could not keep up.

But that was not the end of it. History continued to roll out events, to grind out destiny, to surprise the future. However, something strange happened to the story about the Battle of Kosovo. Namely, as time passed the consequences of this crucial battle lost all the clear characteristics of a historically tragic defeat and took on the contours of less tangible facts, and more shades of the possible. This is not about changing historical truth but about a *different understanding* of that same truth. Interpretation took sway over sense, the system of priorities was disrupted: the significant became unimportant, the marginal became the essential. This defeat determined the destiny of the entire nation for the next several centuries. It is doubtful that mythology crept into the events beforehand. It is more likely that the change in the understanding of the defeat came about afterwards, simply as a defence against the inalterability of history. With time, how can one explain acquiescence to a defeat that lasts two or three centuries, or even longer? That is indeed hard to accept.

Is Kosovo one of the birthplaces of the ideas of courage, honour, murder in deceit? Did all of that determine the course of events that lay waiting in the twentieth century?

Could defeat dare to range from suicide to subjugation? If you could not kill your enemy, you could always kill yourself. If you could not defeat him, you could defeat yourself.

Was desperation born from such an understanding? And are extremes actually born out of desperation?

The battle became a myth. The defeat became a victory.

On the other hand, wishing to show what it was like when the victor overdoes it in his conceit, Pamuk cited some examples from the Ottoman sources about the Battle of Mohacs (when, by the way, the Serbs finally lost all hope after the Battle of Kosovo that the sun would rise again or that there might at least be a chance for or a hint of a *better tomorrow*).

According to Suleiman's personal war diary, twenty thousand dead infantry and four thousand cavalry were counted on the battlefield on the side of the infidels. The victor did not make note of his own casualties. It is known that there was celebration, looting and indeed that several thousand prisoners of war were killed. In the accumulated battles that followed the one at Mohacs, sources say that over two hundred thousand people died on the Hungarian side, and less reliable tallies for the Ottoman army indicate that they lost between twenty-five and fifty thousand men during this campaign. It was a real massacre, and it shows just how great the Ottoman desire was to capture Vienna, and the strategic and symbolic importance the city held for them. Actually, each new campaign was a repetition of that unsatisfied desire.

Probably in order to justify the fierceness of the battle, the number of casualties, the possible remorse of the Sultan himself at allowing the unnecessary murder of prisoners in some of his orders, the conqueror's chroniclers wrote of the Battle of Mohacs that, on the 'enemy side' those who died were – this is followed by an incredible series of epithets (as if the victory was not enough) – 'sons of hell, demons, sinful vagabonds, swine, stubborn men, obstinate men, tramps, dogs, infidels, hucksters, evil-doers, hypocrites, monsters, unclean spirits who had taken on the face of a demonic torturer'.

It is likely that this deluge of insulting names functioned as the celebration (or perhaps justification) of this important victory. But after the victory, the murder of prisoners of war and peasants caught in the fields (there were four thousand of them, not counting women) could not be justified by any sort of strategy. Or by hatred. Much less by epithets.

Maybe it seemed to some that the unnecessary murder of several thousand people was not even worth noticing, especially if they were the victims of mistakes or of an inconceivable passion for death. Obviously, they could easily have been mixed in with the many dead. If the numbers are correct, and most of the sources confirm them, then one should truly keep in mind what an enormous number of casualties that was in that period of history!

Whatever happened, in this way Suleiman quite successfully attained his qualifier 'the Magnificent' among the terrified Europeans. But what if it all began just so that he would receive that epithet?

CHAPTER 9

Three years after his first military experience, Bajica once again rode behind the Grand Vizier Ibrahim-pasha, who was now also the *beylerbey*[20] of all of Rumelia, and had received the title of *serasker*, or high commander,[21] in the Ottoman army. Passing through Edirne, the Grand Vizier again gathered the best young men and encouraged them by claiming that their actions would be remembered for the fame of the great sultan.

They followed the same road they had been on several years before. Bajica was now able to know about some things ahead of time, either by foresight or recognition. But, Sinan was not riding among the officers. To Bajica's surprise, he did not find him among any of the other cavalry units from Istanbul.

Sinan did not join them until after Edirne, in eastern Rumelia, in Thrace to be precise. And that was something that Bajica could not predict. To make the riddle even more complicated, before this meeting he so longed for, as they drew new the River Maritsa,[22] Ibrahim-pasha frequently cast puzzling glances at him, obviously wanting to tell him something. Soon enough it became clear why this was so. At the town of Uzunköprü[23] they were met by a crowd dressed in holiday fashion, specially organised lower level officers, vassals, musicians and folk from the surrounding area. And there in front of them stood – Sinan Jusuf! After Sinan had bowed to the Sultan and ordered the crowd to make way, Bajica saw the reason for the earlier secrecy and the present pride: a bridge rose above the river, one that had not been there three years before, made of white stone and of exceptional elegance. It was quite long, but also wide, set on twelve massive piers. The piers were topped with arches and they were actually the essence of the beauty and stability of the bridge. At the same time, their massiveness spoke of their strength and their intention to last. They left space for the water to flow beneath them, but they channelled it with their bulk. As if they respected the water's power, but were proud of their own strength at the same time.

He took pleasure in seeing the joy of the inhabitants who obviously knew best just how much this joining of the river's banks would change their lives. Although it was also interesting to see the satisfied Sultan upon whose orders the bridge had been built. Yet, Bajica knew, it would not have been built were it not for Sinan's patron, his countryman by background, Ibrahim-pasha. And the lesson: it turned out that the Grand Vizier's support of someone (and their common faith) was not the mere use of power for the sake of power, but a practical and positive act intended for everyone's benefit.

Although he was now already a commander of the Escort, whenever he did not have other things to do on the rest of the journey, they often demanded that Sinan stayed close to the vizier and Sultan. Now they both often called him 'Mimar'. Through his own example as well, and not just Sinan's, Bajica better understood the ruler's need to take public pride in his chosen ones, who were often young. Moreover, that is why they frequently dressed them much more fancily than was permitted for those in even higher positions than they. Although this showing off did not quite suit him, it was thus possible at this rank for Bajica to be close to Sinan.

As they travelled, Sinan told him about how, after all the work he participated in during the previous campaign to Budim, the ruler seemed to be satisfied with his knowledge and ordered him (though he used the word 'offered' when talking to Bajica) to try his hand at bridge building, such that he would do all the plans and calculations and then supervise the actual construction. So, immediately after returning to Istanbul he began to do the drawings and projections for the bridge, and a few months later he began organising the construction work on the banks of the Marica. The job took a year and a half, up to the ceremonial crossing of the great Sultan across it.

"Since such a large army just crossed it, especially the artillery and my unit with all the weight it carries, that bridge will survive for centuries! Do you know what it feels like, Bajo Mehmed, to know that something of yours will outlast you?!"

It was hard for him to respond positively. Nothing tangible that Bajica had done was still around. His work was there, but it could not be pointed at. He was silent. He let Sinan speak because he wanted to talk so badly, and he did have a lot to say.

"After all the ramparts, walls, trenches, temporary bridges and scaffoldings, and especially knocking down and rebuilding *whatever* was destroyed, it seemed to me that I had learned how stone, wood and metal behave under what conditions," he told Bajica. "It's quite important to differentiate materials and conditions. No single structure, not even the commonest of huts or wells, is the same. Likewise, not a single structure of a given material is the same. Everything is new each time, and is being built for the first time!"

Bajica was listening to him but also watching how passionately he was speaking of mud and stone as if they were living beings. Sinan was thoroughly obsessed with his thoughts about creating things. As Sinan began talking about what he might dare to build, and all that he had still to learn, that Bajica realised he was in the company of a man in love.

In telling him of all the fears he had while struggling with the bridge, he offered an interesting view of what he was working on. For him, the bridge was not built only of stone, scaffoldings and adhesive materials, but also of water! Not just any water, but the very water that was supposed to be traversed by a bridge.

"The water *there* was of a specific quality only there and nowhere else. I had to build the bridge *for the water* first, and only then for the people!"

Bajica was a bit frightened by this enigmatic sentence. "This business about the water you might want to keep to yourself. I'm afraid they won't understand you."

But the business about the water also made Bajica start thinking; Sinan was not at war with the river, nor was he fighting *against* the water. First, he studied the water carefully; how it behaved toward different materials, what it withstood, what it liked, what it snatched for itself – and also what it could not stand, what it rejected and destroyed. When he caught himself thinking like this, Bajica became worried. After all, the water was not alive! Then again, how many times had he, as a boy, experienced the differences between streams, rapids and rivers? Each one that he dabbled in or crossed over was different. Each hill and mountain, why everything! – each tree was different from the others. Just like people. Each one a story in themselves.

Perhaps Sinan had an exceptional gift for building; this was obviously true. But it was becoming clear to Bajica that this was not the only secret, and certainly not the only reason for his success. The most important thing lay most certainly in his approach to what he was doing, and this was something Bajica knew what he could work on in the future. The approaches to things needed study.

As approached Belgrade, he saw that changes had occurred since his last stay there three years before. Now the banks of the Sava and Danube were large ports where commerce was developing with regions theretofore unknown: the Asian shores of the Mediterranean, Venice, Dubrovnik, the northern regions of Africa. Goods were arriving from everywhere, and with them new people, new customs, the languages and stories of other peoples. However, at this moment trade was pushed into the background for Belgrade. Around its edges, since they had filled up all the surrounding banks on the delta and both rivers, Turkish warships were anchored for miles downstream. Both near and far, on both banks and all around Zemun, thousands of army units had raised their camps. They were gathering from all over, from Bosnia to the Suez, all the power of the Ottoman Empire with the obvious desire to penetrate deep into the very heart of Europe. The goal of this campaign was Vienna. The city which was, if not the centre of the continent, was certainly considered to be one of its main pillars. That was the phrase that Sinan, the engineer, actually used.

Bajica was not surprised when they were hosted inside the fortress by the *sancakbey* of Smederevo who reigned in Belgrade, which was now much larger and more important than Smederevo, which remained the official centre of the Belgrade frontier. Belgrade was now the central port of the Turkish fleet on the Danube, commanded by that same *sancakbey*, none other than the young Mehmed bey Jahjapašić. Because of his well-known lack of scruples, he had actually been a prime choice of the Sultan as an ideally useful local administrator.

Those were simply the ruler's decisions that no one could sway except for the Grand Vizier. Once the campaign was set in motion, all nuances of the characters of individuals that went outside the framework of the one and only goal – the future victory – were not only no longer of any importance but were even considered to be non-existent. The Ottoman forces tightened their ranks, eradicating all unnecessary differences that could spoil the mood of the troops. The Sultan placed a lot of faith in the overall atmosphere.

The one thing that Bajica and Sinan could do was to decide to stroll around the settlement at Belgrade. Each of them separately used their strengths to take in what was important to them from the particularities of this place. Bajica heard a variety of pronunciations of his mother tongue, and he amused himself by guessing from which region each of the speakers came. In addition, the intermixing of many other languages that reached him like some sort of amalgam, pleased him greatly. He thought that all places should have such a combination of a variety of languages and about how that would enrich everyone.

Sinan was busy observing structures instead of people. He was looking more than listening. His language had obviously become space and how it was filled. By Sinan's was quiet and wide-eyed demeanour, Bajica could only guess the direction in which his thoughts were leading: accepting the beauty of some buildings, rejecting others and constructing different ones in their places, and who knows what else. It was quite strange how they were together, and yet each of them in his own solitude. Neither did they bother one another, nor did they express how much they were both enjoying this togetherness in silence.

Only later, in the heat of battle, did they understand how their minds and bodies had sought this sort of purification. What was about to happen was greater than them.

When the Sultan gave the order to march, the Ottoman armada had over one hundred thousand soldiers on land, several thousand camels and horses (both for cargo and riders), three hundred cannons, and a fleet of four hundred crews sailing the Danube with twenty thousand *Armatoles*. A larger part of this armada once again passed through the mud of the Mohacs field where this time they were met by the genuflecting Turkish favourite, the inheritor of the Hungarian crown, János Szapolyai, with six thousand cavalrymen. Together they headed for Budim whose troops surrendered without a battle, but this did not prevent a massacre. Suleiman believed that, along with the re-enthronement of Szapolyai, this was the proper message to send to the Austrian ruler and pretender to the Hungarian crown, Ferdinand of Hapsburg, who had taken refuge behind the walls of Vienna with twenty thousand soldiers.

It was no wonder. Ferdinand had also received horrid news about the terrible killing and razing that went ahead of the main body of the Ottoman army. In order to ensure the safe passage of his forces, to clear the route, this time Suleiman used some thirty thousand light cavalrymen led by the savage *sancakbey* of Smederevo, Mehmed bey Jahjapašić. He was accompanied also by the Tatar horsemen, and they were followed, under the same command, by the *akinji*,[24] whose job it was to plunder from the dead whatever was left behind. The Sultan's main goal was to have his enemies quaking in fear before he ever showed up. This way, he managed even more than that: he frightened the whole western world.

Observing the tactics of the Sultan and Grand Vizier, Bajica began to understand the policies of war. Things that were normal policy in times of peace (they were few and far between), obviously did not apply in war. Leading the army meant deciding on the prioritisation of goals and then meeting them one by one with various tools and tactics. This also included extremes such as cruelty and mercy, but only if they ensured victory. Everything that was not effective was immediately changed. Commanders who did not accomplish their tasks were immediately replaced or beheaded. It became clear even with the example of Sinan how, depending on momentary need, priorities changed: Sinan was in command of a support unit when certain jobs had to get done, but from time to time he was put in charge of a janissary *orta*,[25] or even regular Anatolian troops. Although, it must be admitted, he was never, ever sent to the front lines. He was too valuable in too many ways to take such a risk. However, at the same time, his patrons did not want to miss the chance to teach him about as many things as possible in the milieu of war. Ibrahim-pasha, seeing that the friendship between Sinan and Bajica was lasting, assigned Bajica to the engineer, figuring that Sinan would teach the younger student something along the way. As a military commander, he assigned them to Lufti-pasha, whose job it was not only to supervise and train them but also to, even more so, watch out for them.

The army arrived at the walls of Vienna on September 27, not disturbed by the fact that it was already autumn and that the rains came often. However, the courageous and fierce defence by the defenders (though many times numerically weaker), the thick and forbidding ramparts and the consistently bad weather meant that the siege produced no results even after twenty days, all the way up to October 16. The Sultan ordered that the camp be broken and the army sent home. Even this decision came too late. Bajica did not know what was worse for him, seeing all those who died in battle or those who, during the retreat, wounded, ill and exhausted, left their skeletons in the bogs of the flooded plains of Slavonia and Hungary. Now he understood the influence of the weather on the campaign – both in terms of how long it lasted and also what climactic change meant for the troops. Even with winter preparation, a campaign from the Ottoman capital could not start before April, and again because of considerations of weather, it had to end before winter. And therein lay the problem that he called 'reachability' in his discussion with Sinan.

"What does that mean?" Sinan asked him.

"You should know this better than I do. It is a calculation of your reach. If you know all the facts before the campaign, from the numbers of soldiers, horses, camels, cannons, wagons, weapons, the rest stops, down to the unforeseeable and foreseeable hurdles and all the rest, and if you know all of that about the later return of the army, then it should be possible to calculate precisely *how far* the campaign can go. The outermost boundaries reachable by the army would be known, and therefore where the point of no return is."

"That's right. But you are forgetting that the boundaries of the conquered territories are constantly changing, expanding, and that means new places from which the main army can move forth."

"Yes, before Belgrade, that place was Sofia. That's also something that changes. Still, some things simply cannot be changed. The Sultan and the high commander always start the campaign from Istanbul, and that distance always remains the same, or even gets bigger. When Belgrade fell, it did make it possible to gather the army under its walls and then to move forward from there. Among other things, due to that fact, the empire has been able to set off on the conquest of Hungary, and even Austria. Even if a large part of the army from other, closer regions is already there early, the arrival of the Sultan still takes just as long. The main army from Anatolia and eastern Romelia still comes with him. The problem would disappear if the Sultan were to reign from Belgrade and if he started the campaign from there in the spring. That is impossible. Understand? I'm afraid that this problem of the army's reach is already unsolvable. Unless the siege was shorter and victory was achieved much more quickly. But above all, unless you or someone else could figure out how a heavily armed and massive army could move faster and reach its goal much earlier than in the past."

Sinan thought about it.

"Well, even when the army's return is begun too late, see how many soldiers are lost outside of battle. What you're saying does require serious thought, for sure. You're starting to act a bit like me. I would call this the distance you can, for example, throw a rock. This is precisely the way you have to think about such problems. It is important to see the problem. If you don't see it, you can't solve it. And, on the other hand, if you don't see it, that doesn't mean that it doesn't exist."

CHAPTER X

Pamuk wanted to change the subject.

"Let's take a break from the dead. Here's a quote from a chronicler, a contemporary of the Ottoman campaign of 1529; after the unsuccessful siege of Vienna, the army was accompanied by merchants with thousands of slaves, many of them women, whom the writer describes like this: 'At the bazaars they sold beautiful women with foreheads like jasmine, thick, arching eye brows, voluptuous like divine houris. Their charms were incomprehensible.' You see, a salesman is always a salesman! However, the latter abstract sentence means that people believed words, and also that in such cases of obvious and exceptional beauty, words became insufficient to express what the eye had seen. It actually speaks of the attempt at being romantic, truth is, by means of clumsily composed praise."

And then he refuted himself.

"I could, in the name of my proposal to get away from the dead, finish here, but life was obviously a marriage of the pleasant and unpleasant even back then. I made a break here, but after the romantic moment I'm talking about, this chronicler goes on as cold as ice, without taking a breath, to feed us the following statement: 'Goods, portable and permanent, people and animals, sentient beings and insentient ones, everything was left plundered or placed under the sabre. So the command was fulfilled in the Prophecy about what should be done with the infidels.' All at once now there is no beauty in people, they are 'sentient beings', yet, he still differentiates them from animals but puts them in the same category with 'insentient beings.'"

It was my turn to make a remark.

"But, look now at the next to the last sentence! Do you see how he calls killing here? 'Placed under the sabre'! So, even here the author is trying to be, if not romantic, then at least linguistically original. He probably got bored of calling common phenomena by their real names."

He chuckled.

"You got me there."

"That's not the point. I've been thinking for a long time about man's duality in possessing the beautiful and the horrid within himself at the same time, about the doing of good and evil by the same hand. I found the most drastic example in the work of a reputable Serbian historian.[26] He offers a strange depiction from 1551 when Mehmed Sokolović, during the Temisoara campaign, conquered the strategically important town of Lipovo. The campaign pushed forward, but he left a strong unit behind, headed by the Persian, Ulama-bey. The chronicler says that once this, obviously idle, commander was strolling through the town and entered a church, which they say was built by Charles I, and he spotted an organ in it. Interested in the instrument, he asked one of the Capuchin monks he found in the church to play for him 'and he felt most satisfied by it. Then he ordered that they pull five of the monk's teeth to force him to reveal the location of the treasure that a church with such music must possess'. You see, I am completely confounded by the sequential subtlety and banality that are separated by a few seconds, but I do not know what separates or joins them *in essence*. How can such traits be found so *close together*?"

Pamuk surprised me with the speed of his intuitiveness.

"Well, what if one is inside the other?"

"I don't know if there is a rule for this. Can some general conclusions be drawn, or is every example a case in itself," I asked him and myself.

"I lean toward the idea that every story is a story for itself. There is, let's say, an example from when Cyprus was conquered in 1570, of what might be called 'tragedy because of beauty'. When the Ottomans occupied the capital city of Nicosia after five weeks of siege, they murdered all twenty thousand inhabitants. Exception was made for young men and women who were, as it was said, set apart for the pleasures of the soldiers. After eight days of plundering the city, all the valuables, from gold and jewels to cannons, were loaded onto three ships, together with a thousand of the most beautiful girls who were supposed to be taken to Istanbul as slaves. However, just before departure, one of the girls discovered a load of gunpowder on one of the ships and she set it on fire. All three ships, together with the girls and the treasure, sank in a matter of minutes.

"Somehow it seems to me that, here, beauty decided in favour of tragedy. If beauty is subtlety, and this act of (self-)sacrifice is banality, then we have another link." Thus thought Pamuk.

He did not mention that the high commander of this campaign was Lala Mustafa-pasha who was to be my next example of 'cruelty out of nowhere'. Anger was insufficient as a justification. Unless it was also significant that he was indeed the younger brother of Deli Husrev-pasha, of the Sokolović family, and once long ago a member of the blood-tribute from the Edirne caravansary where, as the youngest, he was protected and counselled by his cousin Mehmed-pasha Sokolović. At the time of these events, the former was the high commander of the campaign of one hundred thousand soldiers against Cyprus, and the latter was the Grand Vizier of the Ottoman Empire.

Whatever the case, here is the story I had prepared for Pamuk.

"My example comes right after yours in time. And it happens in the same place; it's more of the same story. So, right after Nicosia, Lala Mustafa-pasha headed for fortified Famagusta, which was being defended by just seven thousand soldiers. It was October 1570, and in the spring of the next year he found himself still digging underground tunnels to the walls of the fortification and raising bastions for seventy-four cannons. The fierce battles went on for another month and a half, as long as the Venetian and Greek defenders had ammunition, and then a pact for honourable surrender was signed. The pact said that the defence commander Mark-Antonio Bragadin together with the surviving defenders could freely board some borrowed Turkish ships and sail for Candia. While that was happening, the Turks were to stay at a certain distance from the city.

"Once all the remaining fighters and inhabitants had left the fortress, the high commander of the defence, accompanied by ten of his officers, came into Lala Mustafa-pasha's camp to turn over the keys to the city. It was then that, contradictory to the pact, the pasha demanded that Bragadin leave some hostages behind as a guarantee that the ships would be returned! Demanding that the given word be honoured, the Venetian roughly refused, and the pasha reacted to that with terrible rage and ordered that all the officers be executed immediately.

"Then Lala-pasha's behaviour became incomprehensible. For the beginning, Bragadin's ears and nose were cut off, and they tortured him for another twelve days. In the words of the chronicler: 'First they tied a stone wheel to his feet, and then raised him with ropes to the top of the mast and then let him fall into the sea. Then they would hang two baskets full of soil on him and force him to climb up the walls that the army was fixing and repairing. Each time he passed by the high commander, he had to bow down to the earth. Finally, in the town square, in front of the pillory, where Turkish slaves used to be whipped, Marco Antonio Bragadin was impaled while still alive. The Venetian, instead of cries of pain, spoke the name of the Lord, to whom he was thankful because he gave him a pure heart, and soon after, he died. "Where is your Jesus now, to help you?" Lala Mustafa jeered the dead commander, and ordered the slaughter of three hundred Christian slaves. The other prisoners were, immediately afterwards, publicly emasculated.'

"And this, my friend, is not the end of the incomprehensible atrocities," I could not resist commenting on what I had read. "Here, it goes on: 'Bragadin was flayed, his body was quartered and hung above the four gates of the city, and his skin appeared stuffed with straw on a stretcher beneath a red canopy in the streets of Famagusta, as if he were alive, as if he were going to see Lala Mustafa and hand over the keys to the city. In the end, with the heads of the other officers, he was sent like that to the Sultan in Istanbul.'"

It must be admitted, I reflected, that not many crimes like this have ever been recorded. Perhaps the limits of humaneness, even when such horrors occurred, stopped the chroniclers on whatever side from giving testimony to them. Regardless of whether they were horrified by them or proud of them. On the other hand, there are exceptions like this one. Perhaps they hoped to explain how the high commander thought the defeated should behave, so he 'repeated' the ceremony of the giving of the keys in his own way.

And then I continued out loud.

"However, the story still doesn't end there. Only when Lala Mustafa-pasha returned from the campaign and triumphantly entered the capital, bringing the crowds to delirium because of the capture of Cyprus, only then did the Sultan find out the bitter truth."

Pamuk drew the wrong conclusion: "You mean, he realised how his high commander had gone overboard with his brutality?"

"No, he realised something even worse for the empire. Namely, these acts of evil by Mustafa-pasha could be explained by something that only he knew up till then, but not the Sultan or the Grand Vizier: that an

97

incredible fifty thousand Ottoman soldiers had died on Cyprus! No one could believe the number. No triumph was worth such great losses. However, in order to celebrate the victory and for the sake of history, the Sultan did not punish him publicly, but secretly he did, by a special decree. The shocked Lala-pasha was informed of it — all of the captured income from Cyprus was given to the Grand Vizier Mehmed-pasha Sokolović! This was the procedure according to a kind of in-house justice, but the question is whether this lessened the evil done."

I did not dare to open up another question on the causes of this evil that peered out as a possibility somewhere on the edges of Lala Mustafa-pasha's former religion. This sort of proving his loyalty to his new faith still seems incredible. Wasn't his immediate higher up actually the Grand Vizier, a man with the same past and a similar present? Truth be told, with quite a different understanding of faith, belonging and humanity.

Or was Lala Mustafa the only one so disturbed by the awful length of the siege itself? Perhaps those six months of temporary and obvious futility actually overwhelmed his feeling of confidence in the ultimate victory? Perhaps he tried to erase every trace of the intimate defeat which he actually survived, in spite of the indubitable victory for which there were so many witnesses.

Instead of asking those questions, I attempted to defend myself with irony:

"I thought you wanted to take a break from the dead?"

CHAPTER 10

Once again they had to part. Bajica stayed within the walls of the court at Edirne, and Sinan went with the Grand Vizier to Istanbul. The Sultan chose to rest at Edirne, although he was impatient to go on to the capital. The successful campaign was properly celebrated everywhere. As if the ruler wanted to say, 'There are myriad victories yet ahead, so I don't have to celebrate every one of them at the Topkapi palace.'

The fact that they were together at the same court did not change anything in Bajica's everyday routine. Only there was a strange feeling that he was being observed, but that was probably just his imagination. The ruler did, however, invite him in once for an audience. In his mind, Bajica termed this meeting their 'watching'. The reason was that the Sultan just stared at him in silence. After a while, he told Bajica:

"You are the one who measures the reach of the Ottoman army!" and, not waiting for an answer or a comment from his subject, roared out in laughter.

Bajica felt humiliated. He had been happy because he thought that Sinan had obviously said something to the Grand Vizier, and that he had passed it on to the Sultan. If it was like that, and it could hardly be any other way, then what he said must have been praiseworthy. But now, with this laughter, it seemed to be something to be made fun of. On the other hand, he reflected after the ruler had dismissed him, the Sultan remembered it for some reason. Just because he thought it was funny?

The answer to his question came a few years later.

Near the end of winter, Suleiman left Edirne and went back to the Topkapi palace. Bajica did not even see him leave.

Now as fate would have it, and again after a three-year wait, the Ottoman army mounted a new campaign against King Ferdinand, who had retaken the throne from János Szapolyai in Hungary. The Ottoman chroniclers called this one the 'campaign on Germany'. The army was set in motion in the spring of 1532, and it arrived, after retaking

Budim, in Graz in September when, as usual, it was too late to continue on to Vienna. Once more, this city was out of range...

Bajica was not taken on the campaign this time. He did not know why. Anyway, it was none of his business. At Edirne he went on studying all the subjects and languages he had started, now with additional lessons in court etiquette, relations to foreign emissaries, battle tactics and the tactics of political leadership.

He heard that Sinan participated in this campaign on Graz, and that he had once again entranced his ruler with his engineering feats that contributed to their continued victory. Bajica did not see Sinan on the return either, because the entire entourage was in a hurry to get back to the capital, he found out why later on.

In the meantime, the Edirne palace was visited by the state treasurer, one of the most important, powerful and wealthy men in the empire – the High Defterdar,[27] Skender Çelebi.[28] He was known for his colourful entourage that he took everywhere and which looked so extravagant that it very nearly threatened to challenge the magnificence of the Sultan's. But the ruler did not touch him for two reasons. First, the *defterdar* did his job perfectly as the caretaker of the empire's income and expenses. This reason was less important because it was not directly connected to the Sultan's vanity: it was his job, and he had to do it well one way or another. The second, more important, reason that excused the learned man's strutting about was also why he was so well known: the *defterdar* prepared the pages he took with him exceptionally well for the business of state, in every possible imaginable sense. He trained the most talented among them in the field where he himself was best – in finances, but he taught them all martial arts as well, and everything they needed to know about the etiquette of the court and of diplomacy. He was the one who most successfully equipped those specially chosen students, after they finished their schooling, in the subtleties of the skills and knowledge they needed for the most important jobs of country and court. Thus, from all the effort invested in the most talented, the Sultan once again made the greatest profit.

The high *defterdar* did not come to the court this time to balance the books, but rather to choose new pages for *his* court. His choice turned out to be almost identical to the one that Deli Husrev-pasha had made long before, where the chosen, by simply being chosen, were expected to rise to the top of the government. It so happened that Bajica was among the dozen of them. The only surprise was the additional choice of young Mustafa, whom Bajica continued to look after in the absence of his brother Husrev.

So it was that all of them, this time together with the fledgling Mustafa, set off to conquer Persia in 1533. This military baptism for them passed, surprisingly, without the usual cruelties: in the middle of the following year, with the aid of some Persian allies, the Grand Vizier, together with the pages of the high *defterdar*, entered the capital of Shah Tahmasp, the city of Tabriz – without a fight. The pages did not even witness the usual plundering, violence and ransacking in the streets by the victorious troops that usually, practically always in fact, accompanied the occupation of a town. Before long it became clear why the Ottomans were being so courteous toward the defeated: a bit later, the Sultan stood at the head of the army and, on the last day of 1534, marched with dignity into Baghdad. His dream, to capture the capital of the Caliph[29] as the ruler of the Islamic world, had come true! He could finally call himself a *padishah*,[30] at the height of his rule. And, as such, he had to prove himself righteous and worthy of the title, especially in the eyes of the newly-conquered Persian subjects.

Two significant changes happened to Bajica during this campaign. One was the result of the conflict between his master the High Defterdar Skender Çelebi and the Grand Vizier Ibrahim-pasha. Their bickering had gone on for a few years, but the Persian campaign was used as an excuse for their final showdown. The Grand Vizier had the advantage because he was the Sultan's favourite, and also because he was still married to Suleiman's sister. The end was brutal: at a public Dīvān in Baghdad, Skender Çelebi was sentenced to death by hanging in the central square. When the execution was carried out, all of his possessions were confiscated and handed over to the state treasury. In addition to his entire court and various other buildings, he left six thousand bodyguards, servants and slaves behind. Among them were also the three hundred pages of which he was most proud. They say that the vanity of the Grand Vizier was most affected by precisely this: he only had a hundred or so pages like that (while the viziers just beneath him had sixty to eighty).

Although this meant that Bajica would move into the service of the Sultan (and perhaps even into the court at the capital), he felt sorry for the *defterdar* who had been so kind to all of them. However, it was here he learned how important it was to respect the hierarchy and to not overstep one's position.

The second great change consisted of two parts, and it had to do with Sinan. In executing the first part of the plan to conquer Persia, Sinan was given the task of quickly building a large number of troop transport galleys. Managing to carry out his orders in record time and to deliver completely equipped ships to the high commander of the campaign, Sinan got the credit for the speedy deployment of the Ottoman troops over Lake Van, thus cutting off the Persian army. The victory was clean, quick and indisputable. Sinan was rewarded by being appointed as a *haseki*[31] in the Sultan's bodyguards.

And then Mimar Sinan arrived at the Baghdad bivouac to visit Bajica.

Neither of them hid their great joy at meeting again. Bajica was proud of his older friend and conveyed to him how the entire army was saying that there would have been no victory if it were not for his galleys. But Sinan did not lend much significance to that. Not that he was ungrateful, but he confided that he had had enough of weapons and destruction and the rebuilding of military fortifications. He was longing, as he intimated, to build something for life, and not for death. And then he surprised Bajica:

"It is time for me to tell you my Christian name."

He paused as if to give himself time to realise that this confession was proof of his preoccupation with life.

"My name is Josif. Since my father was a mason and a carpenter, he named me after a carpenter from Galilee, Mary's husband and Christ's stepfather."

Since Bajica, surprised by the sudden announcement, was just gaping at him, Sinan tried to lighten things up.

"What, do I have to show you some kind of proof for that?"

They were sitting in the so-called guest tent. While Bajica, rightly so, answered this question with silence because it was not a question, suddenly several pages of the Grand Vizier burst in, followed by him personally, and Bajica was frightened. They were acting skittishly, nervous and rushed. Ibrahim-pasha then told them why.

"The great Sultan has heard that Mimar Sinan is here. The Sultan wishes to see him. And here he comes."

Neither Josif or Bajica, and goodness knows neither Jusuf or Mehmed (inside them or around them, depending on how you look at it) managed to gather their wits before the Sultan was already there, in the tent, surrounded by his bodyguards. Everyone fell to their knees and bowed, waiting the result of this surprise visit.

The ruler told them to sit on cushions across from him, and told the Grand Vizier to sit at his side. To Bajica's great amazement, the Sultan spoke to him first:

"So, you are the one who is more important than his master to our hero! He came to you, O measurer of Ottoman strength, to brag about his accomplishments! Did you calculate for him whether the galleys could make it to Van? If you had, by chance, said that they couldn't, he probably would have also refused to carry out my orders and wouldn't have made the ships!"

Emphasising the words related to measurement, the Sultan completely paralyzed Bajica. For one he let Bajica know that he remembered very well who Bajica was, and for another his cynicism sent fear down Bajica's spine.

"Luckily," he went on cruelly joking on Bajica's account, "your calculations supported my orders."

The Grand Vizier was also quite surprised, but he was also the first to recognise the limits of seriousness and – he was the first to laugh out loud. When the Sultan did as well, Mehmed was relieved, and so was Jusuf.

Laughter was Bajica's only protection. No one dared to contradict the Sultan, not even in jest. Yet, if laughter helped a little bit, it did not free them from the situation. What would happen next?

The Sultan almost choked on his laughter, he enjoyed it so. However, when he realised that perhaps it might not be so funny to certain people, he suddenly stopped.

"Don't worry, I have come here with the best of intentions."

He turned to Bajica once again.

"If Mimar Sinan comes to pay homage, or to share friendship with someone, that someone is worthy of notice. But you, as you can see, I noticed even earlier. Now I'm sure that it was supposed to be that way."

Then he turned to Ibrahim-pasha.

"I think I shall reward both of them. What do you think of that?"

To Bajica it seemed that this question was meant to provoke the Grand Vizier. Or it seemed like a question that sought no answer. But Ibrahim-pasha did not take the bait.

"Well, you already rewarded Sinan with a new posting. And you can't reward this young apprentice in advance."

"Yes, but that title means nothing to Sinan. He wants to prove himself as an engineer. And young Mehmed has already proven himself by measuring out Ottoman success."

Josif and Bajica gaped at each other. These two, the highest in the Empire, were taunting each other in front of them like little children. Were they just having fun, or was this actually a provocation for Jusuf Sinan and Mehmed Sokollu? It was best to remain silent. A man is, most certainly, wisest when he is silent.

"You want to reward him for his impertinence?"

"Call it what you like, but he showed how to think reasonably and just how important it is to plan properly!"

But the pasha did not give in so easily. He continued to tantalise the Sultan.

"If anyone else in the Empire had said something like that out loud, he would have been beheaded. And you would like to show him your gratitude!"

"Because he dared to cast doubt on my opinion. I admit, anyone else would certainly have killed him if they had heard his comments on the Sultan's actions. But, since I was the one to hear it as I did, and you were a part of that, I would like to praise him for that impertinence. And anyway, why shouldn't luck play a role in all of this."

The Grand Vizier finally surrendered.

"All right, but how are you going to reward them?"

"I have already rewarded Sinan, but you don't know it."

The Sultan paused here so that everyone would see the vizier's surprise. And then he continued, "In honour of my victory at Van, achieved in part because of him, I've ordered him to immediately build a mosque with my gold and my name at that place, close to the lake carrying the same name!"

Then he turned to Sinan.

"I want to see how you get along with such measurements. Or did you come to get them from your friend? If it is so, then in the future let the young page bear a part of the responsibility and so feel the weight of his own predictions, and especially of his own reach!"

The news that Sinan had received such a magnificent offer and order aroused such joy in Bajica that it overrode the Sultan's cruel mockery aimed at him. At this moment he was not important in the least; his close friend was standing before something that he could only dream of, and that he dared not even mention out loud. And he had actually, it seemed, come straight to Bajica, maybe first, to tell him the news!

And anyway, he did not have to worry too much about himself; the Sultan had insulted him perhaps, but – he had done so gently and with a clear feeling of affection. And now the Sultan would prove that, as he explained what he had decided to Ibrahim-pasha,

"If it is already his destiny to be in my court, then I shall place him literally at my feet. Let him be my *rikabdar*."[32]

Having said this, he stood up and left. The invincible ruler paid no attention to those he left behind. Bajica did not even begin to understand what position the Sultan had just appointed him to, and a new surprise occurred. It came from Sinan who explained to the new *rikabdar* and the Grand Vizier that he had already finished the mosque and that he had not dared to tell them anything, on the command of the Sultan Legislator, about its construction. Then he pulled out several large papers from a cloth scroll and, unrolling them, showed them the blueprints of the mosque that he had built in Suleiman's name.

"I did these before the construction. Now they are out of date. If the two of you only knew what a magnificent feeling it is to see something lasting, something that arose from the illusion of imagination! Now, I could go ahead and die."

Bajica had been right. Sinan had indeed come to him to share the joy of his first, as he would say 'peacetime', job, but not at its beginning, rather when it was already finished. Though it sounded unfortunately warlike to say so, this was a huge victory. With no casualties. The very way Bajica dreamed that wars could be won.

Construction, and not destruction.

CHAPTER XI

In accordance with our previously unsuccessful agreement to take a break from the dead, I tried to give a different understanding to Pamuk's reading and my initial interpretation of the chronicler's sentence where he says, '...everything else was destroyed or placed under the sabre'. I originally thought that this *placing under a sabre* meant killing, but it did not have to be so. Later it occurred to me that it could mean 'mastered', 'taken into ownership' or perhaps something else as well. In that case the author was trying to be original in his language use, and not to obscure another brutality with language.

Pamuk congratulated me on my good intentions, but not without a bit of mocking. Understandably: I was using language, a bit naïvely, to attempt to justify actions, regardless of their nature. However, a clearly seen act was more convincing than words. It was good to use words like false witnesses: then, truth and lies are received with equal weight.

But, if mocking was in play, I had a weapon of my own at hand.

In mid-2006 (more precisely May 3), unasked and whether he liked it or not, Pamuk was caught in the favourite American pastime of numbers, placed on a rather unusual list in *Time* magazine, among the '100 Most Influential People' of the world, somewhere between George Bush and Bono Vox. If memory serves, he was actually the only writer on the list.

"How do you defend yourself against such gaudy public displays, when you have no say in them unless it's later, and only then if they ask you, and only if they ask you at all, about your opinion? And when it's too late for your opinion, especially if it doesn't agree with that of the general public. Well, maybe if it's not altogether too late."

I asked him this, in such detail and a bit rhetorically, because the event was fresh; the list had been published just before he arrived in Serbia.

"With humour. I try to be funny. Isn't that what the journalists actually asked me in Belgrade: why hadn't I stayed in America for the celebration of the occasion in New York, when I was already there? I answered, if you remember, that I had an appointment in Belgrade! Isn't that right, and at the same time funny?"

"That's right. Still, it's interesting that you were placed on the list between two 'warriors for world justice', which classifies you with them. In fact, a pretty good argument could be raised about the various ways different individuals fight that battle."

"And that is something people discuss. Even the activities of the front man of U2 are often criticised. Those who think nothing good about the American president condemn Vox's meeting with him. That's understandable. On the other hand, maybe Vox is just shrewd and knows that without the top man of the world's greatest power he cannot achieve his goals. I am another story. My words are heard and read with additional care, but I have no illusion about my own influence – especially about my power to change things. Perhaps all I do is encourage others by saying out loud some of the things they don't say which, and even if the words came from their mouths, would otherwise never reach the public."

"You don't have the power to influence things directly, but it can be seen that you do so indirectly or with a time delay. You pulled none of the levers, but you pointed at some. That perhaps, at least partially, relieves you of responsibility. Which is not such a bad position to be in. Still, it has another side to it: it's easy for them to misuse you if they so wish. It's hard to defend yourself from that. As if everything has its price."

"Fortunately I don't have such grandiose ideas about changing the world, nor the desire to be the one who implements them. Anyway, I'm already paying the price for much less important ideas. The bills come in from various sources."

"Seems to me they're coming in from *all* sides."

Already in my own mind, I staved off the possible entrance into an open conversation on politics, remembering Pamuk's perfect defence against it: "Politics bores me!" No matter how arrogant this may sound, no matter whom it comes from, such a qualification of politics is excellent. It places politics in its proper place: among useful, necessary activities, but far from essential creativity and the source of motivation in man.

Among other things, as long as we kept to the story about numbers in literature, it made sense and was an essential connection with the humour in it. The mathematics in and mostly around literature was an inexhaustible topic, perfectly suited to creative thought. Those were waters we swam well in.

For example, both of us had the habit of asking the other how many pages the novel will have that we are currently writing, to what page of a manuscript one of us has reached at a certain moment, when we will bring it to an end... Although those simple calculations made some sort of sense, we often used them as a cause for joking, if not for something more difficult and serious. From this humorous phantasm came our little stories about books as 'fat babies' or 'middle-sized babies' or about the 'more or less frequent bearing of those children' and so on.

Anyway, in addition to this amusing arithmetic, I also quite liked geography. I could get myself into such a situation that I could no longer write what I wanted to as an author... without the use of maps and geographic charts. And once I have delved into them, they are quickly joined by the irresistible use of photographs, pictures, graphics, drawings, engravings – generally anything considered to be visual. Taken as a whole, dealing with these interesting puzzles sometimes seems like a return to the lower grades of elementary school. I admit it, this makes me happy because it returns me to that unrepeatable excitement that comes when one learns or discovers something for the first time! I know that nothing can be compared to that feeling. Except for, perhaps, the very act of writing? In fact, writing does not indeed differ much from that original learning and discovering.

I wrote one of my novels, after the usual preparatory research and then after discarding everything I had learned (which was in the spirit of the book in that case), holding a booklet of photographs in front of me that served the whole time as a guide through my imagination. Paradoxical? To base one's fantasising on photos that were, as someone noted, 'facts frozen in time'? In other words, to use the real live (visual) *document* for creating its very opposite – the unreal. Whatever, I had an unforgettable time.

On the other hand, another friend of mine, Alexander Genis, has no problem coping with numbers, not even in jest. He has his own rhythm of writing, most certainly – and a set length (in his case it would be better to say – shortness) of his texts, but he is not burdened by this in the least. Actually because he writes most of his texts primarily for the Russian program of a radio station in New York and therefore has to take great care about the number of minutes – air-time on the radio is an absolute and obsessive ruler (Legislator – Kanuni) – and yet he seems like someone who could not care less about time expressed in numbers. I am enchanted by that. You see, since he is greatly enamoured with the ancient wisdom of China and Japan and even more knowledgeable about the art and skills of the Far East, everything inside this paradox is in its place: he and time and the cosmos.

A Russian who has never been Americanised, Genis is actually an orientation point for me. Whenever I forget myself in unjustifiable detail, I remember his economy with words. Of course, that economy would make no sense if it did not produce highly condensed wisdom, and often with it a discriminating humour. For example, when I recently returned from my first visit to China (where Genis has been several times) and wrote him about the wonderful impressions I brought back, he answered me: "I think I was Chinese in my previous life. The only problem is I have never believed in a previous life."

This paradoxical character arises from this (present) life, and not just from his nature. And his life is full of it. Once when I asked what all of them – the Russians – were doing there in America, remaining consistently apart from all the others there for decades, he told me that they constantly criticise Americans. He had to leave the Soviet Union in 1977, for example, in order to realise that *the shortest route* to making his dream come true about writing and publishing *in Russian* – was to leave Russia! And where (or better said – *from where*) does all of that become a reality? As if to spite logic, at the completely (ever) opposite socio-political pole. That the USA and USSR/Russia today are not what they once were, has not stopped people from all over the world from seeing them as perfect examples of difference.

Actually, a word for word quotation is more precise and better and more all encompassing than an interpretation. So, here is what Genis said, exactly, using Martin Luther King, the Bible and the blues simultaneously, "I had a dream. I dreamt the freedom to write and publish in Russian. Paradoxically, the shortest path to that dream was to leave Russia." When one adds to the 'American pie' (a black human rights leader, God and music) 'some Russian vodka with a pickle' (melancholic sadness, tragedy and eternity), one gets a proper mix of the western-eastern view of the world. For me, Genis is the best medium (mediator), and not just a writer, of these relative extremes. If I could by chance convince all the countries on the globe to make a single universal textbook on the differences and similarities of the most intriguing countries in the world – America and Russia – but with an ideal, far-eastern distance in position, I would entrust the writing of it precisely (and perhaps exclusively) to Alexander Genis.

CHAPTER 11

Having become a courtier, for the next ten years Bajica followed a sure path to success. However, it should be kept in mind that such success in most cases and with most people was not a given. He often asked himself, indeed, what was protecting him from temporary setbacks and, God forbid, complete failure. Although the answer to that question came to him much later, it did not diminish the significance of what he learned: he had been lucky with his very *first appointment*! Namely, unlike the others, he was not appointed by the Sultan's underlings as was the custom. In the intertwining of known events, he had been chosen personally and directly – by the Sultan himself! While not even this was a guarantee for his future and certain ascent to the top, it did eliminate all the others who might make decisions about his destiny, and there were many who would have liked to. Now and henceforth he was available, come what may, to just one man, although that one man actually had unlimited power. The good and the bad thing about this position was the fact that he was under constant observation by the great ruler. This forced him to be cautious all the time, and made him learn everything possible about the tasks at hand. It was almost as if he could not blink without it being noticed by the Sultan. Not that the Sultan spent his time constantly watching Bajica, of course, but the *fact* that he could see him at *any* given moment kept Bajica on the tips of his toes. This actually helped Bajica to see his position not with the fear of possibly making a mistake, but as an opportunity to see straightaway if his master was satisfied with his work or not. In fact, it was a chance to constantly prove himself. He thus had an enormous advantage over all the others. He just had to free his mind for it.

Such freedom did not remove the suspicion he had, based on other cases, that no matter how great the protection was that he had from the great ruler, it could not ultimately and completely save him from the attempts of the envious, jealous and evil to take vengeance on him, hurt him, to take away his position or even his life. The first rule of entering the arena of the court was to put his naïveté aside, or even expunge it completely if that were possible. The very thought was a sign that he had already begun to do so.

The Sultan himself offered him a lot of help: all of the positions he was about to be granted were located in closest proximity to the ruler. Yet, even though this given proximity saved him from unknown, and later surreptitious, competition and opposition, it also increased the intolerance and even hate of some people toward him.

In addition to being close to the Sultan because of his position, Bajica spent a lot of time with his ruler for one other reason: Suleiman was constantly on the move throughout that whole decade. And when he was outside the court, he was relieved of a large number of various protocol and often excessive responsibilities that otherwise drew his attention to other things and places. Absurd but true: outside the court, his range of movement within the camp or outpost was actually restricted! Thereby he paid far more attention to his entourage and underlings. For Bajica, this meant doing service without interruption, practically non-stop, because this interpersonal focus selfishly demanded his constant presence at the Sultan's feet. Because of that, the ruler was often in a position to test his loyalty and capability, which pleased him, of course, and so he depended more and more on his page. This series of actions and reactions turned into a sort of magic circle.

But something else was also happening. Bajica also saw that being too close to the Sultan was dangerous. The case he saw could not have been a better example. The ruler's best friend from childhood, the first man beneath him in the empire – Grand Vizier Ibrahim-pasha – lost the Sultan's confidence at a certain moment. Because, it seemed, his power went to his head. The ruler had to remind him of his place, and that the first minister of the Empire was still just his slave (in this case – Greek slave) and nothing more than that. And he punished him – with death. One night in 1536, a silk noose arrived in his bed.

With the Sultan (and with the new grand viziers, Ajas-pasha briefly, and later Lufti-pasha) during those ten years, Bajica went through all manner of things: through a six month campaign from Istanbul to Valona and a battle with the Venetians over Corfu in 1537; half of the next year he spent on the road between Istanbul and Moldavia in order to punish a disobedient vassal, Count Petru Rareş, at Suceava on the Prut River. In the summer of 1541 he marched on Buda, occupied most of Hungary, and two years later he repeated this pilgrimage with new conquests. When he was not heading war campaigns, out of his own vigour Suleiman organised frequent hunting trips so that his did not give his entourage a moment's peace.

As time went by, his unwavering trust only changed forms through the positions he gave Bajica. When the time was right, he appointed Mehmed to be his *çohadar*.[33] And so Bajica was ever close to the Sultan, even in a literal and material sense, coping with his kaftans, turbans, sables, golden stitchings and hundreds of other details that created the ruler's look. This position made it possible that others began addressing him as an aga. The next form of this strange intimacy and literal proximity was attained through a special degree of trust: in addition to his expected ceremonial tasks, the Sultan began to entrust him with special assignments of a diplomatic, military or semi-confidential command character. With that, he gave him a new title: he appointed him to be the *silahdar-aga*,[34] which made him even more visible, and even imposing, being so tall and slim, as he had to walk beside the Sultan on his right arm with a sabre over his right shoulder. Later he appointed him as the *chesnegir-basha*.[35] With this gesture as well, it was as if Suleiman was showing everyone his even more complete trust in Mehmed, and that without him nothing could go on. But that was not the end: he appointed him the high *kapidzi-başa*.[36] Bajica now had an open path to the high offices of the state. Because this, the *highest court position*, in addition to including jobs such as escorting foreign emissaries to the ruler during official audiences, it was also of such significance to the Sultan that he used the basha for confidential missions, for delivering secret letters and messages of the Porta to administrators in the provinces, for delivering the Sultan's silk nooses and *katil-fermans*[37] and so on. So it was that Bajica became an influential person in the court, and a new position was on his horizon, the first outside the court – the office of *sancakbey*.[38]

In all of the Sultan's business, and especially on his military campaigns, Mehmed was not eager to show his soldiering skills. Aware that they were not attractive to him, and that he did not really have them, he directed all of his capability from warring toward the skills of planning, organising, negotiating, making agreements, and later giving orders...

What the Sultan found attractive about him was that Mehmed could turn vision into action and then both, vision and action, into success. Because if he did not know how to execute this final stage, his skill would not have meant much to Suleiman. In doing so, Bajica showed that his way, as opposed to that of all others close to the Sultan, produced clear and tangible results, and not just whimsical outcomes. The Sultan tested him quite skilfully on small and almost unimportant examples, carefully, and then practically unnoticed placing ever larger and more responsible dilemmas, problems and tasks in his hands.

In this period when Bajica/Mehmed became the Sultan's favourite clearly and publicly, his friend Josif/Sinan got his own protégé in the person of the grand vizier, and not just one of them. In that same period, in addition to and after his military commendations, after the campaigns on Corfu and Moldavia 1537–38 Sinan was also awarded with civil recognitions (among other things, because of the swift construction of the bridge over the Prut River, though once again – for military purposes, and it contributed to the victory). He was appointed the *subasha*, the official supervisor of construction work in certain parts of the Empire. Soon after, death and dismissals in high places in the court raised him to the highest possible rank among engineers, the *mimarbasha*, the top engineer of the Empire. In 1538, the imperial architect Achem Alisi-aga passed away, and the new appointed *sadr-i azam*, Grand Vizier Lufti-pasha could hardly wait to appoint, heart and soul, Sinan to his place, under the official title *Koca Mimar*.[39] In any case, there was practically no one better or more desirable who knew of his construction feats to that time: namely, Lufti-pasha was Sinan's last troop commander at war in the earlier military campaigns in Rumelia and Persia, and he was in a position to constantly check first hand Josif's many capabilities. In addition, he had also tried him out in the skills of constructing urban edifices: two years before he had charged him with building a proper bath. So, Sinan built a hamam in the Yenickbahce quarter of Istanbul.

Both Mehmed and Sinan used the campaigns on Corfu and Moldavia to spend time together whenever that was possible. They were first to cross Sinan's wooden bridge (later award-winning) on the Prut River, proving that its construction time of just thirteen days did not mean that it would only last the same number of days (to the contrary, it was used for years and years). It was that example where Bajica saw how the impossible becomes possible: the Sultan and Grand Vizier were indeed surprised by the speed of the construction, but more importantly the enemy was even more surprised by that speed. So much so that they did not even manage to stop being surprised in time, and much less to prepare themselves for their defence.

On these campaigns, actually in this decade of warring and constant absence from the capital, both Sinan and Mehmed became conscious of the huge changes in their own lives and the changes in the sum of their years. Sinan had already passed fifty, in full maturity, crowned with the highest of titles, but knowing that his real and most important works still lay ahead of him. Mehmed, in his thirties, rewarded, but still not as much as he was to be... Less than his friend, just as much as the difference in their years would not allow him to catch up. This was the external form of their relationship. In essence, Sinan (often openly, out loud) did away with the difference in their ages because Mehmed had attained a special, quite early type of wisdom that made up for that difference; already early on, it was obvious that that wisdom would draw even with Sinan's engineering practicality of mind, and place them both in the position of being complete equals.

And indeed, that happened before they even began to think about it.

CHAPTER XII

All of us spend a lot of time looking for similarities and/or settling differences (of all kinds). For instance, the differences between Russia and America. In addition to the rare self-critical, objective citizens of those countries, I have received help from living mediators in discussions on these matters. Two of them are Canadians. They are, however, quite different from each other: one of them is the writer, David Homel, an American who moved to Montreal and became a Canadian citizen, and the other is Leonard Cohen, a Canadian who moved to Los Angeles and kept his Canadian citizenship. There is a third who, in fact, I do not know personally, named Ronald Wright, a Brit who writes from Canada about America. That is probably why I do not know what citizenship he has chosen. Why do I bring all of them up? Well, because they all, like Alexander Genis, are attempting to qualify (modern) America, in addition to other things. But the importance and wealth of their various positions is not founded only on their differing characters but also *on the places* (origins) *from which they speak.* You see, they do not watch that world from a normal window, but from a box seat of differing and not quite average identities that give them the ability to see, in addition to what the object of their attention is (in front of them), a few important things in the periphery of that object (to the sides, left and right). And no matter how wide that horizon is, what they see is not the same. Or, if it is the same – they do not see it the same.

It is understood that they have entered that society by everything they have written and said earlier, both in general and especially on this topic.

It is my duty to explain to others and to myself why I have chosen the example of America from all the possible choices.

Well, because it is such a challenge, being so enormous (both as a topic and as a country). It is exceptionally easy to fail, miss the mark, or make a mistake on this topic. It is extremely difficult to make judgments about it. And it is a great success if one manages to say something coherent and correct about it. In order to do so, as in all other things, one must be *authoritative*.

Yet, authoritative people are those who the general public has hardly ever heard of. Many important people have met them, of course, and it was important that they meet them. But such people, the authoritative, are withdrawn and quiet, and in their withdrawal and silence they do an enormous job for the culture of their country. In that very America, I also met some significant, I cannot say famous – but certainly – important people who are indeed considered to be important, and they were also authoritative, but because of the fact that they were so publicly visible they lost their essential authoritativeness as time went by. But why? In most cases because they accepted the offered role of being an entertainer, probably satiated with their own intellectual efforts, and powerless to resist the offer of be(com)ing very famous. When talking about this, I remember that Allen Ginsberg in New York told me, without provocation or my insistence, a rather weird truth, essentially important for the Beatnik movement and for him personally: that the officially accepted date of the *beginning* of the existence of the Beat movement of 1956 (the time of the lawsuit related to his *thereafter* world famous poem 'Howl'), actually, was the date of the *end* of the Beat Generation. This was the incontrovertible truth, although the Beat movement was still alive then (in 1984, when he told me that): most of the main characters were still alive and active, above everything and everyone – Ginsberg himself. Furthermore, a new generation – followers of the movement – had arisen who carried on with it (for a reason). However, at the same time, the climax of the Beat lay behind its creator and all of us. Was that statement Ginsberg's preparation for justifying his future literary and popular culture behaviour which, said politely, went far from the source? Yes. Several years later I reminded him of that, and told him that in Belgrade, although I hedged at an open conversation with him on that topic. However, it was then that he took me in anew: he admitted that I was right! He rose above his own fall and (by his admission) proved that there was a reason why he was the forerunner of several generations. He said that after all, for the sake of the fall, he had to think about how he would be remembered. Well, he is the symbol of that kind of exclusive people who history turns into phenomena, like the Beatles and Bob Dylan! After all, aren't his meetings

117

with them considered to be historic dates? And when he died, death was the loser because he surpassed it by being remembered well, as he should be. As for me, I agreed, with piety and respect, to the request of a daily newspaper to write a farewell text to him on that occasion. I even gave the editors one of my most beloved photographs of Allen and me together, with Peter Orlovsky somewhere in background (the photograph was never returned after it was published). Hopefully I atoned for my friendly admonishment.

For the sake of that same atonement I guess he had 'revealed' his thoughts back then about the important dates of the Beat (I actually believe that he began talking about that openly afterwards, when he realised that such an 'admission' did no harm to the movement). But he did so because I placed him in the situation of being *his very self*. Here is what that means: while making a documentary TV film about him at that time, my crew and I taped him for several days in a row and got him to be everything he is in a compact period of time. In front of the camera, he 'had to' answer my questions, to recite lines from his poetry and poems, to sing, to play instruments, to perform Chinese martial arts (on the roof of his building) and a lot of other things, all of it exclusively in the atmosphere of his home. Thus, without any sort of conscious intention, I got him into the state of being the 'sensitive self', the 'omnipresent', focused on himself to such an extent that he went numb and sank into what he was in essence, so that even meditation was unnecessary (although he sat in a lotus position during the interview and, breathing rhythmically, occasionally pronounced his mantra 'OM'). In fact, we had meditated together on some earlier occasions, in one of my former little apartments in Belgrade (which he liked terribly, though to this day I do not know why). But then meditation had been necessary for us to isolate ourselves from the excesses of the world and to return to our true selves.

In the case of his apartment on the Lower East Side of Manhattan, I dared to think that Ginsberg, alone there, was able to come back to himself and I got him into the state where he was what he was, only slightly more so.

This, too, falls under the topic of keeping and/or changing identities.

On the other hand, it is worthwhile to clear up a rather large mistake, at the cost of perhaps being the first one to say so: although it looked like he was dealing with selfish questions of his being, and he was quite focused on himself, Allen Ginsberg spent his whole life dealing with the idea of the United States. Because of that persistent search, he had many serious problems with the government. He rose above that government because, as opposed to it, he was capable and courageous enough to speak publicly of not only the truths he discovered but also of the mistakes he made.

Beneath the questions of identity, nation and 'collectivity' are not the only issues (as they are often treated in the Balkans in 'old' Europe). The question is *who we are* in essence; personally; individually. Although seemingly more limited, this is an incredibly wider view of identity.

There is one more, almost completely hidden, reason for that part of the intimate search for the identity of America and of the self in America, ultimately strange and perhaps only incidental: most of the people mentioned (I knew) had or still have family ties with Russia, be it their grandmothers who came from who-knows-where, to distant, complicated Christian Orthodox-Jewish roots. If this conclusion proved to be just a possible speculation, the fact remained that some of them worked on the question of America through an almost monolithic vision of Judaism and Christianity (whether western or eastern). Right or wrong, they thus certainly expanded and enriched the specific question of the understanding of identity in the USA.

That which is a specificity in the phenomenon of identity is contained in its very basic meaning. Namely, both the scientific and linguistic explanation are constructed of the convergence of opposites because it is said that "the identity is a collection of symbols that characterise a person or object by which it is differentiated from other persons or objects". Thus, the set of *different* symbols is made up of a sum of *identical features* that then become (again) *different* in relation to others! When we know that the word 'identity' has 'identicalness' at its root (New Latin, *identitas*), thus 'sameness', it becomes obvious that this concept in essence is manifested only after going from sameness to differentness. It is as if language, from the very inception of its work, wrapped this concept in contradiction. Therefore, it is not strange that everyone has been dealing with this question for so long, more or less successfully, but in any case – without interruption. This contradictory character, desiring to expand the circle of those who might understand it, often floated into mere populism and thus dulled the edge of its own significance, only to end up abused and in the shallows.

It is worthwhile to return to the authoritative but quiet.

CHAPTER 12

Their birthplaces meant something after all. In terms of their personal, intimate feeling for the soil, Josif and Bajica were different. This became especially evident when their travels to ever more distant territories that the Empire ruled over or had recently annexed became more frequent. Persia, Arabia and Rumelia spread across three continents! The Ottoman Empire had footholds in Asia, Africa and Europe, its fleet sailed on all the seas that connected and separated them.

Being from Anatolia by birth, Josif more lightly accepted and experienced journeys around the east. They were harder for Bajica. In contrast, campaigns around his native Rumelia returned him, in truth, more to a familiar, awakened feeling for that region than he actually recognised in reality. His furtive joy at travelling to that land had its price. Under the surface of the basic and inevitable reason for going there – because the Sultan had so ordered – was hidden a reason for him alone: deep in his soul he had to accept an image of himself as a powerful warrior who took whatever should be his without hesitation. Not after he had conquered it, but rather after he had even *thought* that it belonged to him, and then resolved (because of the thought) to conquer it as well. This was the sacrifice made in order to be in the place where he was loyal in an essential, primal way. Even after all the time since his original departure from Bosnia and Serbia, he still got the jitters (less evident but more persistent than those he felt when standing in front of the ruler) whenever he set foot there or even drew close. He understood, using the example of his own name, that Mehmed then turned back into Bajica, and upon returning, Bajica became Mehmed again. As time went by, this duality became his natural state; constantly and unceasingly demanding that he think about it; it broke him, tortured him and sometimes rewarded him, but always demanded that he wrestle with it. As if it forced him to admit that he himself was the duality.

Jusuf was a little more Ottoman than Mehmed only by virtue of geography. Bajica could not deny him the fact that the territory of the original Empire was Josif's natural surrounding from the earliest childhood; he was born in the very heart of the Ottoman lands, even though his parents were not. Because of his different place of birth, and not only because of that, of course, they had managed to implant enough of the Christian in him that he could do battle with his duality. In Rumelia, which in terms of personal experience of territory was unknown to him all the way up till the conquest marches in which he participated, Jusuf had built military structures and torn a few down, but in his dreams he built places of worship, schools and hospitals all over the Ottoman lands, including its eastern part. To him, Serbia and Bosnia were on the fringes of the Empire.

Bajica gave him this difference, but there was no way he could make peace with it. He told Jusuf that views can and must change, and that one day he would begin to build on the fringes as well, even if he never began to dream about them.

"Doesn't the Sultan himself consider Serbia, Bosnia, Slavonia ... as equal parts of the Empire? Even when he says of them that they are *his route to reach* Hungary! Well, then he could say that of Hungary that it is *only his route* to reach Vienna! And if he had plans for conquering lands even further north, where would the end be? Therefore, we can call every part of the Empire the 'fringes'. Anyway, at a certain moment almost every part of the land actually is distant from the centre, isn't it? New conquests constantly change all the borders, and thereby not just the position and shape but the very meaning of the centre and the periphery."

"You are certainly right. But you have to understand that I come from a place that always belonged to the Empire. The place where you come from is nothing like mine. Perhaps it will remain a part of the Empire forever, but just recently it wasn't, isn't that right?"

"Whether it remains in the Empire or not, would you build something there if given the chance, and not just if you were ordered to?"

Sinan did not have answer him. Both of them knew just how much the mosque at Van had aroused his desire to build. It was talking to him, with its perfection it was showing him that the things he dreamed could actually exist!

CHAPTER XIII

Authoritative and quiet.

In the 1970s and 1980s, Belgrade seemed to be the centre of the world. Or, at least, one of its centres. Or perhaps the whole world, in its head, was like that? An exaggeration? Sure. On the other hand, the spiritual side of life always excelled in this milieu, and that is actually not any kind of overstatement. Into that Belgrade world, so many interesting (so-called public) figures came that there were those who arrived unnoticed and departed, and everyone found out about their sojourn only after they had left.

Already at the end of this cycle, this trend... whatever we call it, in October of 1989, a poet from the United States of America named Kenward Elmslie arrived in town. He stayed in Belgrade for seven to ten days. As his host and as the translator of his poetry, and also as a fellow writer, I showed him the sights of the city, and above all, the people. There was a plan to introduce him to the public at the end of his stay. I just had to figure out how. It turned out not to be quite so easy. Namely, Elmslie was, as they say – a multi-faceted artist. In addition to his profession – the epithet poet – he was known for several others: 1. Fiction writer – the author of several books of stories and novels. One of his publishers was the famous magazine *Paris Review*; 2. Playwright; 3. Writer of librettos for operas; 4. Lyric writer for so-called popular music. Some of his songs were played on jukeboxes, sung by Nat King Cole. 5. Composer; 6. Publisher, editor of Z Press. The American audience used two rather rare expressions to describe him: one was the *singing poet* (because he often sang his poetry), and the other was *songsmith* (after the model of the 'blacksmith'. So, they considered him a maker of songs). Kenward Elmslie actually belonged to the real American, non-populist elite. That is why there was an occasional voice from the outside that supported him along with the one-time criticising of the public, as the famous writer John Ashbery did once in the magazine *Parnassus*: 'Elmslie is a uniquely underrated poet'. Yet, perhaps this was compensated for a bit by his guest appearances at American universities where he held his literary 'performances' in front of hundreds and thousands of young people. He did the same thing, as a lover of travel, in various places in the world.

That sort of satisfaction was what probably gave him the idea to hold some kind of performance, together with me, in Belgrade. So it was that an older New Yorker and a youngish man from Belgrade practiced their roles for a few days, reciting, singing, dancing, reading and all of that to Elmslie's recorded music in the background played on cassette. On the day of the Event (scheduled at the Student Cultural Centre), I was experiencing excruciating pain from an attack of pleurisy. Ken wanted to cancel when he saw that I could hardly move, and much less walk. But I did not. I faced the public stoically. A moment before that Elmslie had again wanted to cancel, but this time because there were only four and a half people in the audience. Of whom, two were from the American embassy. Probably on assignment. Again I refused to give up. I smiled and said that we had to be professionals. I acted like I did this every day! And in the end there was applause after all. The essence was fulfilled.

Since the time came soon after for him to depart, I proposed that we play a joke on the public. I was able to pull this off because (I also had several simultaneous professions, thank you very much) in the weekly *NIN* I was the editor of the column 'People' which briefly informed the readers of interesting things that were happening with public figures. So, after the biographical data about Elmslie in my article, to my question about how he managed to live from writing (elite literature) and reading what was written, he answered that it was difficult (and then explained that), and at the end he added that he got a little financial aid when something 'trickled down' from his grandfather. Of course, the question followed of who his grandfather was, and the answer: Joseph Pulitzer.

Just as one might expect (it would be more correct to say – as we expected, and not to say as we directed) there was a proper public uproar. The interest of journalists in him was enormous. But it was too late. The article was published, as we had planned, after Elmslie had already gone.

And here at the end is the lesson. Being a descendant of Joseph Pulitzer from birth, as this grandson grew up, he realised as time passed that the creative future he had embarked toward was threatened by his name. He wanted his creative work to represent its ultimate quality, unburdened by the name of the famous family. He figured out that, bearing that surname, he would never be sure if Art accepted him as an authentic artist or if it was only/mainly because of family privileges. What if he thought that he could not even write like that? That sort of honesty, of course, was a two-edged sword: the artistic life was not easy, but it was real. As opposed to him, his brother did not change his name and, the irony of it, the so-called yellow press was constantly full of his various affairs (to which he was prone). With time, Elmslie began to 'add' his grandfather to his bibliography because he (Kenward) had already achieved an undeniable reputation as a serious artist. Now the public omission of the Pulitzer surname, mostly in broadcasting situations, defended him from the excesses of people and 'cheap' stories. And, as we have seen, he was able to joke about it.

To be honest, there was one facet of Elmslie's identity that I was not sure I should meddle in. That is, it should be remembered that Joseph Pulitzer (1847–1911) was the creator of yellow journalism, together with, somewhat later, William Randolph Hearst (1863–1951). The two of them were the owners of a large number of newspapers and magazines, reaching millions in circulation actually by publishing sensationalist texts. (Hearst was the creator of the comic 'Yellow Kid' whose name was the origin of this type of journalism.) It is possible that grandfather Pulitzer began to feel remorse, so in 1903 he founded journalism studies at Columbia University. That personal journey toward becoming serious continued *post mortem* when, in 1917, the Pulitzer Prize was established for journalism, caricatures, literature (fiction, poetry, drama, biography and history), and after 1943 for musical composition. It must be admitted that he achieved his goal, because it is generally accepted that only one other award is more respected than the Pulitzer – the Nobel Prize. Or, said more precisely: after the Nobel Prize, *the most famous* is the Pulitzer, if not the most respected.

So, obviously I concluded that these facts should be mentioned *because* I realised that they were actually the main drive of Elmslie's behaviour in public. Not to mention his behaviour in private; for example, much later when he asked me to come visit him in America so that we (that is *he*) could translate one of my books into English together! My humbleness won out over his: I declined.

Elmslie's partial, 'majority' concealment of identity (like escape from the yellow press) *is indeed* a story about America. His behaviour in itself said a lot about modern America, and then it further gave him the right to explicitly sketch, explain or qualify his own culture and country, based on the example of his own grandfather – the magnate. Not because 'we asked for it' but because he (K.E.) deserved it.

Kenward Elmslie was quiet, and he became authoritative.

The confusion arises because his grandfather was so loud (worldwide), but in the end, the literal end – after his death, he also became authoritative.

I suppose that is another part of democracy.

CHAPTER 13

It was as if they both simultaneously felt an irresistible urge to build and not tear things down. Or at least to build more and tear down less. This followed on naturally after feeling the blessings of making something that was useful to others. And after they had left behind enough destruction, in which they had indeed participated, and which had made others unhappy. Yet, the strongest motive lay in their personal satisfaction that had mastered a hard-to-control destructiveness. Both Bajica and Sinan knew how thin the line is that separates a decision about a good action from a bad one. They had witnessed such decisions. As long as they were just observers or the executors of others' decisions, those decisions could be withstood. However, as they drew close to their new responsibilities, those coming with each new higher position, they were forced to cope with making their own decisions, and they had to begin to think about how they would handle themselves and those decisions. Briefly stated, they needed to prepare themselves. They dared not allow themselves to be surprised by much of anything. In addition to the rest, because being surprised began to cost more as the level of their responsibility grew. It did not cost others more. Rather them. They thought about this and openly discussed it, though only face to face, the fact that greater authority also meant greater responsibility. Though it was not the same for everyone. There was a rule, but not for everyone. There were those who only took on greater authority without the proportionate increase in responsibility. Some people even reduced their responsibility, encouraged by possessing greater power. Such people were taking a risk, blinded by their own greatness or forgetting that they had gotten where they were because someone more powerful than them made it possible. Until that powerful person warned them, sometimes too late. Then they lost their money, properties and title. And occasionally their heads. And those who did not use their heads – lost their lives.

The need to build (not only literally) appeared as a natural defence against destruction. But it also happened when it became clear to Josif and Bajica that they had irrevocably begun to live as Jusuf and Mehmed. And this was only made possible due to the inclinations of the Grand Vizier and the Sultan, who kept appointing them to higher offices. They had to face the truth that a full return to what they had been until recently was no longer possible. Yes, they could do so in part; they had time to come up with ways of returning. The issue that imposed itself by its very nature, from the moment when it became obvious that their new lives were following an upward course, was the need to take care of their families. They consulted each other on how to do this.

When the re-settlement of the non-Turkish population to Cyprus from Anatolia began on order of the Sultan, Mimar already felt free enough to intervene on behalf of his parents with the Grand Vizier. His request was granted and his mother and father were left in peace, and they were actually given additional security as demanded of the local authorities.

Bajica's family situation was much more complicated. His entire family lived much further from the centre of the Empire (although they were now *inside* it), and there were many more of them. For many years he did not even know if they were alive, much less if they were in good health. Using his passages through Belgrade on military campaigns, from there he sent messages to his family in Sokolovići in various ways, but he never found out if those messages had reached them. His help to his family began when he was the Sultan's sinahdar-aga, and when he was encouraged to do so in 1540 for the first time, encouraged by his comrade Ahmed-bey from the court school, likewise a Serb. Ahmed-bey, familiar with the lay of the land and the people, was sent to collect taxes in Bosnia, and he offered Bajica a favour because his visit would take him to the area they were from. Bajica got general permission to do what he wanted with his family, so he asked his friend to bring any of the Sokolović family he found to Istanbul if he could. So it was that, after all those years, he finally had his brothers and father standing before him. In fact, he did not know at the time that his youngest brother had stayed with his mother in Bosnia, and that the person in front of him was a cousin who looked like his brother. His mother had held him back because she refused to part with *all* of her sons, saying, "If they are not with me, then I don't care if they are dead or if they are living like kings."

Unfortunately, after only two years the older of the two brothers, now known as Mustafa, died at the Galata court, and Bajica passed his name on to the youngest brother who was relocated from Galata to the Sultan's court, and was thus under the watchful eye of his brother Mehmed for the next seven years. He converted his father Dimitrije to Islam and renamed him Dzemaludin-bey, and in honour of his friend the engineer he also added – Sinan. Since he obtained a *ziamet*[40] and founded a *vakuf*[41] in Bosnia, he appointed his father to be his *mutevelli*.[42] His mother also soon came to visit and was fascinated with her son's success. But she was in a constant hurry to get back to Bosnia, and Bajica realised that she had left someone dear behind. Who could be more dear to her than he was unless it was someone like him, but who was unprotected. After a while, she admitted that his real brother was back home, and she apologised for tricking him by switching the two cousins.

Mehmed, however, did not have a single reason to complain that his nephew Mustafa ended up next to him. After learning how to be a barber and masseur, he became the official court barber,[43] and then on the Persian campaign[44] he also showed exceptional courage. Because of that he was deservedly appointed a tax collector in Bosnia and went on advancing, becoming the Bosnian *sancakbey*, the highest possible position – the military and civilian administrator of Bosnia in the name of the Ottoman sultan.

When he found out that his younger brother was in Sokolovići, very soon he sent for him. That was cruel to his mother, but now when he was sure that she had seen what a good life he had, he thought it would be easier for her to take the departure of her last son to safety (overseen by Bajica) before he eventually set off from home into some uncertainty, which was surely what awaited her one day, as it does every mother. After all, sooner or later every child must grow up. To be honest, in convincing her, he counted on the support of his father Dimitrije/Dzemaludin Sinan-bey.

However, with his brothers came also misfortune. Soon after he had settled the youngest one in for his education at Ibrahim-pasha's court at At Meydani, the young man got sick and died soon afterwards.

Bajica felt deeply shaken. It occurred to him that he was partially guilty for their deaths. He asked himself aloud, in front of Sinan, whether the Christian God was punishing him through his brothers for the fact that he had changed his religion. Sinan, spontaneously and suddenly, asked him with great cunning and wisdom:

"Did you ever renounce him?"

Without even a moment's hesitation, Bajica answered:

"No."

Sinan replied:

"There you are."

And that saved him.

CHAPTER XIV

In 1984 in New York, five years before Elmslie, I met another, quiet and authoritative, very important guardian of the written word. Actually, I knew him much earlier by reputation, reading (others') books that he published. The man was James Laughlin, legendary publisher, founder of New Directions Publishers.

Where does the originality of his identity lie? Yes, his ancestors came from Ireland. Yes, from his grandfather forward his family was known as the owners of the fourth largest steel company in America. Unoriginal? Yes. But this is where his personal (super)construction of his identity begins. Nothing was further from his mind than continuing the family business. Young James found his studies at Harvard equally tedious. With an impressive literary education, he wrote a letter to the already famous guru of thought, Ezra Pound, who permitted him to come to his informal, private Ezuversity in far away Europe. So Laughlin left America in 1935 and arrived in a little town called Rapallo, near Genoa in Italy. Enthralled by his professor, thirty years his senior (1885–1972), his whole life he remained a loyal admirer, propagandist and student. So, here we have come to the tailoring of Laughlin's identity. To be someone's lifelong student! By one's own decision to be not someone's shadow, but to be in someone's shadow. Here is how that happened. In fact, a lot of this is known because James Laughlin is no longer among the living (1914–1997) and because since a few years ago the Harvard University library came into possession of one of the wealthiest documentations of the intellectual history of the USA, precisely because of Laughlin's will. Yet, I heard a lot of this from him in the abovementioned 1984, but also later in our correspondence.

Before his return to America, Laughlin screwed up his courage and showed some of his literary opus to his professor. His imagined fear of the 'grade' he might get, in reality turned into a 'day-mare' and a true horror. Not even his poetic imagination was free enough to guess at the words Pound would speak to him (I am using a quote that Laughlin himself reported, even into a microphone): "It's hopeless. You'll never be a writer!"

To say something so cruel to a young man in his early twenties who had placed all his hope in the verses he had written, as much as – if not more – he had in his idol, was the fruit of insanity. Or genius? In retrospect, it was the latter. Because, no matter how truly shocking this evaluation of his writing must have been to the young student, after a breath Pound continued with the (comforting?) sentence: "But you could do something useful for literature." Perhaps a more important sentence than that was produced when Laughlin found the strength to ask the (expected) question: "What would be useful?" Pound answered him: "Well, why don't you take up publishing?"

Maybe Pound's greatness lay in the fact that he edified this human being, a moment after shattering his dreams, with a new and unexpected proposal, giving him hope for an exit from the fall, not affording him the time to hit bottom. Or maybe it was something else: in recognising the strength of his student to withstand the cruelty and to rise beyond it to other, more attainable heights.

This is also where the true magnificence of James Laughlin begins. Listening to his teacher, from a tiny printing house, over the next sixty years he created and ran, right up to his death, what was probably the most important, and perhaps the best (but certainly not the wealthiest) publishing house in the United States. Doing that job he became *his own*, though wrapped in the cloak of Ezra Pound. He said openly that, even after thirty years of experience, he still took advice from Pound! Not because he was not ashamed of it, but rather because he was proud of it.

Pound kept his promise to Laughlin: first he gave him his own manuscripts to publish, and then he asked his friends to do the same. So it happened that Laughlin became the publisher of William Carlos Williams, Lawrence Ferlinghetti, Gary Snyder, Henry Miller, Tennessee Williams, Kenneth Rexroth, Michael McClure, Denise Levertov, Jerome Rothenberg (these last three were hosted by Belgrade and myself) and hundreds of others. His merit is actually twofold: in addition to giving the world whole generations of avant-garde and modern American writers, from that same world he introduced the USA to the most important authors of Europe, Latin America and Asia: Dylan Thomas,

Joyce, Lorca, Goethe, Sartre, Camus, Queneau, Cocteau, Borges, Paz, Nabokov, Pasternak, Kafka, Montale, Mishima...

After a long time, once he had become the touchstone of value in world publishing, he dared to admit publicly that he was again (and still) writing poetry. And after that he began to publish his poems. Then it could be seen that Pound had left an indelible trace in them. In any case, Laughlin showed that openly: his verses often sounded like his teacher's, their topics were often similar, Kanto poetry was peeking around the corner, Chinese calligraphy, epigrams were popping up everywhere – Pound's favourites. For this loyalty, abstract justice awarded him one other prize: Laughlin's poetry was not only NOT just a (bad) copy of Pound's, but became excellent poetry in itself in and of itself, and original too (even though Guy Davenport wrote about Laughlin's poetry, 'The real poets are always someone else').

Thus, this brave man decided to modify, to transform his own identity. He became a good poet after he fulfilled Pound's promise. Because for decades he, without an ounce of vanity or jealousy, with no complexes, published the books of others and not just for others. He did not become a marvellous poet, but he 'just' became a good poet. Perhaps out of exaggerated humbleness or from a consciousness that one's teacher cannot, and indeed should not, be surpassed. In his case, emulation became independent and turned into an original of its own. But Pound, after half a century, in terms of the talent of his student, was no longer right.

Or perhaps he was right the whole time, in another way? Convinced that James Laughlin from the outset was a good poet, he lied to him in the belief that Laughlin was 'called' to become a publisher. With this lie he took a risk, but he succeeded: Laughlin went on to be(come) an excellent poet and an exceptional publisher. An improbable option? Yes, but a possible one. And the result was, above all, justified and more expansive. And much more useful to the world.

CHAPTER 14

Although Sinan had comforted him because of his feeling of guilt for the deaths of his brothers, Mehmed had to find an additional way to cope with, or to make up for, the fact that he missed his loved ones.

Upon returning from collecting taxes, Ahmed-bey obeyed him, fortunately, and made him a detailed list of all the Sokolović family who were still in the homeland. So, Bajica was able to bring them to Istanbul. In addition to Mustafa, the new life was quickly assumed by Ferhad, Alija, Derviš and one other Mehmed, his namesake. One of his female cousins also came to the capital. His younger cousins were not the only ones to advance in their schooling and service; his female cousin also 'advanced', to be fair, by marrying Dzefer-bey, the son of the Bosnian *alajbey*,[45] and moved with him to Pecs where she gave birth to a son, Ibrahim.[46]

That was what he could do *externally*, which could immediately be seen and which was very tangible as a source of comfort. But what should be done *in essence* in order for the pain to subside, in order for death to be understood? It seemed to him that the two deaths of these young beings disturbed his understanding of the natural *order* (of everything). First, and literally so: shouldn't the old die first, and then the younger who have gotten old, and then the youngest who had enough time to get old? He did not want the path to dying in peacetime to become the same as the one in wartime. In war, death means to lose one's life. It is not natural. At home one dies 'naturally', but only when the time has come. There is no good time for a child to die! No time of death should exist for children.

But, it had happened. Twice. One after the other. From one to the next. The natural order was changed.

Perhaps one can die first, and then live?

Maybe that is exactly what happened to him. First he had died when he left his home, and now he was alive in another place. First he had

133

written from left to right, and now from right to left. First he had obeyed others, now others were obeying him. How many books had he read turning the pages with his right hand to the left, and how many after that with his left hand to the right? How many had he copied in Church Slavonic letters, and how many with Arabic? First Slavic and Greek books, and then Persian and Ottoman. Holding the quill with one hand and then the other had equally confused him when he picked up a yataghan, dagger or sabre. He would rather pick them up with both hands at the same time. Or to toss them from one hand to the other. While they were teaching him to fight at the court, everyone thought that was his tactic, and they did not stop him from confusing his opponent that way. This shifting of weapons did not lesson his skill in battle. To the contrary. His weakness became an advantage. He actually became known for it.

These deaths somehow had no connection to God or to Allah. With them there was no story about another life in Heaven and in the heavens. These deaths seemed to be unjust and unjustifiable.

On questions of death as well, he had someone to talk to in his friend Sinan. Sinan was also having a strange experience with death during that time.

"Did you know that I got an order from the commander of our navy, Hayreddin Barbarossa, to build him a mausoleum!? Thinking it strange, I checked: he's not even sick, much less dead! I don't dare to ask him why he's asking for this ahead of time. On the other hand, I do understand. If he waits till he's on his deathbed, it will be too late for him to be buried there straightaway. And of course, if he's dead then he can't order anything at all."

This stirred Bajica up.

"All right, what you say is true, even though you're joking a bit, and rightly so. But, for something like that there must be more profound reasons than whether death will be faster than the grave or vice versa."

"Well, it could be the desire to get to see where he will rest in peace."

"Or to repel death from himself?"

"Or to invoke it?"

"And what reason did he give for you to build him a mausoleum? He must have said something to you!"

"Well, he said that he was quite satisfied with the way I had built the mosque, *medresa* and *mekteb*[47] to honour our empress, the Sultan's wife, Haseki Hürrem."[48]

"Then that's a good excuse for any real reason."

At that moment they did not even imagine that soon after this conversation about graves they would be talking about another, this time caused by a real death. Bajica was once again forced to think about the natural *order* of things. Namely, suddenly and with no warning, the Sultan's oldest son died, Mehmed Shehzade, the heir to the throne and Suleiman's favourite of three sons. He was only twenty-two when he passed away. An addition to his death was the small child this young man left behind. Shehzade's daughter was only a small comfort to the Sultan who never got over the loss of this son.

Although it was difficult to compare and measure these events against each other, it seemed to Bajica that this kind of order, when a child dies before the father, is something even more terrible than the pain that he felt when he lost his brothers. Regardless of the fact that he could not experience something like that, he was horrified by the very thought of how a parent must feel when his child leaves this life before him. Then he began to think about his own children for the first time, children he did not yet have.

Sinan received an order from the Sultan to quickly build a luxurious mausoleum for his son, and to prepare the plans 'proportionate to the great pain' for later building the Shehzade mosque as an auxiliary wing.

Both Bajica and Josif realised that they needed to protect themselves from so many deaths. Bajica especially did not know how to cope with them, since he experienced the Sultan's personal drama as his own, quite intimately, unable to set a depth for them, because he was constantly close to the Sultan. In addition, after Shehzade's death, the Sultan more and more often sought out Mehmed-aga as a confidant and disclosed to him his belief that, after the loss of his favourite son, very little in life made sense like before. In truth, Suleiman showed none of these intimate misgivings in front of the others; before everyone else he remained a stable, invincible ruler.

Sinan, on the other hand, had it somewhat easier. He turned these deaths into action. He melded them into some other material form. Mehmed was left only with his thoughts, which is not the best medicine. He would have to find another. Having no choice, he found another way, perhaps not just a temporary solution, and proposed it to Sinan. He thought that they should somehow come up with a plan together.

"I would like to join you in the work you are doing. You leave such clear and visible evidence of yourself behind. I envy you. Perhaps my actions, if the Sultan ever allows me to consider them mine, will prove to be the same one day. But until then, I can't find a way to overcome these attacks of death around us..."

"What did you have in mind?"

"To somehow get involved in the construction of *hamams*."

Sinan looked at him with a bit of scepticism.

"Hamams?"

"Well, the baths are places with a lot of meaning. One does not wash only the body there. Or just its surface. Everything that isn't pure is cleansed from the body. The pleasure the baths offer us extends far beyond that which is normal enjoyment. And it is good for everyone. You have already built hamams for great statesmen, but it would be good for us to make them (you see, I'm already using the plural!) for everyone. Public baths! As many as possible! If we build kitchens for the poor, why not baths, too? But you and I could thus (both building and bathing) wash from ourselves some of our misdeeds, if they exist."

"The idea is not uninteresting in the least. No one ever had anything except good from a hamam. And how do you see yourself in the actual construction?"

"How else than as a patron? If I knew masonry, I would take stone in hand... Like this, either some of the baths will carry my name because I will pay for their construction or I will find other benefactors who are wealthy enough and who want to leave something so clean and beautiful behind. Of course, I am not yet so rich that I can pay for everything myself, but that time shall also come. And maybe the time will come when the two of us will have enough power and influence so that we can choose where, how many and what kind of hamams there will be in the Empire or in some part of it. And when our wishes and plans will be paid for by the imperial Dīvān. In any case, you are already very close to such a position. Maybe one day we'll have enough influence on the grand vizier and even on the sultan himself, and the Empire will open the treasury for its ritual and literal bathing."

"If you were a Roman Catholic, I would think that you are seeking indulgences for sins. But, according to my Greek and your Serbian Orthodox renunciation, it will be enough for us to simply purify ourselves that way."

CHAPTER XV

Just as Italy (more precisely, that part of the north Adriatic that makes up an arch from Genoa to Trieste) is connected in the correspondence and encounters of Ezra Pound, James Joyce and the Serbian guru Dimitrije Mitrinović, so it connected me with two other dear and significant writers. A story by one of them (about the two of them) helped me to see my own position in similar situations of the (in)equality of personalities.

And 'the two of them' are Juan Octavio Prens and Jorge Luis Borges.

After a literary reading that I had in Trieste in November 2006, where the introductions were made by an older gentleman dressed in enchanting warmth – Juan Octavio Prens, an Argentinian with Belgrade in his biography, at that moment the president of Trieste's PEN (!), having just met, we realised that we needed to see each other in private. Already the next day we were sitting in a fish restaurant over a leisurely French lunch, enjoying each other's company. The connecting person who we both knew had brought us to the above-mentioned story. That was Maria Kodama, the wife of Jorge Luis Borges. Prens had been friends with both for years, and I had had the pleasure of watching a theatre performance at the BITEF Theatre Festival with Maria Kodama, and afterwards of having supper with her in a bohemian restaurant in Belgrade. I caught her attention because I was one of the few people who knew that she was a writer, who was interested in her stories (and not just in those of her husband), and because she knew that I had written a novel about medieval Japan (her father was Japanese). Her exotic appearance was also a subject of conversation between Juan and me, of course, from the most noble of motives. Yet, Prens' little story held her absence as a motive, as opposed to her monumental presence among us.

So, the anecdote actually happened in Morocco. There was a conference being held there and Prens and Borges were participating. Since Maria

Kodama had gone somewhere, in their free time the two of them walked around Marrakech, enjoying their conversation, and then they headed over to the abovementioned conference. As they entered the lecture hall, applause broke out among the professional world elite present. Borges turned instantaneously to Prens and said, "It seems as though they've recognised you."

My host wanted to say by the way that the guru of imagination was a mellow and funny man, quite opposite the commonly held belief that he was a stuffed shirt, a snob. But, above all he was trying to show me indirectly what it is like to be close to a great man, and not to denigrate oneself by thinking of one's own (in)significance or by making nonsensical comparisons. The message was: in that hierarchy, there was a place for everyone. Just as Prens could have felt threatened in the presence of the Great Writer, Borges' wife could have felt the same way, as a writer as well. She could have felt that way even after his death, when not even the echo of his name protected her any longer. Well, couldn't she have felt that way also at the theatre festival in Belgrade, right then while she was with me (of course, though not because of me)? Or I in the presence of so many Famous People that I have known in my life. Or someone in the presence of Prens or me, someone who considered us to be Well-Known, Famous or Great? Yes, the roles could be exchanged so easily!

Or Prens' other example that snuck into our conversation when I explained to him what it was that interested me in terms of (the change of) identity in the book I was writing. He told me that he was currently writing an autobiographical novel (not an autobiography) and introduced me to his vision of the difference between those two genres using a personal example: on his birth certificate next to the year of birth, in the place where the month of birth was supposed to be – it said he was 'born in the 25th month'! And these were Prens' words (spoken in Serbian):

"If such a fact, so true, is used already at the beginning of the autobiography, then it is excellent. However, if it is put in a novel with elements of the autobiographical, then it is just a cheap and naïve joke."

I added: "And no one would even bother to check that you had used a real fact, a real mistake that you did not make up, which is precisely what a writer would do!"

How strange all of this is! A fact from real life, an absurd mistake (by some bureaucrat) made sense in a realistic text about the self, but in a book about the self which is fiction – it does not manage to 'take root' because it is not (in a literary, phantasmagorical sense) refined enough.

I was sorry to have to part from this dignified and charming, cheerful man. I could have learned a lot more from him.

However, James Joyce was waiting.

I often sat in the 'Joyce' café in Trieste with its view of the Piazza Ponterosso, so famous and important to Yugoslavs in socialist times, when Tito's western-communist country, as opposed to all the other countries of the Eastern Bloc (to whom Yugoslavia was itself a window to the world), had its special train into the world that departed from Belgrade and, passing through Zagreb and Ljubljana, created the concept of 'brotherhood and unity', and as a reward arrived in the 'decadent west' – in Trieste. Ponterosso was socialist reality: it was a proper flea market created for the Yugoslavs – an open-air market with cheap and low quality merchandise, from clothes to all sorts of knickknacks. The average visitor from the East could not afford anything more expensive, nor could they find those articles in a normal store back home (except in the famous store called 'Giovanni'). For such people this street was reserved, and moreover – in the West! And that street was a symbol of the market. Perhaps also a sort of vague picture of a possible, different kind of freedom. It offered the possibility of creating the phenomenon of the retail black-marketeer, which was a replacement for private entrepreneurship in early and middle socialism. This place was probably also the embryo of the future stock market among the Serbs, and among others. The square next to the Red Bridge offered, at various moments in time, raincoats made of almost non-existent material (once they caught fire, they vanished in an instant) – the ever popular 'rustling' sweatpants, nylon stockings, chewing gum and the most important article of the liberated mind – blue jeans! Even though the name of the square, and the bridge, could have hinted at something else, including merchandise that might have gone 'in the tour package', I do not remember ever seeing ladies of the night in this place.

The excitement of arriving at this square covered and obscured the closest building nearby in which, once upon a time, on the third floor (with a view of Ponterosso), James Joyce lived, and also the very visible

Orthodox church built by the Serbs in diaspora who had a close-knit community and a longstanding mercantile tradition in Trieste. The customers were not even aware that the famous American article of clothing that they bought there, invented two hundred years ago – jeans, was first produced in Italy (in nearby Genoa) and then taken to the USA so that the material could be made into the pants of the working class, and later into a legend.

The average fellow did not dare to look up and ultimately be amazed by the architecture there, or to go walking around town. Even though he could have done his sightseeing mostly for free. No, in the morning after arriving, everyone went shopping till they could stand no more, in the street they would eat a sandwich brought from home (it was an unplanned luxury to get to eat one of the famous Italian pizzas), and in the evening it was time to board the train home. Overnight was spent on the seats of the train compartment. But before that came the real nightmare – would the customs officers 'find' all the jeans, t-shirts... or among the more affluent customers – shoes. Paying customs or, God forbid, having your 'merchandise' confiscated – that was a real tragedy. In any case, the traveller was still returning home *from the West*, and therefore as – a victor.

I was a kind of special case. My trips to Trieste were somehow schizo-phrenic: I went there many times, like everyone else, in the manner described above. Especially in the earlier phase of socialism. But those trips alternated like cake and icing with a completely different kind when, having just turned legal age, I got in my mother's luxury sports car (though she never lived with me or shared my usual living standard for most of my life) and drove it to get serviced in that very same city. That really was the reason for going. But by the way I would stop to see friends of my mother's husband in various parts of Slovenia and Croatia (from Ljubljana, Šmarješka Toplica, Novo Mesto to Kopar, Opatija, Portorož and Umag) and saw another kind of socialist life that few even knew was possible. But in Trieste, while I was waiting for the car to be serviced, amazed by the sight of auto-mechanics who did their jobs in clean *white* lab-coats, I would check in at luxurious hotels and watch that same city and those same people, my own and foreign, from a different perspective.

There was one more comfort for the common visitor: it was said that 'Trieste lives off the Yugoslavs' and that they would 'go bankrupt if it weren't for us'. But, unfortunately, only later when 'we weren't there', the other/real face of the city could be seen. Yet, this truth is also only partial: my current view through the café window reflected a parking lot for cars that covered half of this important square, but the rest of the view was more interesting. The other part of the square (so, half of the area that used to be taken up by their competitors) has been inherited by immigrants from the African countries. On the stalls, also in the open, they were selling hand-made articles from their own homelands, but also pieces of low-quality clothing like the Italians used to sell us. Domestic fruit cart peddlers wandered among them. The difference was that these folks who have inherited Ponterosso were not in a hurry to get home. They were staying there and not rushing to catch any kind of night train.

The only thing I did not understand was whom they were selling their merchandise to (when they couldn't do so to the non-existent Yugoslavs): to 'their own' or to 'someone else's'? And who was their own and who was someone else's, anyway?

CHAPTER 15

Bajica could not have even guessed that, in presenting his plan about the baths to Sinan, he was actually invoking water on his own behalf.

After the Drina River at Višegrad, the Sava and Danube at Belgrade, the Rivers Prut and Marica, and Lake Van, it was now time for... the sea. And everything had its own reason. Rivers were hard to master, like cats, each with a will of its own and each trying to be lovable. Lakes were calm and they seemed to be inanimate. The seas seemed to be tamer than rivers, often because of their expanse – unending, and therefore threatening without a real reason. Yet, they could be loyal like dogs, less inclined to selfishness and thereby more predictable. But salty in different ways. He could not claim the same thing about rivers: their waters were all equally sweet.

While he was thinking about how water had, almost imperceptibly, gotten under his skin, he remembered that, for example, in all the waters where he had stepped, ridden and sailed – he had also swum. Of course, if the conditions allowed it. He remembered how everyone always watched him with enormous surprise, whether as a boy or on military campaigns, because he was one of the very few who knew how to swim. Less in childhood, but many times in battle – he saw a lot of people who drowned in the very same water that liberated him. The encounter with and touch of a larger expanse of water caused most people to be afraid. So, he noticed that his relaxation and lack of fear of water caused many people to be afraid of him.

Perhaps this story about his 'courage in the face of water' had reached the Sultan as well, when the ruler invited him to come see him before the viziers' council. Upon receiving this invitation, fear arose in Bajica for the first time in a long time. Among other things, maybe it was his turn, now, at this moment, to be afraid. To be fair, why shouldn't he be afraid: this was the first time he was invited publicly to stand before all the highest officers of the Empire! The natural reaction to such a position, the first and unstoppable thought, was – I have been called because I did something wrong, and so that I may be punished.

And when he did stand before the Padishah and the Dīvān, his fear flared even higher because of the Sultan's first utterance to him:

"Mehmed-aga, it is time for you to leave the court!"

Bajica went numb. He had not heard a single hint of any mistake he had made, and so this was a real shock to him. With lightening speed, every action went through his mind, even the smallest one that he thought might be the reason behind his master's rage. But he had executed every order without objection, and he had used his imagination to improve those that he could by adding elements, and he had always received praise for that. He used all the methods he knew to figure out where the mistake might lie, but to no avail. The only thing he could do was to let destiny run its course, that is, to follow the Sultan's new command.

"Our loyal Heyreddin Barbarossa has passed away. His position must immediately, without delay, be filled. Therefore, I will deprive myself of your years of closeness and appoint you to be the Admiral of the Ottoman Empire. I want you to be the master of the waters just as you mastered yourself in my personal service."

Ah! Relief flooded over him. He was completely numb. That is what 'leave the court' had meant. To go on his first assignment, his first position *outside the walls of the court*. He was actually being rewarded!

However, after the relief, when the first fear had died down, a second one appeared: he did not see himself as a person who was capable, who was trained, to lead the entire fleet of the Empire. Especially after the legendary pirate, the Greek Barbarossa, who had turned an arrogant, pirating fleet into the dignified and powerful Ottoman navy, through his long years of loyal service. The greatest powers of the Mediterranean had begun to be serious threat of Heyreddin and his 'pirates' who they considered to be an enormous danger.

The Sultan read Bajica's thoughts. He told him:

"Our rule in the Mediterranean is not enough. I want us to rule the seas in the eyes of all of Rumelia!"

In 1546, Sokolović did not have a problem with his new and demanding admiral's title, nor even with the heritage left to him by Heyreddin Barbarossa. Behind it all there was an honest fear toward himself and his own uncertainty that he could do more than the confident, brave and talented warrior, as his predecessor had been. So, he was not afraid of the legend which follows all the famous great men who pass away, but he was afraid that he would not be able to measure up to such person in a wartime situation. Then again, he had been given the freedom to figure out a *different way* to achieve the results demanded. And that had to be possible.

And it was. Barbarossa had created a mighty seagoing power, but he had not made it efficient enough because it was not well organised. That was exactly where Bajica's chance lay. Already in his first plans for the reorganisation, he immediately added some very visible preconditions: with the Sultan's aid, he raised taxes and began to build a large shipyard in Pera, across the way from the imperial city and the court. Several hundred engineers and supervisors worked there in thirteen different bays, building that number of ships simultaneously. A new line of ships was created that way, with larger dimensions, better handling and modern features. As soon as one of the galleys was launched, work began on the next one. In just a few months, the fleet had several hundred new ships. At the same time, military units were trained to be the crews on the galleys. The command hierarchy was completely redone, the main change being that all of the *reises*[49] were controlled by one high commander – Mehmed Sokolović. Even those captains who were famous for their fearlessness and their inclination to rebellion were brought into line; they realised by themselves how much stronger they were under a common command than if they went on like free-lancers lacking internal organisation. This change actually did not even lower their chances at catching future prey, which was something that did worry them. To the contrary.

Mehmed did not have to worry about victory at sea. Among the commanders and captains there were some war-hardened mariners. For battle, quite enough of them. The job that he was doing was much more significant: he made it possible for them to win. Without his persistence, methodical work, cold-blooded decision-making and clear idea of what needed to be done, none of the long-term successes would be achieved.

Ultimately, death brought him new life. Many of the deaths he experienced till then had horrified him, but here was one, the first but by no means the last, which was so useful to him that he did not have to invest any effort whatsoever in the profit it brought him. Death did it all for him.

This death had, in fact, caught him in the middle of his thoughts about another one, which had depressed him utterly because it showed that there were absolutely no untouchables: it was when the Sultan's childhood friend, Grand Vizier Ibrahim-pasha, was actually strangled to death in the room right next to his friend – who gave the order for it, and who was above all his ruler. The Sultan had intentionally had the death take place so close to him so that everyone would know that he was the one who decreed it and that he feared no one.

The right to take a life was his alone.

It turned out, especially after the murder of someone so close to him, that the Sultan's best friend was – death itself.

CHAPTER XVI

The Joyce Café did profit from the fact that the brilliant writer began his difficult tenant life in March 1905 on the third floor of the same building, and remained there only two months (he was evicted because of Nora's visible pregnancy which had not been sanctioned by a formal marriage). Anyway, the symbolism that arises from the fact that this was his first address in Trieste of the nine existing ones from two periods of his life in this city (1905–1915 and 1919–1920) mitigates this rationally conceived profitability. Among other things, it is worthwhile to pay for the opportunity of having the same view today, from the same place (to be honest slightly skewed because you are on the ground floor) where Joyce saw things in his time. Maybe it was that very view (of the Grand Canal or the Piazza Ponterosso) that inspired him for the end of *Dubliners* or *A Portrait of the Artist as a Young Man* or the poem *Giacomo Joyce*, the play *Exiles* or the beginning of *Ulysses*. Because all of that came into being, or was conceived, in Trieste at various addresses, from the moment when he arrived from Pula so that he could teach at the famous Berlitz language school, several streets over from the Piazza Ponterosso. From his relationship with Nora, in 1905 his son Giorgio was born here, and his daughter Lucia in 1907.

The thing that most intrigues and interests me is the modern day relationship of the people of Trieste with Joyce, and his with the city back then, where he lived in a variety of ways, but in any case never easily. It was indeed employment that brought him to Trieste, but it cannot be said that he was forced to go there: he applied for the job of his own free will. It was not even the constant lack of money that drove him away. After all, his brother was his ubiquitous guarantee and also the constant victim of Joyce's debts. Still, it is strange that, at the same time, persistently residing in Trieste, he also remained persistently obsessed with Dublin and that Ireland of his that he, likewise, left of his own free will. I want to say that it is possible to see his life in Trieste in two ways. The first proposition is that, if the city did not really suit him, he certainly would not have been able to write so many wonderful lines there. And there lies the second, visible fact that, while living in one city, he constantly wrote about another. A bit insulting for Trieste. On the other hand, we have to remember that he gave his children, once and for always, Italian names! Was it only gratitude toward those who had taken him in? (In a letter to Nora, at a time when they were both not living there, he indeed said that Trieste was a city that had taken them in protectively. And not just that. In several of his letters he expresses unreserved emotions toward the town, even writing them in Italian.) It is likely that the sum of these two statements produces the closest thing to the truth about Joyce. In any case, the people of Trieste returned his love in a dozen wonderful ways, posthumously. They ignored all the negative aspects and took him in as one of their own. They placed a bust of him in the park, named one of the public staircases after him, set a bronze statue of him (life-size), on the Ponterosso bridge, striding toward his first home there with one hand in his pocket, a hat on his head, and a book under his other arm. For the tourists there is an itinerary of forty important spots that represent *Joyce's Trieste*, they have hung a plaque with his name on every building that had any kind of relationship to him, and they published a guidebook about him. All of this came about in a special project 'Laboratorio Joyce', initiated by the local university. This relationship of the writer toward the city and the city toward the writer seems like a gentlemen's agreement based on mutual acceptance, recognition and respect. With it, this identity became unquestionable. Even given the fact that it was solidified, after the fact, by elements of cultural tourism.

That is why it is quite normal that, in Trieste at this moment, there are writers of sixteen different nationalities living and working, at least that is what I was told. With that in mind, it is no wonder that their PEN centre is led by an Argentine (who has two daughters born in, of all places in the world, Belgrade!).

Just as Trieste and Joyce used to be like magnets of opposite poles, so today there is a common pole on the magnet of internationalism, drawing pilgrims of literature and attracting new fans of Joyce and most certainly his followers.

CHAPTER 16

Mehmed's new appointment was only a surprise on the surface, and rightly so. The people – the general public – had seen him long enough at the very feet of the Sultan. To them, such a choice was reasonable: if the ruler kept him so close to himself, why wouldn't he appoint him to an important spot which is, what a surprise, further away from him. In their eyes, it would be strange if a decision was made that incidentally brought him even closer to the Sultan. But this way, everything was fine. In fact, they had exchanged distance with position.

Those who were still closer to the court itself, and therefore knew a little more about the events there, did not have a single reason to oppose such a decision: Mehmed had not taken a single mistaken step in proximity to the ruler. Yet, they also could not see any special reason why Sokolović should be recommended for such a high position. If the 'pros and cons' were all added together, it turned out that, for Bajica's new appointment – it made no difference at all.

The third group that had the right to make comments about such a decision included those whom it affected most. They were the commanders, captains and sailors of all kinds. In addition to them were all the war-hardened military commanders. The latter had no complaints about Mehmed's actions in the military campaigns: many of them were convinced by his courage, but also by his careful planning that had visibly aided him in everything and prevented him from rushing headlong into an untimely death. The naval officers, however, had reason to be jealous, and also to be distrustful of Sokollu's future capabilities because it really was true that he did not have experience in the *naval* strategies of war. But he himself was the first to drive away their fears and mistrust, immediately: he told them that he would not involve himself in things he did not understand, but he would rather enable them to achieve their very best as quickly as possible. Therefore, battles and victories were reserved for them. Eventual glory belonged to them, and then to him, of course. And to the great Sultan above everyone. And to omnipotent Allah above all.

After he had finished the promised reorganisation of the navy and built a large fleet, he invited all the commanders to an audience. Having reported to them the completion of this enormous task, he told them:

"Now it is up to you to win our victories. With the help of omnipotent Allah, and by the command of the Great Sultan Suleiman Kanuni, I will command you where to sail and tell you what you will conquer to the glory of our Empire. Even now I am making plans for the day when we will conquer far away India. Till that day, we shall rule the Mediterranean, the Red Sea and the Black Sea. And all the lesser seas we come upon. From this day forward, no one can snatch your fame and glory from you. It is your task to take them before others do."

With these words, not only did he change the minds of the doubting officers, but he even managed to win their support to the extent that they began to swear by him. Now he could say that he was commanding the navy.

Sultan Suleiman kept an eye on him, occasionally in secret, but most often quite openly. He was pleased that his presumptions about Sokollu had been correct. Now it was obvious, Mehmed had proven to be an excellent organiser, a convincing orator and a good strategist (which had been assumed to be his weak point). After all, weren't his achievements with the navy a special kind of battle? And he had proven to be more than just good.

The Sultan's heartstrings hummed: he had formed a top-notch servant and a perfect slave.

For the Empire.

And for himself.

CHAPTER XVII

But what are we going to do now with the non-existence of the Yugoslavs? A hundred books about the topic of that identity, and especially the search for it, would not render a clear answer. Just like those that have already been written about it. I will hardly do better in a few sentences.

For now, until history refutes itself in the future, as it always does, 'Yugoslav' will remain just one more, almost geographic, concept, an insignificant toponym, an ethnographic definition, melted in among thousands of others, like the old 'South Slav'; or it will, more broadly, signify a grouping of peoples or tribes like the Slavs. And nothing more. And so it will be until a new utopia is achieved in the Balkans, until some significant assassination occurs, or among the intellectual elite a new hybrid post-mega-plus-injection romanticism is born.

Or unless the old-new Yugoslavs are ultimately recognised, at least on paper, like the twenty-seven national minorities in the state of Serbia. And such demands are already being made in public before the Parliament of Vojvodina, the Serbian province with the highest number of nations in its make up. However, the legal interpretations of this idea are not beneficial to it: the law says that a national minority can only be one that has a language of its own, and not one of the dialects of an existing language. But officially, the language that the Yugoslavs spoke – Serbo-Croatian – also no longer exists, disappearing in the package with the non-existent nation and country.

The Yugoslavs are, until further notice, in a state of hibernation.

The Yugoslavs are a virtual concept.

The Yugoslavs are memories. Not just the past. There are some still among the living. More precisely – among the living dead, something akin to vampires

What if there is a desire for blood...

After all, the highly developed Europe of the 19th century stuck the Balkan areas with the name of a non-existing place – Ruritania – in order to cook it a few more times in the cannibal cauldron. Or was this role also just episodic and undeservedly blown out of proportion? Perhaps in the case of that particular political feast, it was not the main course, but just one of its spices. In its lack of interest, didn't that Europe mix a little of everything in the homeland of Count Dracula (starting with vampires and werewolves); and who was found where and who came from where? In the jungle of place names (the Danube, the Carpathians, Romania, Rumelia, Serbia, Transylvania, Šumadija, Bulgaria...), this Ruritania easily found a home. Oddly enough, this is almost the only case when (Anglo-Saxon) fiction had an actual influence on reality and inserted an imaginary, fake and literary truth into actual history. It managed to do something considered impossible, though so longed for by writers and literature, and thus obtained the right to be proud of itself. Still, why did they have to use the Balkans?

Perhaps history, like a sort of living organism, or like a character from a literary work, planned it on its own initiative, by repeating the enlargement then shrinkage of the Balkan humus and stone. It seems that the existence of that plan is almost certain, and that its circulation is still not finished. That which is not certain is the answer to the question of why? For dialectical reasons? Out of greed? Because it had to be so? Because they thought it was true? Because of a higher power? Just for fun?

The Yugoslavs also had the mission of enlarging and then shrinking the Balkans. The first mission went slowly and was brought to fruition after the wars, and the second one went quickly and with the aid of wars (so quickly that it might have actually been done before the wars). And that is why it was always unclear to me how one makes tools that make tools. Or machines that are meant to munch up other machines. Was it necessary to design and develop an alloy, thus, a mixture of various metals, which would be stronger than any one of them alone? The associated forces of nature against the one and only?

An alchemy that creates in order to destroy.

Like people.

CHAPTER 17

Mehmed's command over the Ottoman fleet was the first period in which, his presupposed submissiveness to the invincible Sultan notwithstanding, he participated with his mind and voice in the making of important decisions. Since this high position displaced him physically from his master, in order to mitigate this change, he made a clever move: he decided to command from Istanbul and to not head off for campaigns and battles in which he ought to be personally at the head of the fleet. In this way, he also enabled his war-hardened commanders to go on returning triumphantly to port after victory, leading their galleys with a heightened sense of their own contribution. Thereby he maintained the invaluable possibility, even more important to him, of seeing the Sultan and consulting with him, at times in addition to a bit of conversation that was not always to do with command and subservience. This five year period was important for both of them because they could show each other their capabilities: it was fortunate that they complemented each other well in the evaluation of events, and in the similarities of the proposed commands that they exchanged. Kanuni (Suleiman) would challenge his admiral, waiting first to hear his decision, and only then giving his own opinion or command. This sort of shrewdness, oddly, did not create either open or hidden anger, rage, worry, fear or anything like that in Bajica. On the other hand, Suleiman enjoyed Mehmed's calmness, which he did not confuse with arrogance, nor did he interpret it as a lack of respect or obedience. To the contrary, all of this brought them even closer.

Actually, both of them were surprised by this closeness. Bajica could not and dared not dream of drawing so close to the ruler, no matter how much time he was spending close to him and no matter how much confidence the Sultan was showing him. The Sultan, on the other hand, did not know that he could build such a relationship with someone who was not a comrade from childhood, not really a friendship (because it could not and dare not be), but rather a strange confidence, at times between them alone – a conspiratorial complementation in ideas. It could not be said that their relationship seemed like a game, but it was indeed a kind of training.

As a reward for his work, the Sultan promoted Mehmed from aga to pasha. Bajica thus reinforced his position also with a title unrelated to the military, in addition to his governmental one. This new position enabled him to increase both his monetary accumulation and all his other properties as well. And that was how he was able to bring his nephews, from among his more distant relatives, to Istanbul. In the schools and various imperial services, Alija, Mustafa, Ferhad, Derviš and his namesake, Mehmed, were all coming along nicely. Bajica raised his self-confidence with their help, and with their presence he brought back and reinforced his feeling of closeness with his original and essential homeland. Having the scales balanced in this way seemed fairer to him, and it made him feel better.

Not to mention the significantly increased intimate presence of his mother tongue.

This latter both empowered and saddened him. For several reasons. The first was a reminder that his mother was the only one who did not wish to move to Istanbul or to change religions, persistently saying that at least one of the Sokolović family had to remain at home, and that she was the one who had to do that along with one of her boys. She got over the transformation of her husband Dimitrije into Dzemaludin-bey, she gave her blessing to her son Bajica during her short-lived visit, even telling him that she felt that his sister would probably 'marry a Turk', but that she did not want to exchange her lonely home with a new one at any price.

The second reason for Bajica's sadness was the realisation that, among all the women he saw around him, not a single one could be his. Young, tall and slender,[50] he was quite desirable among the girls and women at the court and outside it. Even without his position at the court, he would have been equally attractive. Even more so than he was later when he was most revered. Young women, but married ones as well, let him know that, because of his youth, handsomeness and slave service to the Sultan, they did not take him seriously in their planning. He was ideal for their physical pleasure, with no serious consequences for anyone. Furthermore, he was an obligation to no one. Bajica did not reject them, nor could it be said that he did not enjoy himself with them. But he felt no tranquillity. He supposed, and he had even heard, that in such relationships, 'a certain tranquillity' can perhaps appear. At the time, he did not know that this could also be called – love.

The girls liked to boast in their intimate conversations about how they had tried young Mehmed (calling him young even when it was no longer actually true)... And many married women hinted at the same, but very carefully and ambiguously. Bajica did not show any signs that he was anxious or in a hurry to get married; this persistence of his in refusing to choose a future partner grew into a trait that everyone knew about – they proclaimed him to be a perpetual bachelor!

When these rumours reached him, Bajica was angry at first. How could anyone dare to proclaim such a thing about him! But when he thought about it for a while, realising that there was nothing he could do to stop the rumours, he accepted them as useful: due to the rumours, they would leave him in peace; if and when he decided to prove otherwise – the wedding itself would have the last say on the matter. Among other things, even if he had to, it would be difficult for him to offer the one particular reason why he had not found a spouse: he wanted to speak Serbian with her! No, this did not mean above all that he wanted a Serbian woman for a wife, but he did want a person who knew that language as well as her mother tongue. He was convinced that the kind of intimacy shared by spouses also meant a commonality in language, and not just in body and soul. Could anyone really understand that?

CHAPTER XVIII

When certain phenomena are occasionally slightly tilted (or the angle of perceiving them), they take on different forms, new features, and lots of things change about them. Under such circumstances, even Yugoslavs are possible: in fact, as time goes by, the memories of their existence will probably turn into a feeling.

Here is another example of something that is impossible at first glance, but existing, though basically non-existent...

In Syria, down to this very day, there is a Greek Orthodox monastery by the name of St. Tekla, built in the fourth century, where the liturgy/mass (in a more recently built church) is held in Arabic. (Sources say that the monastery and church are also found in a Greek village, but that it is Catholic!) Both the priest/monk and the sisters, some not looking very Greek, lead the procession in which one can see believers of all races and skin colours. In addition, there are the ever-present, active participants and Moslem pilgrims who stop at the monastery on their way to Mecca, as do the Christian pilgrims and Jews on the way to Jerusalem. Their hosts, Christian servants of God, who take them into their service with wide-open arms, believe that they are in the service of all faiths and religions. Meaning, not just (their own) God, not just themselves. And why would something like that be impossible? Among other things, in one part of the liturgy, the priest says a prayer in Christ's language, Aramaic. This language in itself is largely considered to be non-existent, isn't it? Or somehow half-dead? This village, called Maaloula, is one of three remaining where only the language of Christ is spoken. Whether because of the language or because of loyalty to serving all faiths, I don't know, but St. Tekla's is the oldest existing complete mass that is still in use. If nothing else, from an ethnic point of view, that fact must set the standard for all other, and all younger, communities of the faith.

This positive crowd of faiths, races and this chaotic openness toward the Other and the Different, relativises the one most confusing fact (that

I already mentioned, by the way): this Greek Orthodox church and monastery are found in a Greek *Catholic* village! There are two explanations for this absurdity. One is that the German editors (the authors of the information) were wrong, and the other is that, well, there is something among the Greeks that is on the very edge of the impossible: an entire settlement of Catholics with an Orthodox faith!

It is of interest that the mass at the monastery of St. Tekla on Good Friday was filmed by a German TV crew (broadcast April 8, 2006 on one of the Serbian TV channels) and that the camera caught a rather unusual icon of this monastery, which has Saint Mary and one other small character, a Turk, in its bottom part. The narrator explained that this depiction was of a man who, in his time, wanted to turn the monastery/church into a citadel, and that Mary convinced him otherwise. Stated in modern language: it seems that they came to an understanding and cooperated well with each other.

Why should there be amazement then at the even more obvious example of the reconciliation of two faiths (even) in one man; Mehmed-pasha Sokolović went as many as nine (!) times on the Hajj, to convince those in the Ottoman Empire who claimed that he was not entirely honest and that he was not a fully committed Moslem. That is why Sokollu Mehmed-pasha can sometimes be found under the name Hajji Mehmed. Even back then, therefore, you practically had to prove that you were dedicated to a certain faith if you had ever been dedicated to another. Still, these proofs of faith do not necessarily have to be any kind of proof of faithfulness. They are formal, confirmed tests. Yet, only the one who hears the heart and soul in question knows which god (or gods) are being addressed. Mehmed-pasha's pilgrimages are actually no different from one of today's modern trips into the (un)known. Above all according to the destination, and then according to the questions, apart from the ultimately religious ones, that appear along the way. Every journey is dedicated to something (more rarely to someone); after that, a weight falls from one's soldiers; answers are found; something is sacrificed for a higher cause.

Although surprises have been known to appear. I could even use my own example. Namely, over the last few years, probably because of all the miles behind me, I began to have a different feeling before a trip and, Lord knows, also before coming home. In what way? Well, once it had meant excitement or nervousness before departing, including a suppressed joy, but it was replaced with a fairly strange sense of melancholy because I was leaving. That same thing began to repeat itself even when it was time for me to return from a trip: the pleasantness at the thought of returning to those who are mine and to what is mine, was supplemented by a feeling of sweet and gentle sadness (if that exists) because I was leaving the place where I was. If someone forced me to differentiate this kind of departure and return, I am sure that I could do it. It seems to me that I have a better understanding for the melancholy I feel when leaving a place where I have been temporarily than the one I feel when I leave home on a trip. The melancholy of leaving one's own is much more complex; it seems like premeditation, like a dilemma, a secret surrender.

Perhaps the secret is in getting older. It is known that older people find it harder to leave their home than the young, even for a short time. With old age comes a physiological insecurity which, likewise, influences the psychological and it is therefore understandable; when the body begins to betray us and becomes dependent on the help of others, of the family, of those close by, and while travelling they are not around, then the image of limited independence becomes absolutely clear. The body sets conditions on the soul! And even when the body is old, the soul still is not. Here there is no victory of the soul over the body. To claim otherwise would be as if a discriminating smoker of pure Afghan oil mixed with tobacco claimed, stoned from the concentrate that had landed him in bed and disabled him from moving for the next twenty-four hours, while his mind worked/raced at 200 miles per hour, that he had run several miles in his mind. Yes, it is true; a thought could cross that distance in a single second. But the body would not have moved even an inch.

However, I am not (at least not that much in that way) that old. I have just entered that aging process for the first time. Or I have just become aware of it for the first time. Though my body has still not betrayed me. Although I do not know whether that boundary for the beginning of aging exists at all, much less where it is and how one finds it, I have started thinking about the process, with the help of others, more experienced, but I have also been able to draw some conclusions on my own. In any case, perhaps the very beginning of thinking about aging is also the beginning of aging itself?

Still, to be honest, I remember when, probably because I had the good fortune to get serious about literature, I asked someone the first time about old age, about memory and the enduring. It was in the early eighties, I was about twenty-five (hopefully that was not the beginning of my aging?), after reading the book *Up to the Impossible* by the surrealist and linguist Đorđe Kostić who described there his childhood with Đorđe Jovanović and Oskar Davičo (all the way up to beginning of the famous almanac *The Impossible* in the 1930s). In writing it, Kostić was already along in years, while I was fairly young when reading it, and I was amazed at his memory and the description of such bizarre details from his early childhood. Through my good friend Bora Đoković, one of the most talented writers I knew (but who soon after, unfortunately, left his talent behind, at least publicly), I had the good fortune of being able to tell Đorđe Kostić of my amazement. His response was equally amazing and unexpected for me, perhaps because it was cruelly true and quite possible. Among other things, in this way as well, this charming and quiet member of the Academy who, in his waning years, printed and published the books of young authors, in Calcutta (!) on 'fine wood-based paper', thus proving how authentic he was as a surrealist writer and painter.

'In old age, a man realises how the time ahead of him is shrinking. Because of that lack of future, as if to compensate for time, a man returns ever more deeply into his youth and childhood. He thus creates the illusion that time lasts equally. As if the past will replace the future and even make it happen. The truth of no tomorrow becomes clouded, and the images of yesteryear clear up. Or, said more simply: the less time a man has before him, the more he searches for it behind him.'

This was a kind of *reinforcement* of memory. And through it, new conclusions could be drawn. I suppose that is how wisdom is born. By re-examining the known, but using the personal energy of the future, which is automatically melted into the energy of the past. In that state a man becomes hypersensitive, and thus more able to see phenomena better, more lucidly, precisely and perhaps truly.

Still, we dare not forget the most important part of the *journey* into old age. That is the eternal return related to emigration, the diaspora, moving 'there forever', and which almost always ends desperately in the longing to return 'back here in the end' – to the homeland – to the place of one's birth, and if it is no longer there, then to an abstract place bounded by geographical provability. Old age always returns people to their homeland. Closeness to death especially. The desire to die 'in one's place' is almost perverted. And if death overtakes life, last wishes (which must be fulfilled) are found in the wills and testaments, so that the executors return either a casket or an urn to the place of birth. If in *no other way* you go home dead. The expression *at any cost* in this case is carried out mercilessly and is brought to its most literal meaning.

Death is always were it belongs. It is life that is scattered around.

CHAPTER 18

If he did not manage to speak Serbian with his imagined wife, he did manage to do so with almost the whole world a few years later in 1551, as the commander of the campaign on Hungary. This is how.

As the commander-in-chief of the fleet, seldom leaving the capital, Mehmed-pasha quite skilfully led the Ottoman policy of conquest with the aid of his exceptionally brave, skilful and seasoned sea dogs. They were satisfied with the admiral's respect for their wishes (from equipment and galleys to money), and they obeyed his carefully planned orders. They chose the means for executing the orders themselves, and in return they brought victory. To be honest, there was also incredible wealth from which they had personal benefit. They owned the surrounding seas.

And the Sultan was pleased. From their intimate proximity, he knew Mehmed-pasha's character well, and now it turned out that he had been extremely wise by showing so much trust in Mehmed, certain ahead of time that the pasha would command successfully from such a high position. To show him additional gratitude, Suleiman promoted him to the position of beylerbey of Rumelia. Bajica could now be certain that the doors were open to him for the most important offices of state. Although it was unwise to measure the significance of one office over another, he was aware of just how much power, supervised of course, the Sultan had placed in his hands. Rumelia was a spatial community of highly different powers, including the Hungarians, Hapsburgs, Germans, Franks, Spaniards, Italians, Serbs, the not so distant Brits and many others, and it seemed to be a dangerous construct because of the padishah's idea of conquering it. However, at the same time, that was also why it was so vulnerable: it was hard for all of them to come to an agreement on anything – so many kingdoms, empires, principalities, city-states – even on their own defence in the face of the rather obvious intentions of the Ottomans.

However much that forced him to think seriously about the difficulty of overcoming such large number of enemies, no matter how disparate they might be, one thing brought a smile to his face, barely visible: the possibility that he would also see Serbia brought him a furtive joy, and with it came his real name, temporarily out of circulation.

Soon he got orders from the Sultan to begin accelerated preparations for a campaign on Hungary. That part of his job followed a well-known path: once set in motion, all parts of the mechanism worked perfectly. For the technical matters of the task, he was practically unneeded. His job was to come up with a war strategy. His heart told him that, if he listened to himself, he would certainly introduce a new strategy into warfare, and more diplomacy as well. However, he knew that unless he proved his courage on the battlefield, he would never gain true respect among the Ottomans. So, he whole-heartedly prepared to connect his giftedness in management and the certainty of its execution in reality. Said in simple terms, it would be good to mix his ability to negotiate with his fearlessness in destruction.

The word and the yataghan, wine and blood.

It was easier to step into war than to get back out of it. He had to use all the shrewdness he possessed. Actually, two kinds: one for his enemies and the other for his friends. In good time he understood that this campaign, however it might end, would be remembered by his name. Therefore, he could not allow himself a single mistake. Searching carefully and diligently, he found a possible formula, perhaps even a saving one: without the Serbs on the campaign – not a chance!

In parallel with his war preparations, he sent out messengers and missives to the Serbian feudal lords, officers, and military leaders (regardless of whose flag they were serving under), calling upon them to join his campaign or, if they did not want to do that, then at least to avoid serving under enemy command. In return, he promised all Serbs an especially privileged position in the Empire. Of course, all of the letters sent out were in Serbian. In the beginning, this gesture reduced the risk of someone understanding the content of the letter if it fell into the wrong hands, and later it proved to be a good political move as well. Most of the Serbs answered favourably. And why wouldn't they? For the first time an Ottoman in such a high position addressed them directly in the name of the entire Empire, in Serbian at that, whereas for decades they had been torn apart and pressed by the lies, deceit or attractive but unrealistic promises that had arrived in equal number, in alternation, from the Hungarians, Austrians, Italians and Russians! If this was also another of those empty promises, somehow it was easier to take than most, if not all, of the preceding ones: even an untruth was nicer to hear in their own language.

Sinan supported him in this idea.

"I would do the same thing if language was my most important tool."

Mehmed was grateful to him. But he returned the compliment.

"Your language of construction is more all-encompassing. I envy you because of that. And it lasts longer because of the materials you use."

"I'm not so sure. It is more solid, harder and seemingly more difficult to destroy. But, think about it – what the written word has had to endure! How many words have survived catastrophes and come down to us!? So, some of your words will also survive this time and reach someone who doesn't exist yet."

Bajica reflected on this. He liked Josif's power of belief. As if he read his thoughts, Josif continued to persuade him.

"Well, and unwritten, orally spoken words have also survived. Isn't that enough for you?"

As if that was not enough for him.

"Your engineering language is easier to understand: it is enough to look at it to understand it."

"Yes, but what will we do with it when we use it to destroy? Do you think that then it is enough to 'understand it'?"

Mehmed fell silent. Sinan had to make an extra effort. And he did. He proposed something that went beyond everything the high commander had thought of.

"I think that, when you reach your resting place in Belgrade, while you're re-grouping your troops before the final attack, you'll have the time and the need, even the necessity, to send one last warning to our enemies. Now, I think that you should send that warning to all of them – to the Hungarians and the Austrians and the Italians and those from Dubrovnik – in Serbian."

Bajica gaped at him. He did not know whether this suggestion was gross impudence or pure genius!

CHAPTER XIX

The question of identity in collision with numbers often produces conflicting results. And in the conscious attempt to *preserve* identity – a disarray of differences.

The Kosovar Albanians are solving this problem in the simplest and quickest way: with an aggressively high birth rate. Large numbers. Their neighbouring Albanians in Albania – with the transition and the conflict of politics and culture. With small numbers. And with greater nuances.

Example: Besnik Mustafaj, the writer from Tirana, after the end of his tenure as the Albanian ambassador to France (before that he was in parliament, the founder of a political party, etc.), went on writing and making public appearances as a writer, but with a dose of a politician's conceit and arrogance (which I experienced personally in several public outbursts). I do not know if that extended feeling of power aided him and elevated him in the political ranks, but in this new life-phase he became the Minister of Foreign Affairs for his country. But, not for long! There was another turnabout: a mutual French acquaintance of ours told me that the writer rendered his resignation to the *politician* (on his own and exclusively, so that he could go back to writing)!

The most important conclusion from this example is the given fact that Mustafaj is a good writer. The question remains, if the writer turned in his resignation *as a politician*, was literature the victor?

Can literature ever be the victor?

Another example: a writer, also from Tirana (this time, in fact, born and bred there), named Bashkim Shehu, was practically forced out of domestic politics (which does not mean that he especially wanted to take part in it in the first place). He was actually expelled because he belonged to a political family, and therefore, because of the political inheritance associated with his last name. Namely, for years his father, Mehmet Shehu, was the Chairman of the Council of Ministers of Albania, inheriting that position in 1954 from Enver Hoxha who, in that transfer of power, became the head Secretary of Central Committee of the Communist Party of Albania and the president of the country. However, in the difficult struggle to safeguard the political identity of the country (and for a long time Albania was an original creation even within the Socialist Bloc), best friends and closest comrades went their separate ways, in a way very similar to that of many of the sultans and viziers of the Ottoman Empire: Hoxha had Shehu killed. His family was also stricken: his wife and sons wound up in prison and Bashkim, at one moment finding his way to freedom, decided to move to Spain. He became the General Secretary of the European Parliament of Writers and continued to dedicate his gentle spirit to writing.

It is as if both of these fighters for the future of their country, in addition to the political and civil battle, while differing drastically from one another, struggled for personal and national identity through the more long-lasting survival of that battle – through literature. Although books sometimes seem to be the mere remembrance of events (even if they deal with that which just happened or is still happening), they have a miraculous power to last longer than politics. Good books.

As opposed to these examples from the Mediterranean south of Europe, an example from its Atlantic extreme north – Iceland – has a more obscure battle for identity, if not for mere survival.

I made friends fairly easily and quickly with Sjón, the singer Bjork's friend and songwriter, a member of the band the *Sugar Cubes*, 'a man with a dozen professions' it seemed to me, and he had a really interesting answer to one of the questions I asked after meeting a large number of very creative people in Reykjavik. Namely, I noticed that almost all of them had two or three professions at the same time and that this was actually almost the rule; this is even stranger since even with the naked eye it is visible that Iceland, an island cut off from everything and made from volcanic rock without any kind of greenery or natural resources (apart from the sea, the geysers and fish), there is no really visible multitude of job choices that a man could do there. Sjón himself is an amazing example of this multi-faceted character. He even multiplied his own name: the stage name Sjón was created from his family name Sigurjon Sigurdson. So, in addition to being a songwriter (he is the author of the song for Bjork in the film *Dancer in the Dark* by Lars von Trier, and was nominated in 2001 for an Oscar for that text; with the English composer Julian Nott he wrote the composition for the Brodski

Quartet that I listened to last night (!) or, better said, watched in a guest performance at the Belgrade Philharmonic performing the *Song of the Traveller in the Night* by Isidora Žebeljan – he is the author of the song 'Oceania' which Bjork sang at the opening of the Olympic games in Athens in 2004) he is also involved in art and the stage, to say nothing of his activities in literature.

Anyway, my question was about why so many people did so many different types of jobs at the same time and why all of them had several professions (an answer explaining that more money is the reason was excluded from the outset: even without additional jobs, Icelanders enjoy a higher standard of living than the Swiss or Norwegians). Sjón answered, and later others confirmed this, that it is because there are only 320,000 of them and that this is a subconscious defence from the fear that they could disappear as a nation, and that it is therefore a powerful attempt at preserving their identity. At least to the virtually multiplied Icelanders.

A collision with numbers.

CHAPTER 19

The supreme commander of the military campaign took the advice of the supreme architect.

Upon arrival in Serbia, he took the divan of the pasha of Belgrade and, using the pasha's and his own scribes, he made the effort to send letters all over Rumelia, in Serbian. Even stranger than the fact that the conqueror's official missive in the name of the Ottoman Empire was written in Serbian to the rulers and statesman of the Italians, Hungarians, Austrians, Russians and others, was the explicit demand by that ruler for them to *answer* him officially in Serbian! So it was that Bajica, at first not even aware of it, created with his correspondence – a brand new language of diplomacy.

He was a bit worried by the Sultan's possible reaction to such liberties on his part. Although Mehmed explained his reasons for behaving like this ahead of time, and though he had heard no opposition to it from the ruler, he knew that the smallest of insignificant trivia could bring down the Sultan's wrath. Instead, Suleiman surprised him with his understanding after the fact: he sent him a message that, with such unusual behaviour, Mehmed had aroused the interest of many rulers in Rumelia and that he would soon receive some rather uncommon guests to whom, the Sultan was sure, *serasker* Mehmed-pasha would be very convivial. He wrote to him literally: "You turned the Serbs into allies, and confounded the enemy! Two birds with one stone!"

And indeed: soon enough from various places, he received communiqués from all over the Ottoman part of Rumelia proper and from its border areas, from princes, kings, dukes, but surprisingly, like travel writers who come from everywhere – from France, Venice and Dubrovnik and even Germany. If they also served as spies for their masters, this was not of utmost significance: Mehmed-pasha announced his military goals publicly and ahead of time, the conditions of surrender, and even the dates and routes of his campaign. He could afford to do so – he had all the military might on his side. And fear was on the other.

However, the Grand Vizier Rüstem-pasha sent him a message. He had heard of everyone's new interest in the campaign, but also of the Sultan's praise for Mehmed-pasha. He wished (as a Serb by background) to remind Bajica to watch out for 'infidels' and to try not to fall for their provocations, but to turn the situation into his own use and do some spying of his own. In that way, he would be able to check what the public and secret cartographers were really thinking.

Bajica obeyed him. He invited one of the travel writers to the Belgrade court (one recommended to him by the Grand Vizier personally) who was returning to France from Istanbul via Serbia and Belgrade. Rüstem-pasha instructed Bajica on how, while playing host, he could steal, just for the evening, the large book the writer never parted from where he recorded everything that happened on his journeys. Rüstem-pasha had done so without regret while being his host recently at the court in Edirne. That is how he learned the differences between what the Europeans were saying and what they were really thinking. He sent Bajica a copy of part of the travelogue of this Frank, one that had to do with the Serbs, for obvious reasons. It said:

"Serbian soldiers (*delije*) are audacious as light cavalry, and their skill lies in adventure-seeking it in the most dangerous places, wherever they are given a chance to prove their courage and heroism in war. Because of this, they gladly follow the sultan's army without any payment whatsoever (like the *akinji*). Still, most of them are fed and maintained at the expense of the pashas, beglerbeys and sancakbeys, because all of the latter keep a certain number of the bravest and most courageous Serbian soldiers in their entourage. They are found in the regions of Bosnia and Serbia that border on one side with Greece and on the other with Hungary and Austria. Today they are called Serbs and Croats, and they are actually Illyrians, those whom Herodianus described in *The Northern Dream* as men who were quite courageous and large, well-built, powerful, of lion-coloured complexion, but by nature quite malicious, even more so than the barbarians in their customs, clumsy in their cleverness so that it is easy to deceive them. The Turks call them 'delija', which means crazy and brave. However, the name they use among themselves is 'zatočnici' which, in their language, means 'those who challenge other men'. Because, since each of them is required to compete with ten (if they want to take on the name 'delija' or 'zatočnik'), they meet their enemy in vicious hand-to-hand combat, and in doing so use certain clever tricks and deceptions they have learned from their forebears, and do so with such skill and courage that they are most often victorious."

Bajica understood the vizier's message completely. And he was quite intrigued about what he would read, freshly written in this unfinished book.

Welcoming this travel writer and geographer, named Nicholas de Nicole from Dauphiné who was, actually, in the entourage of the statesman D'Aramon, an emissary of the French king, Bajica repeated Rüstem-pasha's rude behaviour and overnight at the Kalemegdan court in Belgrade, he had a copy made of those parts of the travelogue that seemed interesting to him. One part about the Serbs (which was the continuation of the part sent to him by the Grand Vizier) touched him especially:

"I met my first Serbian soldier in Edirne when, together with Messieur D'Aramon, I was at the court of the Grand Vizier Rüstem-pasha, to whom this *delija* belonged. He accompanied us to our quarters not so much because of my request but more in the hope that he would receive a tip, which he did. There, while he was our guest, I sketched his appearance and the appearance of his strange clothing... His weapons were a sword and a yataghan, while in his right hand he held a club, or rather a mace, with golden spikes. Several days later, however, this soldier left Edirne with the army led by Ahmed-pasha (the one who was, later on, strangled in his bed on the Sultan's orders) instead of the Sultan, headed for Erdelj. Then I saw him on a horse covered, instead of with a horse-blanket, with the entire hide of a large lion, with its front paws attached to the horse's chest while the hind paws dangled behind. The mace hung from the back pommel on his saddle. In his right hand he held a lance with a long hollow handle, its tip finely sharpened. All in all, there was something special about him, as you can see, faithfully reproduced in the picture below. In addition, I was curious enough to ask him, through a dragoman, to which nation he belonged and what his religious confession was. He answered me, in wise way, that he was a Serb by nationality, but that his grandfather came from the Parthians, a nation of ancient times who enjoyed the reputation and respect of being the most warlike in the entire East. And as to his faith, he said, he was simply pretending to live among the Turks according to their laws, because he was a Christian, by birth, in his heart and in his mind. And in order to convince me properly, he recited in vernacular Greek and in Slavic the *Lord's Prayer*, *Hail Mary*, and the *Nicene Creed*."

Grateful to Rüstem-pasha for allowing him this insight into a foreigner's view of the Serbs, Bajica made a copy of this and some other parts of the travel-writer's book and sent them to Edirne. He knew that for the Grand Vizier, like for him, this additional knowledge would be an aid in a more complete mastery of the dilemma of his duality which hung above them since not long ago, and which seemed like it would never leave them. Every new example similar to their situation was a comfort in their loneliness.

CHAPTER XX

One of the most subtle, creative and impertinent stories on the topic of identity (and its imaginative changes and variations) was told to me by the Argentine Alberto Manguel, a Canadian citizen who is French according to his place of residence. This writer, in addition to his authorship of interesting titles, owns one of the largest and most beautiful libraries in the world, and such a well-read person is hard to find. Already because of his 'multiple-belonging', it is clear that Manguel is among those researchers of biographies in addition to his own. One of the biographies he has whole-heartedly studied, but which he also witnessed and participated in, belonged to Jorge Luis Borges. However, Manguel was different from other researchers in two delicate and subtle oddities: in his youth he was the personal reader to Borges (precisely so, he literally read to Borges), and when he matured he also wrote about him (patiently waiting four decades!) – he wrote a little bit about him, but also about the Borgesologists. Actually, only about some of them: about those who made mistakes about the great writer, those who ascribed the wrong books or non-existent ones and letters to him, but he studied them closely, those who studiously interpreted other authors convinced that they were speaking of Borges, those who rarely admitted their own mistakes and their unbelievable egotism, but who were also unable to laugh at themselves, even afterwards...

A few years ago, Alberto Manguel was a guest at the Blue Metropolis Montreal International Literary Festival, where I also made an appearance. Our meeting was set up, before our public readings and conversations with the audience, by our mutual acquaintance, David Albahari (who is himself, in part, a Canadian writer). Understanding each other very well from the start, unusually quickly and easily we got entangled in the topic of identity with our own examples and those of others, in a topic that self-reproduces like a spider web – spreading in concentric circles, enclosing an ever greater area, and above all *getting farther and farther* from its creator and thereby *protecting him more and more*. But it is hard to see and even harder to catch; for the uninvited guest caught in it, sometimes it not so strong as it is uncomfortable.

We were invited.

Offering me numerous examples of mistaken identity (besides those done to Borges), he also told me of several cases created by Borges himself. Among other things, that was one of the things for which he was known. But, he started giving me one example that went further, and which he somewhat later told/read in front of the audience (not long afterwards, as his publisher, I published it in the form of a special addendum to his book *On Borges* in Serbian, under the title 'Counterfeiting'. And that was actually the world premiere of that text). And here is a part of that story:

"The Second World Shakespeare Congress was held in Washington in April, 1976. The main event of the congress was supposed to be a lecture on Shakespeare by Jorge Luis Borges, entitled *Shakespeare's Secret*, and a thousand experts were milling about, like rock band groupies, trying to get a place in the largest hall of the Hilton. The theatre director Jan Kott was also in the audience, struggling like the others to get a place where he could hear the Teacher revealing the secret. Two men helped Borges climb to the podium and settle in front of the microphone. Kott described the scene:

'Everyone stood up, the ovation went on for a long time. Borges did not move. At last the clapping died down. Borges began to move his lips. From the speakers, only a faint buzz could be heard. Above this monotonous buzz, only one single word could barely be heard again and again, like a repeating shout from a distant sinking ship: Shakespeare, Shakespeare, Shakespeare...

The microphone was placed too high. But no one in the room dared to approach the podium and push the microphone down in front of the old blind writer. Borges spoke for an entire hour, and during that hour only one repeated word – Shakespeare – was heard by the audience. During the lecture, no one got up and left. When Borges finished, everyone stood up and it seemed that the closing ovation would never end,' Jan Kott reminisced with wonder. Doubtless, Kott, like the others, rendered his own reading to the incomprehensible text, so that in the repeated words 'Shakespeare, Shakespeare, Shakespeare' – they all uncovered the secret.

Perhaps there was nothing else to say. With a little help from the imperfections of technology, the master of counterfeit achieved his goal. He turned his own text into a sonic forgery which was made up by the audience..."

The beauty of this story is its multifaceted character: are you convinced that you have gotten all the meaning from it? I have not. For example, did Alberto Manguel intentionally leave his comments so open that he could also lead the reader, additionally, by imitating Borges, into making a mistake? Before him, Jan Kott was also not that comprehensible either. Are we dealing with a personal or communal conspiracy? Because, ultimately and after all, you are still unsure whether the technology was really bad or if the Eternal Magician was so rude in his creativity that he dared to flirt with the great Shakespeare and with his (great and small) interpreters.

But when would it end, the starting of a discussion of idolatry (toward the Teacher) that is caused by hypocrisy (in the expert audience)?

I like the idea enormously that the possibility exists that there are no invincible greats. That attitude (not mine but Borges' himself) was applicable to Borges as well. Ask him, he will tell you so.

Yes, and I forgot to add something to what I have said: Alberto Manguel is Argentine by birth, a Canadian citizen, a resident of France, *but he wrote, and he still writes, in English*. Ultimately, even if he had wanted to hide his imperfect knowledge of English, he could not: in his correspondence with me he did not use English or Spanish, but the language of literature. Still, the various paths are many, both for DNA and for the language identity of the words of such wizards. One important connector of East and West (like Orhan Pamuk), a Lebanese from Beirut, Amin Maalouf has mixed his Arabic background (not confused but joined, or even better – hybridised) with his family's Catholicism, and the Arabic alphabet with the Latin. He wrote all of his books, most of which deal with Arab culture, history and civilisation, but above all with questions of identity – in French, his non-mother tongue. And as such, multi-talented, open-minded and at peace with the world, at the world congress of International PEN in the arctic city of Tromsø in Norway, in order to communicate as well as possible, he read his speech in perfect English and finished it with an apology for not speaking that language as well as he ought to. Before supper, immediately after his speech, I asked him why he was being so humble. He replied: "Well, shouldn't people like you and I, who struggle to find perfection in words, aren't we duty-bound to know language the least of all others?" What more could I have expected from such a humble man and real world-traveller (as a journalist he had been a correspondent in the most unbelievable parts of the world, and even reported from Belgrade at the funeral of Josip Broz Tito in 1980) than an answer that I could not have predicted?

Then again, Maalouf was famous for his sentence explaining his background and his environs: "For whoever lives in Lebanon, the first religion he has is that of co-existence." He could apply that sentence literally to Tito's Yugoslavia. That is the reason for his interest in this non-existent country. Unfortunately, no matter how different they are, those two countries negated the concept of co-existence. The former harmonious cohabitation of people of different religions within a common border was exchanged in both countries by the use of the worst possible, once again mutual, tool – civil war.

It turned out that Tromsø, a city in the far north of Norway, was one of the last stops of the 'civilised' world from where all the North Pole expeditions departed, and was equally attractive to writers (the members of PEN). As if these creators of words also believed that the purity of renewal can be conceived in such a faraway, cold place, from where so many headed off into the uncertainty of their own life but into the certainty of the search for the unknown. And indeed: this un(over)populated expanse woke the need for a personal purification and for a fresh start. It takes a person back to an embryonic state that implies innocence and naïveté. That is why such remarkably diverse writers had arrived there from completely different parts of the world: in addition to Maalouf, there was our host Jostein Gaarder, and also the legend of Latin American literature and the revolution – Ernesto Cardenal. It was a shame that Alberto Manguela was not there since, intrigued by Maalouf's search for the nullification of differences, he had translated his novel *Ports of Call* from French into English. (The novel deals with the multiple mixing of Ottoman and Armenian in the background of an individual, and with the love affair of a Jew and a Moslem...)

Anyway, all of that is connected. Giving a speech at that same place, Gaarder only confirmed that his native Norway really did awaken a utopian drive and a certain childlike sensitivity in writers: with his words, his smile, his facial expression, his gestures, his whole body, his voice – our host seemed to be more like Harry Potter than a 'serious writer' and all of that – in front of other writers. However... only a year later, the Jewish community in Oslo denounced him because he publicly sought the withdrawal of the Israeli army from (Maalouf's) Lebanon, and thus sentenced him to a voluntary withdrawal from public life. And to a certain kind of expunging of the childlike in him. The two of them, Maalouf and Gaarder, did talk in Tromsø, but they did not forge a conspiracy. Anyway, the Israeli writer David Grossman demanded the same thing from his own government! Just one day after he visited his premier and handed him a demand to withdraw the Israeli army from south Lebanon, his son was killed there wearing the uniform of the Israeli army. And that was when I had published one of his books and had just invited him to come to Belgrade. How life changes itself in a mere second.

The conclusion? Writers – peacemakers – are not welcome. Politicians and those who feel sovereign in politics often let writers know that their role has not changed since the Middle Ages: it is their job to be entertainers, like minstrels. Period.

But not just period... Recently, Nobel prize-winner José Saramago said (unwisely?) of his homeland Portugal that it would be a part of Spain in the future and he experienced a cannonade of political attacks, not counter-arguments fit for a debate, but rather political disqualifications by politicians who told him to stay out of politics and go back to writing. Which would be just fine if those same politicians would do their jobs and not write books. But, there you have it!

An unusual and successful, and of course rare, example of someone who does both, also present in Tromsø, is the abovementioned Ernesto Cardenal.

A revolutionary who, after visiting Cuba in 1970, created his own philosophy of 'Christian Marxism', but who long *before that* had been: a convert – Catholic, priest – Leftist, and *later* the one who brought down the dictator Somoza, then became the Minister of Culture of Nicaragua, and *all the while* – a poet (who promoted the aesthetic standards of Ezra Pound and was a creator of his own *Cantos*). A man who also stepped away from his former brothers-in-arms in the Sandinista movement (in which he used to be an officer), but he never stopped being a Leftist, a monk at heart, a champion against the unnecessary accumulation of wealth...

This friend of my friends was ultimately for me the symbol of the determination of poetry. He was a man who made utopia real: as a future minister in 1979, he seemed to many to be a clown because he read poetry to soldiers and policemen, offering a concept of state in which 'poetry would be of technical assistance to the army and police'. And when he actually became a public servant he did not back down: by reading poetry he uprooted illiteracy in the country where, afterwards, poetry books would be sold in the millions for years.

A man who forced the state to listen to poets.

In Tromsø, at the age of eighty, he made an exhibition of sculptures, held a literary reading, and he was remarkably funny about serious topics – and he was the youngest of all the writers. The followers of James Laughlin from the New York publisher New Directions announced that they were preparing to publish his *New and Selected Poems* (1950–2005) during 2008. As if they knew that in 2007 he would be nominated for the Nobel Prize (just as in those years nominations were received by some others of 'mine', equally rebellious and 'old' enough, people I knew – Cohen and Dylan). Poetry is music. And vice versa.

In fact, I was present at Cohen's public candidacy in Montreal and, together with everyone else, by acclamation, voted for that proposal. Strangely, but something that, at the beginning, was conceived as a sort of joking idea among several of his friends (TV producers, jazz singers and writers...), was seen to be quite worthwhile and serious by the public in his hometown. Soon enough the proposal could not be withdrawn: his readers, the public and the media carefully drove the idea to its end. Of course, for such a creative talent the 'end' does not come with winning the Nobel Prize. It is a bit naïve to believe that a serious man on the cutting edge of the everlasting alternative, to be fair, the oldest active pop-rock musician (he is even older than Bob Dylan), to the doubters ever 'half poet, half musician', no matter to what extent even in old-age he confirmed his own consistency, could ever become the laureate of such a prize. However... one never knows. Even the expression 'half fish, half maiden' was often used to tease, but for those with imagination it, actually, stimulated them to do fabulous things.

CHAPTER 20

Mehmed-pasha's diplomatic conquest of the battlefield was quite successfully replacing the old way – until then regarded as the only one possible, the decisive way – by means of fire and sword. Of course, not completely. But even this much, partially, it saved thousands of lives on all sides. To be honest, it sometimes only put death off for a while, but the total outcome made negotiation fundamental as a replacement for an excess of death, wherever and whenever possible. It was important to Bajica that he first convince himself that he was able to at least partly master the negotiating skills in which he so honestly believed. He knew that without the cruelty of conquering with weapons, a campaign could not be successfully finished, but that did not stop him from trying to use the alternative – through correspondence and conversation whenever the opportunity presented itself. His desire to believe in the word was so strong that it did not leave him even in the moments when, alone and unwatched, he was close to despair. And there were reasons for despair. The long negotiations with the clever and whimsical, dethroned and uncrowned or half-baked pretenders and rulers of Hungary, the Austrians and their followers, divided among themselves, each of them having their own greater or smaller interests in this cauldron, dragged out the results of the conquest: caught in the trap of winter, he had to stop the advance and withdraw the army to its winter quarters, to get rested, fed and motivated for the continuation of the conquest in the spring. The Sultan was almost angered by this decision (more by the lateness than by the decision, which was a consequence of the lateness), but the Grand Vizier Rüstem-pasha took his compatriot under his wing and explained to the ruler that it would be better to wait for the final results of the work of their new military commander, who was, he thought with reason, acting differently than all of his predecessors on this conquest. They had lost some time by putting goals off until the next year, but it was not pointless. The army was kept at the borders of the captured territory, and thus there were no losses in the return from the campaign: the army was waiting in close proximity to the enemy. Bajica had most of the forces encamped in Belgrade and Zemun, on the slopes of Avala and in its vicinity. No one had withdrawn to their starting point, not even in Bosnia.

One more unusual thing happened to him. All of the Serbian military commanders, together with their soldiers, were acting as if they were happy to be all together; they kept gathering in tight groups and this awoke a feeling in them that there were *quite a lot of them*, that they were brave and strong, that they were in agreement and that they could once again fight like this, but exclusively for their own goals. Some of the Serbian leaders, when they had responded to Bajica's invitation within the ramparts of Belgrade, did not hide their thoughts from him. He, of course, gladly received them and heard them out: everyone enjoyed hearing the sound of their own language which could be spoken aloud even *in front* of the highest representative of the Empire, and also with him. The leaders thought, for a moment, that they had their own ruler in front of them. And Bajica was in front of *his own people*. But he was still not the ruler of his own country. How strange! He, the commander in chief, born and raised on this soil, they, his subjects, also of the same lineage as he, all together on one and the same, their mutual soil, but all of them in the service of a different ruler and in a foreign country.

The Sultan Legislator himself, who was given that name because of his actions, was to be credited for the fact that the Serbs felt rightly privileged within the Empire. Of course they still remained only more protected subjects than others, but they at least had the illusion that they were governing themselves and determining their destiny as they wished. In any case, they did not feel like slaves. They were a part of something. In difficult times, *belonging* was more important than being in despair.

Bajica silently accepted this awkward and voluntary union, but he said nothing about it out loud. He decided to act instead. And to do so whenever he had the chance and in a way that would be useful to all of them.

Knowing even now that they would return to this city, Mehmed-pasha ordered that everything in Belgrade be repaired, renovated and cleaned up over the winter (to be honest, not the best of times to do so). For the larger projects, he ordered plans to be made for future works, and on the smaller ones he put engineers and soldiers to work who otherwise did not know what to do with all of their free time. Work maintained discipline in the ranks. Actually, he was the so-called guardian of the fire, the one who never allowed it to go out. Work was a substitute for Sinan.

From his conversations with the Serbian leadership, he got a clearer picture of the state of the people's spirit, about the Orthodox Church and its constant impoverishment and dangerous collapse... He saw that the people had nothing to connect them, being scattered around several different imposed empires. The land was the only thing the Serbs could remain tightly connected to: the ground was unmovable. But, intentionally or not, foreign rulers found a usable means to break this connection: when it came time for movement, they did not touch the monasteries, but they relocated the people. In a variety of ways, cleverly, shamelessly, either voluntarily or by force, they would relocate entire villages or regions whenever it suited their needs. They would move them by expulsion or even by using scare tactics so that the people would make the decision to leave 'voluntarily', sometimes they would buy out an individual, force them into service, but most often they recruited them into the army. In such desperate situations the common people did not have a hold to grasp on to. Even in their thoughts, and certainly not physically, they could not even create an illusion to help themselves resist their fate. All that was left to them was their faith, which was also not supported by the church, because the church was slowly but surely crumbling into dust right before their eyes.

If the buildings were collapsing, one should at least save the thoughts. As soon as possible. But how?

Perhaps thoughts were renewed not just *like* a building but *by means of* a building!

Again, he was sorry that Jusuf Sinan was not by his side. Not Jusuf, but Josif. But not even he, rather all three in one – Mimar. Not the Turk nor the Greek, but – the Engineer.

CHAPTER XXI

I was waiting for my partner in conversation. I was looking for someone knowledgeable to explain to me why the Ottomans never called their conquering of Europe a war, nor did they ever write down the concept of *war*. It was always a *campaign*. It was as if the very expression 'war' necessarily meant the fact that in such a situation there must be, on the other side, equal or not, at least a minimally respected opponent. I would not say that such a definition forced an admission from them that someone might (or God forbid – would have to) be better or stronger than them, but it all indicated that they were acting immaturely in this; like when children mumble, to themselves and then out loud, try to chase away great fear by constantly repeating a swearword. Forbidden words that have healing power in extraordinary situations!

It seems that, instead of calling them by their real names, to phenomena they gave names that fit them, and so the soldiers complied with this timeworn tradition also with the attribute of the great Sultan Mehmed the *Conqueror*. There were battles, but no defeats, so there was no war either, there was only *conquest*. Therefore, the invincible victor did not go to war, but rather just occupied and conquered. His campaigns were those of conquest. One other concept from the same corpus, today we might even call it ideological, became semi-linguistic: the infidels. This was exclusivity without justification, to call the members of other religions infidels. To 'not differentiate' three (!) entire existing religions was too difficult? This connection is not accidental. Both the *campaign* and the *infidels* came about at the same moment, just when Mehmed the Conqueror sealed the fate of the centuries-old Byzantine Empire by conquering its magnificent capital city Constantinople.

Once again, for the umpteenth time, we know, before and after that, history repeats itself to exhaustion and ennui: the conquering newcomers expunged the traces of their predecessors from the past. And they tried to do the same with their very own future: without planning, it was if they did not care about their heirs and much less about those who would one day subjugate them. As if everything started and finished in the present.

The present! Why, that is just another word for selfishness.

Arrogance – that is another word for ruin! It must be admitted, the Ottomans did overcome it with the example of the lost battle at Lepanto. It was then that they understood their mistake once and for all: think the best of yourself and ridicule everyone else. That was a situation, never seen in another example, when the son of the greatest sultan of all (and even greater than Mehmed the Conqueror) – Suleiman the Magnificent – Sultan Selim slid into crisis and into a real paranoia of fear that his empire was disintegrating, and that Istanbul would be overtaken in just a few days. And who saved him with words and actions: by convincing him that everything could be recovered, and by quickly renewing the destroyed fleet? His Grand Vizier at the time (once the fleet admiral as well) Mehmed-pasha Sokollu/Sokolović, of *infidel* stock, brought from Bosnia, that is Serbia, *during a conquest*.

I must now come back to language and why all of that was not called war.

My partner in conversation arrived. Or, better said this time, my audience. Orhan Pamuk. His presence helped me to think that I had one more part of a possible answer to that question. That part was with Bajica. Participating in the campaigns and battles, namely, he was just a normal soldier at the beginning, later an officer, but when he was the commander of the campaign, especially on the soil of Rumelia, he did not have the impression that he was running a war. Strange, even though everything was military in nature, even though so many people died, even though they took prisoners, occupied territory, changed borders and rulers and all the rest, he was simply not prepared to call all of that 'war'. But he had his own reason for that.

"He was aided by the fact that the Ottoman army always started its conquests in the spring and finished them (or interrupted them) in late autumn, understandably because of meteorological reasons. And that made these campaigns seasonal. Like fruit. Or like something temporary, something that starts and then stops, exists and then disappears. Like fashion. Such a view of 'war' made it easier for him to think that Serbia and Bosnia were only temporarily (not to say 'seasonally') without liberty. Although he consciously served his Ottoman masters,

Mehmed still remained Bajica. That is how he retained his belief that Serbia would certainly, and Bosnia perhaps and even Slavonia, (again) be a part of their own former or future empires. He could not make peace with the idea that they would eternally be slaves or servants of someone else."

Pamuk did not just want to listen:

"Or like politics: Because of the same reason of rhythm, the Americans call the battle for their presidential elections... a campaign. It has its own amplitudes: as the goal draws closer, the pressure mounts more and more, and then it explodes either in victory or in defeat. And then they disappear. Thus, that which was known about it from the very beginning, that it is a one-time thing and that at one moment it stops and vanishes. That is why they use this word in their language and keep it also for signifying war campaigns that they did not call war."

He had hit the target. I had a personal example:

"You've probably forgotten that the bombing of Serbia in 1999 was also called a campaign. Actually I think, not just because the whole thing was short, 'just' three months (in relation to the usual length of a war), but also because of the propaganda machine that is the customary accompaniment to such campaigns. But above all so that the conflict (another favourite word – replacement) would not even accidentally be called a war. War is always somewhere else. (In fact, the wars before that on the soil of our former, larger homeland, were also for the president of our country at that time – somewhere else.) I don't know if you knew that the campaign in 1999 carried the exemplary name of 'The Angel of Mercy'. Very Christian of them. A Catholic present for their Orthodox brothers."

"And since we're talking about it," I remembered something more recent, "the recent announcement, long awaited, by the head of the Roman-Catholic church, Pope Benedict XVI, went almost unnoticed; while visiting the Patriarch in Istanbul in the winter of 2006, he stated that the division of Christianity into eastern and western was... a scandal!"

Pamuk took us back to the time of my story:

"No matter if Bajica's and Jusuf's lives were just a bit of time in which Rumelia withstood the Ottoman government, you should not forget that, in this so-called temporariness, that same Europe remained under that government for almost half a millennium."

I said, "True. Bajica could not have seen that on the basis of his own life, no matter how long it lasted. Nor was he that kind of visionary or prophet. We can see that from our perspective."

"But not because we are some kind of prophets or visionaries, but because that is behind us," Pamuk joked.

CHAPTER 21

The Sultan and the Grand Vizier found a middle way for the continuation of the military campaign on Temisoara, Buda and Vienna: insufficiently satisfied with Mehmed-pasha's successes, they assigned Ahmed-pasha, the second vizier of the Porta, to be the new military commander. They did not decide to go to any extremes: Sultan Suleiman did not go to war himself (but he ordered it again symbolically from Istanbul), nor was there any sign of reprimand or punishment for Mehmed-pasha. He left him as the right-hand man of the new *serasker*, wise enough to use him as the commander who had, after all, successfully occupied parts of Banat. And this was not so much smaller than they had planned, but it was done more slowly. But it was done. In any case, the Sultan had many more plans for him.

Bajica did take this replacement rather painfully, but he had to be open to the truth: just as it was clear to everyone that it was his first great campaign as commander and that no one could expect him to have the experience of a seasoned veteran, it was also clear that his persistent negotiations shortened the time needed for greater and quicker successes. This, of course, cast no doubt on negotiation as a method.

Both Suleiman the Legislator and Rüstem-pasha were, actually, exceptionally satisfied by it. Mehmed-pasha had opened another door for them, one of the more subtle means of ruling: he infused cleverness into politics! The Ottoman strategy no longer had to be called shrewd; it now had a name – negotiations. Their enemies had begun to speak with respect of the *Sultan's* new diplomats and, praising him, they let him know that they were likely to cooperate with him. And this meant to his ruler and the first vizier that, in the future, they could achieve victory over their opponents in a roundabout way, but without unnecessarily spilling a lot of blood. After all, there were, of course, situations when more corpses did not suit their purposes. And one other thing: they saw the extent to which Bajica, so respected among their

Serbian subjects, was necessary for them to remain in good relations with the Serbs; these were their best and most courageous soldiers.

In this case, for the sake of the greater public, and because of the visible partial failure on the battlefield, they had to take the high command away from him for the rest of the campaign.

Bajica's reputation as a warrior was in question. This had nothing to do with impractical self-satisfaction. He understood to what extent it was important to prove oneself as a soldier among the Ottomans. A personal example! He remembered. Although it was not easy for him to move from the state of having fallen into the partial bad favour of his ruler and completely in the bad favour of the general public – to the state of readiness and good will needed for renewed success. Not that it was impossible: ultimately, somewhere down the line, the ruler's good graces awaited him again.

However, it was actually the Sultan's mercifulness toward Bajica that became the reason why some of the pashas, agas and beys all over Rumelia began to despise him: among such men, the principle of combative cruelty recognised nothing except one's strength. Thereby, Mehmed-pasha was considered to be a weakling, spoiled by the court, who needed to be shown, whenever possible, what raw courage and the sowing of fear in one's opponents can do. Therefore, certain Ottoman subjects – ruling in Bosnia and Hungary, on their own ground – could hardly wait for the replacement of the high commander, and in the winter of 1552, not even waiting for the new commander to leave and much less for him to arrive – rushed off to conquer and raze on their own initiative. The worst for Bajica was the fact that they even succeeded in doing so, and received praise from the newly appointed *serasker*, Ahmed-pasha. This silently accepted circumventing of the beglerbey was their way of ridiculing Bajica, because under his command they were not given a free hand even nearly as much as they wanted. However, in giving themselves this pleasure, they went too far, of course; they were not wise enough to recognise the Sultan's reserve and to deduce from it that they would all once again be under Mehmed-pasha's command in war several more times. If they survived. This is taking no account of their costly forgetfulness that Bajica was also still the beglerbey of Rumelia, and that they were subordinate to him in peacetime. They were indeed of importance to the Sultan and the Grand Vizier, but only insofar as they served to achieve their goals, very often only in a given moment. No matter how one looked at it, they were naïve. Which did not mean that they should be pitied. To the contrary. No matter how crude it sounded, they were the ones who jumped at the chance to lord it over a wounded body, seeing it as they wanted to in their heart of hearts – as a corpse. That was their mistake. Because after every campaign or war, peacetime came again. And at that moment he returned – the beglerbey of Rumelia, Mehmed-pasha Sokollu, also known as Bajica Sokolović. In this case, it was not known – which of those two names was likely to be more dangerous for them.

The Sultan and the Grand Vizier were not ashamed of the reputation they had developed of the Ottomans among the states of Rumelia – that they were cruel conquerors and bad negotiators. But they also understood that times change. And that, in addition to the existing trepidation that they sowed by the use of armed force, it was not a bad idea to introduce a new fear that was not so visible and predictable. And they admitted to one another that the praises reaching them about Mehmed-pasha were quite pleasing. In any case, they had come to Rumelia to stay. And they had been there long enough that it was no longer a question of whether they would remain. On the contrary, their plans were to settle in its very heart. There was no end to the conquests yet on the horizon. But great campaigns and long-range planning demanded breaks and resting places, a variety of approaches and solutions, varied strategies that would confuse their opponents and keep them on their toes even when the sheer might of the armada was not marching toward them.

For such an approach to planning, Mehmed-pasha was ideal for them. His approach was not so much a new weapon as a commonly used and verbal one, which it would be hard to cope with: a word given could be an obligation, but it did not have to be kept. A single thing can be said in a hundred ways, and it can be understood, correctly or incorrectly, in the same number. The beglerbey of Rumelia had already begun to improve the reputation of the Empire: in him, the infidels saw a chance for putting things off, for withdrawal, political bargaining, and even deception. But even Mehmed-pasha had no illusions. He, too, used this approach for the same goals, but he counted on the possibility that, in this sort of battle as well, the best would be the victor. That is, skill could overcome shrewdness. For Bajica, and for the start, that was enough. The thing he believed in deep within himself

– he did not dare to show it too openly, and much less to say it out loud: in the relationship between the *word* and the *sword*, the word was sovereign.

If nothing else, because of that stance, he had to remain calm and try to overcome all his impatience. He thought about it like this: if it proved to be right and he truly possessed the abilities that everyone, in one way or another, was praising him for, then he would not rid himself of those skills. But he could therefore make an effort concerning those abilities that people thought he either did not have or was bad at, concerning those he was not partial to or did not have in the slightest. Since these were character traits, behaviours that could be learned, he resolved to make them a part of his character. Perhaps he would be able to trick others with this variety of traits and abilities, but he would know within himself why each of them existed, what their purpose was and which ones he would have to keep under control. He did not want to change himself. That was the hardest exercise of all: to become someone else and remain himself.

Hadn't life already thrown him into that cruel game long ago? This exercise was much longer, more important and dangerous: it would have to go on for the rest of his life. His greatest secret, in terms of this exercise, was also the least likely to become reality. How could he, with equal honesty, present two different parts of his personality to himself and the world, and not feel like a cheat, a fake and a liar? And to not be those things in truth.

Perhaps only if he could manage to prove that differences did not really exist.

CHAPTER XXII

I remember my long research preparations, and all the others, before writing my novel about the Druids.

On one of my travels through the Celtic lands, in Brittany, one of my dreams came true. But first, how the dream came about...

It came about from the connection between music and architecture. Namely, while rock-'n'-roll was still considered to be the modern and cutting-edge musical style in the world, parallel with it, in the sixties and seventies of the last century, there was a different kind of music that did not have a name at that time. Formally, it was a kind of rock but it was, let us say – broader, or at least different enough. Its roots were found in the brash individualism of its musicians/composers or in their classical music education (these were people schooled in classical music at the standard music schools and universities). The first of these two lines was characterised by names like Donovan, Bob Dylan... The other, which I am interested in discussing now, was based on the music of strange characters such as Ian Anderson, the frontman of the band Jethro Tull. He/they were, like the group the Gentle Giant and others similar to them, classified most often in a style called symphonic rock. These were people who readily injected the influences of classical music into their compositions. So, they actually used classical music (as opposed to the others who had similar educations but did not use it). The very name of the style, symphonic rock, indicated not so much what the music sounded like as to what it consisted of. Therefore, it was, to say the least, more complex compositionally and more demanding musically than the other leading rock trends of the time. As time passed, elements of the musical heritage of a variety of cultures also began to enter into it, and not only the predominantly Anglo-Saxon ones. Actually, the roots appeared of something that had elements of music that would later branch off into a special style of music called world music or ethno-music. At that time, 'that' actually did not have a name as yet. In rock-'n'-roll at that time, the lead was taken by a mutual musical language that still did not recognise the specificity of individual musical cultures.

In the nuances of such musical combinations, the most varied of compositional voices appeared, all together creating a rich and joyous period of creative work. That was a time when both the creators and listeners of that same music 'competed' in their enjoyment. Who would be the winner was not important. The only thing that was significant was reaching a certain degree of happiness.

But we should return now to the connection between music and architecture. In this story.

Belgrade has several concert halls for so-called serious music, some specifically built for it, some 'accidental'. Although there is not a special hall for listening to opera, there is one at least for watching it – in the National Theatre. It is all somehow superficial. So, in addition to the so-called hall (incidentally musical as well) of a mall, the city also has a philharmonic hall, to be honest in contrast to the former – quite a small one. But there is also one hall that has become a sort of symbol for the city, even though it is the oldest and is not so large. It was constructed originally as a part of an endowment, a marvellous architectural design in which a variety of cultural programs have been held for decades, and even courses in foreign languages have been given there. It was designed by Petar Bajalović, the architect, the one who, *also in 1924*, finished the ten-year construction of the building from which I now speak (which is, truth be told, too highly acoustic for an apartment building), the one built on the foundations of the court and residence of Mehmed-pasha Sokolović. In several of his most important efforts, this remarkable engineer combined the Serbian and Slavic tradition with European trends and left a marvellous heritage behind (for example, the grandiose, but minimalist building of the Law School of the Belgrade University). In this, his, hall called the Kolarac' National University (the endowment of Ilija Milosavljević Kolarac, 1800–1878), all of the significant figures of world and domestic classical music have played over the past few decades. Why is that? Well, not just because plans were made like that but because, if they are not exaggerating, everyone says that this humble music hall has exceptional acoustics. Now, while it is true that Bajalović played the violin and was formally musically educated, this does not guarantee that he would design a room with good acoustics. And they say that he did not hire a single expert for sound while constructing this building, popularly nicknamed as simply 'Kolarac'.

So, it is clear that the engineer's talent was crucial for the acoustics. He had plenty of that. Among other things, it is enough to see, as a contrast to the visually monumental Law School, the tiny house of Mihailo Petrović Alas (1868–1943) at Kosančićev venac, that Bajalović built to order, for private purposes, in 1910. Regardless of the extreme differences in size, the home of this famous mathematician, the forerunner of cybernetics, builder of computers... (and a fisherman, the nickname 'Alas' in Serbian means 'fisherman') is a humble abode, but it also has one detail – a wish that the architect fulfilled for the owner, and by which the house became famous in Belgrade. (It could almost be said that later Belgrade also became famous for that same 'detail'.) The humble and tasteful facade is ornamented by a tiny balcony (the one specific request made of the builder – everything else was left up to him – that one can see the River Sava from it). That little balcony, the most beautiful in the city (or at least the best-placed balcony) inspired this mathematical genius to write a travelogue and so, as a sign of gratitude to give something back to this architect in literature, just as the builder had given Alas a view, and surrounded music with walls and a roof.

And finally, here is the connection between it all.

In 1970, within the existing framework of the ethno-sound (which still did not have a name at the time), an LP appeared, different and very strange, essentially dedicated to rock but above all quite distinctive. Unusual even by its choice of solo instrument – the harp. And what a harp it was! Re-born in the twentieth century – the Celtic harp. In relationship to the usual, standard harp, this one is significantly smaller. It had metal strings, of bronze at that, even though its owner said that the maker of this harp – the owner's father – most often made the strings from horsehair. Yet, the bronze strings produced a louder and more sustained echo. The composer and performer was from France, more precisely from Brittany. His name was Alan Stivell, and the record was called 'Reflets'. And the music was divine! Educating myself later, I managed to define for myself in words what that music represented. Naturally, this was incomparably less important than the feelings that music brought out, but it was a natural need for me to find out where Stivell's inspiration came from (including the origin of the harp and the other instruments he used).

As the years went by, Stivell (his artistic name, in Britannic – *old fountain*, similar in meaning to his and his father's real surname – Cochevelou) went on making records, equally or similarly exceptional. Time was running, he became ever more famous, the hall of Kolarac continued to host world famous musicians... Until one day in 1983 Alan Stivell arrived in that very same hall with his Celtic harp and accompanying musicians. I was ecstatic, convinced that all of Belgrade knew who he was. However, the hall was – as they say – relatively full, but not completely so. For me, this was incomprehensible. Then, the concert turned into real nirvana! It was part of one of his, most frequent, acoustic periods. He also had electronic periods, heavy rock and similar phases, and he was always good enough. But, when he was in his acoustic periods – then he was the best. In his instrumentals, even better than the best. But when he sang, he did so in Britannic, Gaelic, (Old) Irish, French and English. So, in Celtic, if that only existed – as the one unifying language of the former pan-Celtic countries, tribes and nations. He already had a dozen albums to his credit, concerts in Paris' 'Olympia' and at the stadium in Dublin... And that is why I was proud that in such a small room as Bajalović's hall – he sounded wonderful. It should be remembered that for this music at that time the natural surroundings were huge open-air concerts – from fields to stadiums, and even those in enclosed spaces – in the largest spaces possible. At that time, remember, rock ruled the masses. Good for rock. Good for the masses.

Is that my dream come true? No.

That youthful dream was related to Stivell; but everything related to him seemed to include a pause of about a decade...

At that time, my dream was to talk with him. I managed to fulfil my wish some years later, not before the early nineties, in the very heart of Brittany, in Rennes. The introduction to that experience had all the elements of secrecy, conspiracy, false trails, hiding, clandestine meetings... Not because of Stivell but because of a combination of the electrified political atmosphere in France (and not just there) and the very nature of the behaviour and activities of a certain number of Bretons who I knew at the time.

Extremism. New nationalism. Separatism. And many other things.

Thanks to a friend (a Breton) who enthusiastically led me through the hidden modern Celtic world of Brittany, I felt privileged. Encounters of that kind preceded the one with Stivell. And they were preceded by travelling to the places which irresistibly took me back into the deep past of the bards. Then I was present at gatherings that had no sort of official or semi-cultic form but which were private sit-downs of friends, and which emanated an atmosphere of brotherhood, of a special community, of quasi-conspiracy. To this very day, I do not know how (except for the guarantee given by the presence of my friend) I was accepted among those people as if I were one of them, without an ounce of visible doubt. I remember that, at one of those gatherings of very interesting people, I was carefully studied, and I had not even spoken a word. And when someone finally said something to me, in the name of all, they said the following: "You're a Celt!" I was completely flabbergasted by the (pleasant) qualification that did not bear the smallest hint of doubt and even less objection. Many of them did not have any idea of just how much there really is of the Celtic heritage present even today on the soil of Serbia. Only some of them did. Actually, not even the most famous French and Breton experts on the Celts knew anything about it: the multitude of books contained almost nothing about the Balkans except some general comments about how the territory was used by the Celtic tribes to travel to Delphi. And about the fact the Scordic Celts had founded my hometown of Belgrade (actually twice, so that the fact cannot be brought into question), there was not even a hint. Was it that they just did not know, or did they have a reason for not knowing?

Perhaps this question would be excessive if I keep in mind that a similar thing happened in Serbia, though in a milder form because there no one could ignore the knowledge of our cultural heritage which was already a certainty. But it was indeed covered up somehow! I did not understand why a certain number of undoubtedly professional experts so enthusiastically kept shoving these provable and proven truths under the rug. For instance, what culture does not want to show off its knowledge about the deeper historical layers from which it originated? Which civilisation does not enjoy measuring and comparing itself with others? Even the example of the old name of Belgrade shows this unreasonable superficiality or intention: the general public constantly boasts about its Roman name, *Singidunum*, overlooking its Celtic name, *Sindidun*, the name (and existence) of the city from four centuries earlier. Amazingly enough, that is happening to a nation that became famous in the world in the transition between the twentieth and twenty-first centuries because of its drastic events, among other things, and precisely because it literally and persistently insisted on its own ancient character, people and land. Perhaps because the Celts, after all, are not the Serbs. But, certainly we must have learned that, in addition to inheritance through genes, there is also the inheritance gained through land and space.

This unsolved problem from my backyard does not lessen the responsibility of the French-Breton Celtic experts who ignore, in a most un-colonial way, the existence of part of their own heritage in another place. Or, if I could qualify it more mildly – for not working on that part of their heritage.

Is politics to be blamed?

Judging from the example of Alan Stivell, it is.

CHAPTER 22

He did complain that Sinan was not around, but he realised that this was a message from destiny. He had to bear the difficult load of his partial defeat as a military commander alone, and he alone must free himself of it. Sinan was, for now, only in his thoughts.

The next spring, when the campaign against Banat was recommenced with the Second Vizier of the Porta at its head, he understood that pride must sometimes be removed from one's horizons. He had to forget his high position and behave like a regular soldier. And it was actually this return to a subject's unquestioning obedience without any sort of thinking that enabled him to see in others now, and in himself as well, an exceptionally brave soldier. Now he led his unit in several battles, often risking his own life and becoming a true model for the other soldiers. The chroniclers even left a trace of this courage: "Sokolović did amazing things at Temisoara." Or the fact that Mehmed Sokolović in this battle (the one-month siege of Temisoara) attacked the enemy so viciously that "the horse was actually shot from underneath him, but God protected him and he was left unharmed. He mounted another horse and went back into battle." So it was that he attained everyone's trust: both the soldiers when they went through moments of fear, and officers as well, whom he drove to heroism without directly influencing or convincing them.

The word of his bravery reached the Sultan and Grand Vizier faster than the reports of the battles in Banat. When the final official report from the *serasker* arrived about the successful campaign, with the personal and public praises of Ahmed-pasha, especially dedicated to Mehmed-pasha's exploits, they both breathed more easily. Their tolerance of his earlier mistakes now seemed to somehow justify itself. This allowed them to go on showing unbridled sympathy to Bajica without remorse. And he could breathe more easily as well, having blocked the poisoned arrows of those overzealous pashas, agas and beys who had so readily sent them his way. No one dared to doubt in his heroism any longer.

But Bajica had an additional – devilish – plan, now that he was continuing on the campaign in an equal position of commander with the Second Vizier of the Porta. Namely, after capturing so many fortified cities, Ahmed-pasha accepted a proposal from the beglerbey of Buda, Hadum Ali-pasha, too easily and quickly – to put all the commanders together, combining all the armies, and to finish this wartime success with an attack on the famous fortress of Eger which dominated upper Hungary. Just how much importance was given to this proposal – which Bajica opposed in a face-to-face confrontation with the *serasker* but then backed down from his insistence when he realised that they would start accusing him again of lacking courage – can be seen from the numbers and list of participants in the battle: against the two thousand defenders led by Duke István Dobó (close to the Serbian hero Petar Bakić who also fought on the Austro-Hungarian side) a mass of fifty thousand Ottoman soldiers gathered (among them, of course, under Mehmed's command were also several thousand Serbian warriors)! At the head of the Turkish army, besides the Second Vizier, Ahmed-pasha, and the beglerbey of Rumelia, Mehmed-pasha Sokollu, there were the beglerbey of Anatolia, Hasan-pasha, the beglerbey of Buda, Hadum Ali-pasha, the sancak of Stolni Beograd, Arslan-bey, the Bosnian sancak, Ulama-bey, the sancak of Pecs, Dervish-bey, the sancak of Smederevo, Hasan-bey, the *sancak* of Szeged, Mustafa-bey, and the sancak of Hatvan, Veli-bey. These seasoned warriors, desiring to send a message about the decisiveness and importance of this battle, had all the branches of the Turkish army behind them: the janissaries and spahis, akinjis, beshlis (mercenaires), Azapes, Armatoles and cannon-masters. But all of this might was of no help to them. Precisely what Bajica had foreseen actually happened: the numbers were a trap and deception, because this fortress was perfectly placed strategically, marvellously designed and constructed even better, and it was thus easily defended. In addition, for ages the Ottoman army had not seen such insane courage as shown by all the inhabitants of the fortress, from soldiers and old men down to the women and children. After more than a month of siege, a heavy icy rain also began to fall in mid-October, and it seemed that the Almighty had gotten involved, as if wishing to say that, for some people and places, there comes a time when they should be left in peace. It became clear to Ahmed-pasha that he had to recall the army. No one dared speak out loud about the number of Ottoman casualties.

Nor did Bajica have to report anything to anyone: there it was, the Second Vizier also experienced a failure, not to mention a defeat! His 'devilish plan' did not consist of doing anything as much as it meant doing nothing. It was enough for him to know ahead of time that no one would listen to his objections to the idea of laying siege to Eger. He thereby managed to send a message to everyone that flawless warriors do not exist.

This event further diluted Bajica's previous failure. With the additional benefit for him because the Sultan and the Topkapi court somehow received the news that the only one to oppose this plan had been Mehmed-pasha Sokolović. One might say he tried to teach others from the lessons he had learned. Without success. It seems everyone must make their own mistakes.

The enormity of the defeat and the Sultan's anger could not be diffused even by the replacement of the beglerbey of Budim.

However, Bajica was also not satisfied. After such, in his eyes, concrete proof (of his personal courage), he longed for a rather more subtle affirmation.

And once again, Sinan came to his mind.

No matter how he turned it, he envied Sinan for his ability to build. Since he had been reprieved from army service as an engineer on all the campaigns, he had gotten several jobs from high officials in the Empire, including the Sultan himself. He did not have to destroy things anymore. Bajica could also say for himself that he was participating in building the Empire, but he was not willing to be that naïve. He knew how many more bloodbaths he would have to survive (since he had already become such an important figure) because he was still essentially a soldier. And everyone knows what a soldier's job is. To be prepared at any given moment to kill or be killed. From which it seemed that nothing could save him any longer. Still, he was counting on one better possibility: if he got lucky one day, he would no longer have to do things himself, rather it would be enough for him to give an order to others to do that (in his name). Until now that sort of luck had generally followed him: so many years of schooling, of which he had spent many on the battlefield, belonging to the janissaries predestined to hold important positions, he had been protected by the *padishah's* proscription that he not kill anyone himself because that would endanger his life, already highly valued at the time. Although he had been forced to learn how to kill in all possible ways, he had to use that knowledge later in order to teach others how to kill. His future planned job was to command by means of killing. Such a plan saved him from personal, 'excessive' killing. This was of some comfort to him.

He was ashamed of himself. None of the offers he received looked good. Nor did he think that any of them was an expression of him personally.

If he killed and conquered for the Sultan, Josif as Jusuf celebrated his victories by building things. But Bajica still had to prove himself as Mehmed. In truth, he had to honest and remember that his friend was ten years older than he. According to all the numbers, including age, Sinan deserved to be ahead of him. Bajica was thus able to pretend that he was still a young man who, as ahead of every young man, had a bright and promising future ahead of him.

CHAPTER XXIII

The trouble with cultural heritage is in the fact that it always, by definition, divides people into two camps: into those who see in it the preservation of their identity and those who see danger in their heritage. So, it is the same old *pro* and *con*. Thereby all dealings with the purely artistic questions within this topic are subject to political abuse. This was precisely what Stivell told me when we met in a tavern in Rennes. In his case, this question had turned into fear. At the peak of his career, as the biographers would define it, when, for example, just the album recorded live at the concert in Paris' 'Olympia' in 1972 sold 2 million copies, he was seized by the serious fear of the responsibilities imposed on him. The influence he spread with his music in Brittany, Ireland, Wales, Scotland, Cornwall, the Isle of Man, and by Jove in other parts of Europe and on other continents (in Australia, New Zealand, the USA, Latin America) actually frightened him because he realised that many people had misunderstood his desire for reviving an ancient, dead culture. Such people dragged politics into it. All sorts of societies, associations and gatherings with dubious goals started forming, misusing his texts, interviews with him, and him as a public figure. The public reputation of such people was ever more visible, but also ever more aggressive. Stivell began to seriously re-examine things, looking in himself for a sense of blame, which he did not recognise in the least. To love something, to understand it and share it with others, does not automatically mean that it belongs in the political arena. Realising that *his* love, when taken over by *others*, had gotten out of control, he decided to retire from public life. In peace, he went on with his creative activities, but he did not go public with them. He vanished.

Talking with Stivell in the winter of 1991–1992 in a comfortable (perhaps even virtual) log cabin protected from western civilisation, but in the heart of 'rebellious' Brittany, I had that schizoid feeling of my own duality because my country was falling apart at that very moment and people there were killing each other. Feeling heavy, I tried to gently hint to my friends, and to Stivell as well, that I was afraid of all nationalisms, even the Bretons', that was lurking around every corner in the land of the Franks. Perhaps the Bretons would never reach for weapons in order to achieve their goals like the Yugoslav peoples did, but the danger loomed of an idea spreading in a place where it had no influence on them, like the unification into a general movement. One already existed, and this was a perfect chance for it to raise its head.

During the period when he withdrew from public life, others tried to take his place. In a political way. Indeed, the history of the unification of the Celtic peoples and cultures was a rich one. The idea of a pan-Celtic movement in modern times was conceived in the 19th century, and it went on in various forms in organisations like the Celtic Congress, the Celtic Union, the Celtic League and others. Some saw unity only in language and culture, but others saw a united state in the political goals. All the way down to the present.

After the peak of success that he reached at the beginning of the seventies, Stivell made his comeback from voluntary exile and reached the place he had been before. Even then, at the beginning of the nineties, while we spoke, there were those who were using him for their own purposes. But the general political tensions had relaxed, and he was again able to comfortably express his opinions even outside of music. Now he was experiencing, perhaps for the second time (before that, at the beginning of the eighties), a revival or a comeback (to fame): some of his albums/compact discs were selling at an average of one thousand per day! He continued to claim that Donovan was the forerunner, and even the creator, of Celtic rock. Accepting this phrase as a symbol for his music as well, he enriched it with names like ethno-modern, New Age, and even folk. But he did not accept leadership of the (movement of) the neo-Celts. No matter what kind of challenge this position offered. For example: the political champions of the Celtic state, if they took into account all the territories that the Celts lived in over a certain period, they could extrapolate a state that, by size, roughly speaking, could compete with a new state in the process of being created – the European Union. The fact that, long ago, they were mercenaries in the army of Alexander the Great who participated with him in the conquest of Asia all the way to India and were, thus, at least partially the 'owners' of the Middle East, does not have to be taken into their calculations.

How close the pan-Celtic movement was to exploding in several periods, and in this one where I was a witness, is testified to by the sympathy its militant members had toward the Basque separatist movement, ETA, of the day. To be honest, that was understandable: their historical and ethnic motives overlapped a great deal, they were neighbours geographically, practically in each others backyards, and in their mutual support it could be said that their political programs also overlapped. The governments of both countries enthusiastically cooperated in dismantling the faction of ETA that dealt with terrorism. The Pyrenees were the border, but also the pass into a foreign courtyard: the Spanish fugitives used French territory as a logistical base, partisan hospital and temporary station for regrouping and respite.

One day/night I realised how profound these relationships were. My Breton friend took me to a neighbouring town, just smiling enigmatically as an answer to my question about *where* we were headed. And more specifically about how we were getting there? We were driving for so long and on such a roundabout route, and supposedly heading for the *neighbouring* village, that it became clear to me the thing was serious: we were covering our trail! Then we were met at one place by another friend, we changed cars, and went through the whole thing again: driving around, all over the place, just not directly. With the conspiratorial aid of the dark, we arrived at the home of our hostess who was at the wheel.

The evening passed in the usual atmosphere of a three-person sit-down, pleasant but not completely relaxed. After a time, it became clear why. We were joined by a handsome man in his middle years, with dark hair and a swarthy complexion, speaking excellent French and English, but with a lilting Spanish accent. He seemed open and cordial. He did not dwell on the niceties that people usually use when first meeting or getting to know each other. He was quite direct, more than kind and most refined. Only near the end of the evening, when our hostess and Raul T. went to the living room from the dining room before us, did my friend tell me that our guest was one of the four leaders of ETA and that his responsibility was transporting its members over the border along the Pyrenees. I know that a shiver ran down my spine. I think that they were the most wanted people on the continent during those years for the state, police and secret services.

Since he realised that I finally knew who he was, this remarkably educated man changed the subject and began to tell me openly of his movement, its goals, and the tools they were using to achieve those goals. He answered all my questions. His dedication was fatalistic. He placed death on the level of the everyday and did not differentiate it from life. And then at one moment he amazed me. What he said was no longer a matter of his acceptance of me. It was a fondness for my people, to be honest, expressed in a very strange way.

"But why don't you Serbs start undertaking terrorist actions against your enemies?" he asked.

I did not understand him. At that moment in my (former) country, a bloody civil war was being fought! A war that, at one moment, seemed like it was 'every man for himself'. It was cruder and more massive murder than any sort of terrorism. The purpose of his proposal was unclear to me. And then it became clear.

"I don't mean you should carry out those actions in Yugoslavia. I mean the foreign countries who are against Serbia and the Serbs, those who support the Croats, the Bosnians and the Moslems."

I could not believe my ears.

"But I want that war to stop, not for us to export it elsewhere!"

Raul, however, insisted. He compared the Basque situation with the Serbs (he was not bothered by the contradiction that the former wanted to secede, and the latter the opposite – to unify), he drew unbelievable conclusions and offered training for terrorist attacks. In cooperating he saw quite a normal future.

"If we train you to fight the civil war, you can train us as a real army which we will certainly need later on."

Raul was certain that a war was coming for them.

But how could I convince him otherwise? You see, he was using events and experiences from my country to prove that he was right. Were we not, for instance, in the search for our own roots and identities, resorting to killing each other on a massive level? Moreover, in that conflict he found that justice was on the side of the Serbs! Probably because everyone else had proclaimed that it was the Serbs' fault. And I must admit, I who certainly could not directly be a mass murderer (or a commander in anybody's army), in the years that followed, I felt on my own skin the damnation of belonging to my own people. Especially outside of my country, no matter what it was called at a given time. Unfortunately, I was something like a 'damned Serb' for many publishers and literary institutions.

Raul's fiery sympathy for 'the Serbian cause' was even stranger because I knew (as did he) that my friend at the party was on the side of the Moslems in that war, both in Bosnia and in Kosovo. Even though I could justify that by some of her expressly private and intimate familial reasons, I could not justify one other: the French, because of the large Moslem community in their own milieu, inherited from their colonial past, were on their side just to keep reasonable peace at home. In addition to that, besides the needs of democracy, there was France's slightly hypocritical need to protect minorities theatrically and loudly. In that, my Breton friend (let us not forget, by definition a separatist) was French. But she is still my friend because politics does not make a friendship. Or, said more simply: friendship is not politics.

Both her protectiveness of one side and Raul's extremism in the protection of the other side were just one more kind of battle, if not for the finding of lost identity then at least for its return. In all of these radical standpoints, it was at least comforting that they were ready to risk their own lives for them, and not just the lives of others.

And in terms of my life, that was one of the rare occasions I did not celebrate the New Year (1991–92) and Christmas (both Western and Eastern) with my own family, but with someone else's children in a French family. Seeing that I was hiding my melancholy poorly, my wonderful hosts 'set it up' so that, in the loaf (I do not remember whether it was for the pagan celebration or the Christian one), I would find the golden coin, they gave me presents and were the replacements to my virtual happiness.

A month later I returned to my featureless country, whose concurrent symbol of liberation, or occupation (depending on whose side you took in the conflict) was a town by the name of Vukovar. A city that belonged to Croatia according to the existing borders, but which had a majority of Serb inhabitants, that was so horribly razed that it became a ghost town, and instead of its original name 'Vukovar', became known on the international scene by a more fitting one: *Vukowar*.

One month after that, after my return, my friend the Breton, using her own kind of code in her letter, gave me the sad but expected news that our hostess from 'that' evening had been arrested, and that Raul's hiding place had been discovered and that, as he was being arrested, he was... killed.

Death on all sides.
  Does death have an identity?
  Does death protect it? Like mummification does a body?

CHAPTER 23

The fact that Sinan had long before reached the peak of his craft and become the chief architect of the sultanate did not hinder Bajica from comparing himself to him from time to time. When Mehmed, taking into account the difference in years, would think about what might still be waiting for him if he was further promoted in his job, he dared not say anything about it to himself aloud. But the very possibility of the unsaid – for him to catch up to his friend, was enough for him to get over all of the deaths he was thinking about.

Sinan had indeed reached the peak of his *profession*, but not in his *work*. Not yet! Yes, that was the very thing that gave Bajica the strength to believe that it was possible for him to catch up. Both in his professional title and perhaps in his work. Not so much for the sake of competition or some sort of victory as much as to relieve himself of this state of warring from which he still had not freed himself. And what awaited him, he found out quite soon.

First, he was upset to have to leave Belgrade. He was not forced: the seat of his Rumelian beglerbey office was in Sophia so, in order to do his job, he had to administer the European part of the Empire from there. However, just as he had never remained very long in Sophia, because he was often called to move out on new assignments, so it happened again this time. Upon the Sultan's orders, after just a few days, the Grand Vizier called him to Istanbul immediately to take new orders and prepare for the campaign against Persia.

But he did not go to the front lines immediately. They kept him at the court. Happenstance allowed him to observe, close up but from the sidelines, the intrigues of the court that had gotten stirred up, fortunately as a temporary if not accidental passer-by, without getting entangled in them. Namely, as he crossed the threshold of old age, the Sultan began to act strangely from time to time; on the other hand, the love of his life, Roxelana, having lost her beauty, youth and adulation, also began to redirect her attention from her husband to her own influence on the court. Grand Vizier Rüstem-pasha set off on the campaign against Persia with partial success. Not even the fact that he was the Sultan and Sultana's son-in-law, the husband of their daughter Mihrimah, saved him from immediate recriminations: at one moment, in an irrational decision, he was overthrown from his position as the first man of the Dīvān, and the Sultan installed another vizier in his place, Ahmed-pasha, the conqueror of Temisoara and Bajica's brother-in-arms till recently. Although he was a bit confused by the events, Bajica was saved by the shadow in which he remained. If he had not, he would have had great difficulty in choosing a side: Rüstem-pasha was his compatriot who always protected him, while with Ahmed-pasha he had gone through the nastiest of battles which had returned the soldiers' respect of him. Upon the announcement that he would be joining the army against the Persians, Bajica spent the next month doing the assignments of his new orders between Sophia and Belgrade. This relieved him of many unpleasantries. A tragic period came upon the Sultan's family: through all sorts of intrigues, the Sultan was served an untrue story about an attempt to overthrow him by his (not Roxelana's) eldest son, Mustafa. An additional problem was that this young man was a favourite in the army, so that Suleiman's decision – and then its execution – to have him removed not only from all his positions but also from life itself, did not meet with approval among the soldiers.

Bajica was shocked. Although he was aware of similar cases from earlier periods of the Ottomans, it was the first time that he witnessed this kind of cruelty up close, that of killing one's own child. In previous times when this phenomenon was more commonly used, although justified exclusively by the important reason of protecting the throne, it was mainly done in a clandestine fashion or re-worked as a kind of half-truth. No one, not even the ruler himself, dared to speak openly and admit that a father had killed his son. However, Suleiman made his admission public without any kind of remorse, and even repeated it too emphatically. As if he were proud of what he had done! Even with all the possible explanations, Bajica could not understand this act. For a parent to kill the dearest thing he had ever created! To be honest, Bajica also had some secret experience with children: two of his concubines had given birth to two children and he had partially hidden them from the public, but he was still considering whether he would officially recognise them as his own. This secret was a positive one: no one was threatened by an evil resolution, whatever it might be.

The only thing that the Sultan certainly achieved, if that is what he wanted, was indeed to frighten all those around him, and probably the rest of the country as well. The news reached his enemies. They again saw him as a merciless barbarian, but they were also even more frightened by him.

As if wanting to reinforce this image of himself, Suleiman suddenly ordered another public execution: after the convening of one of the dīvāns (which he presided over through his little window above the ministers' hall at the Topkapi palace) he issued an order to have the Grand Vizier, Ahmed-pasha, killed – just as the dīvān adjourned. That very moment, in the middle of the court and before the whole council of ministers, he was throttled with the Sultan's silken noose. For this murder as well an explanation was given (the Vizier's personal use of looting Egypt done at the hand of the Egyptian *valia*[51] who had been appointed by the Vizier). However, again as a witness, Bajica began to connect the lines: everywhere and in every situation, the Sultana Roxelana kept appearing. Immediately afterwards, when Rüstem-pasha was reinstated in his position as Grand Vizier, it became clear to him that he had been removed from office for a short while so that the Sultan's son Mustafa would not be killed while he was the Grand Vizier. Thus, Hürrem Sultana saved him from each and every doubt about his involvement in the murder. Roxelana's son-in-law was to serve as insurance of inheritance: now *her* children were certainly the only candidates to take the throne.

When he received his orders to continue his business in Sophia and Belgrade, Mehmed-pasha gave thanks to both Gods for allowing him to get out of that whirlwind of death. It was much easier for him to take killing done in battle, whether the victims were anonymous or not, but for which it was easier somehow to find a reason. These murders in the capital were proper executions that sent messages to others about morale and whatnot. They were even replacements for threats, for murders left undone, as hints at the next one. And everyone was forced to understand the message correctly. If someone did not manage, punishment or taxation was certainly forthcoming. If not death itself.

When he had already settled in Sophia, he received one more interesting explanation of the reasons behind the most recent murder.

The new/old Grand Vizier himself reported it to him in a letter. In essence, supposedly, Ahmed-pasha and his protégé Dukadjin Mehmed-pasha, administrator of Egypt, were both Albanians by background and they had decided to establish Albanian authority in the government by forcing the viziers with Slavic origins out of the imperial Dīvān, where they were otherwise a majority. The letter ended with an unclear 'company' as the actors, in the words 'we could not permit that to happen'. Who could have been included in that 'we', besides Rüstem-pasha (a Serb) and Roxelana (a Russian), he was unable to discern. But, he also did not want to ask; that would end up dragging him into a game that he had managed to stay out of. Anyway, the last word about the colour, length and weave of the silk noose was always had only by the *padishah*. Whether someone had an influence on his decision *beforehand* was not the most important thing. It was important that no one could do so *after* him.

And then great joy reached him on a visit: Mimar Sinan! He came upon the Sultan's orders to raise several mosques in Sophia and its environs. The first to be built, also his, already had a name – Banya Bashi.

Bajica suddenly, in an outpouring of kindness, without reserve, told Sinan how proud he was of him.

"Look how far you've come! The Sultan sends you according to his plans, to leave traces of your skill all over the empire. Yes, find me a man who would dare to be unpleasant because he envies you!"

"Well, a lot of people already owe me, and perhaps they've started to give back: for the Grand Vizier Rüstem-pasha Opuković I built a caravansary and school in Galata. Though, we ought to be fair, he gave both of us plenty of support ever since we rode with him in Serbia. We are probably still in his debt. At Üsküdar I built for his wife and the Sultan's favourite daughter Mihrimah everything she wanted, from a mosque and court to a spa and a hospital. And since everyone dies, I have built mausoleums for many: to be honest, I was late with some of them and too early with others."

Bajica laughed. This last statement did not mean that Josif was too quick or that he was late with his work but that some of the 'many' had already died when he got the job of making their graves, while some people gave him the job in person, having learned from the experience of others, ordering their graves to be made while they were still alive and without the risk (or at least with a reduced risk) of being too late.

Sinan changed the subject.

"Listen, I want to remind you of our previous plans, especially yours. The way things are going, you won't wait long before you'll be able to build your own endowment. So you should start thinking about *what* you want and *where*, and for the *when* we'll decide together after they have started rewarding you."

Mehmed was a little surprised by the certainty that Sinan was talking about something that he had not even started considering seriously. He went on with that same self-confidence.

"I can't resist suggesting something to you from afar. Actually, that really isn't so far away any more. But, still... Since I have seen so many places and thought about them as an engineer, I could share something I noticed with you, something that stood out from everything else... I compared the positions of Belgrade and Istanbul on various maps, more precisely the parts of them known as Kalemegdan and the Golden Horn, and this is what I concluded: Belgrade has the River Sava on one side and the Danube on the other, while Istanbul has the Black Sea on one side and the Sea of Marmara on the other. More precisely, one branch of the Bosporus canal separates into the narrow bay called Haliç just before the Golden Horn, and then spills its greater part into the Sea of Marmara. Haliç Bay is the Sava of Istanbul, and the end of the Bosporus straits is the Danube. Belgrade even has its own Üsküdar across from the lower city, by the name of Zemun, and its very own Princes' Islands gathered in the river islands that are silting up under the water... Don't let it bother you that one city is surrounded by rivers and the other by seas. That changes nothing. Water is water. What's important about water, and always has been, is its depth and breadth. Moreover, when you examine the maps and drawings of both cities, you'll find a lot of other similarities between them. But if you don't find them, you could also make them!"

Bajica was staggered. Josif had gone, perhaps, too far. Either he was sending him far away messages at close range, or he was joking with him. He had never thought about the geographic position of Belgrade in this way: that it was a city 'with the Sava on one side and the Danube on the other...' Whenever he had to describe the peculiar position of Belgrade, everyone, including Mehmed, always described it as 'the city at the confluence of the Sava and Danube' or 'on the delta of two rivers'. And this was true, but also not as pleasant – perhaps because it was actually supposed to sound more romantic, beautiful and poetic. And it was, after all, less precise. He said this to Sinan. And Sinan laconically answered him:

"Sorry, that is the simplest and also the most precise description of Belgrade. But I wasn't the one who thought of it, although I wish I had because I like it; rather, I found it in a manuscript by Marten Fimet, a courtier of the Duke of Anjou.[52] The Duke sent the manuscript to our Sultan as a gift, and he handed it down to me. Now, listen carefully!"

Here he paused, looking Bajica straight in the eye. And then he continued,

"Our padishah, Suleiman the Legislator, told me to give it to Mehmed-pasha Sokollu! But he didn't say why! Uh-huh! What are you going to do now?"

Sinan was enjoying the uncertainty.

Now this as well! In Mehmed's mind the hint about the similarities of Istanbul and Belgrade still had not settled, and now he had to try to cope with the Sultan's messages.

But, it occurred to him that he was saved from a (hidden) message from the Sultan:

"Well, of course he sent it to me. I am the Beglerbey of Rumelia. Everyone knows that the unofficial centre of it is Belgrade."

Although this did not have to be, but could be, the most important or the least important reason for sending the message, it did not essentially have to do with Bajica. He was much more bothered by Josif's clever observation, spoken almost by the way and incidentally, about the similarity of Kalemegdan (with a horn) in Belgrade and Istanbul's Golden Horn.

CHAPTER XXIV

Perhaps I dealt with the question of identity and its variability, change and replacement most (in this case it would be better to say – most profoundly) during my years of interest in Buddhism, and especially Zen Buddhism. Most and least. The least because this eastern philosophy, according to a simplified (but not incorrect) interpretation, sees dealing with a phenomenon as an act where, precisely when we have focused ourselves on the phenomenon, we are actually not dealing with it. The object of our attention to which we pay no attention. To the rational (European, North American) mind, the Buddhist (India) unintentional contradicting of logic, the Chán (China) seemingly pragmatic 'logicalising' and the Zen (Japan) absurdly simplified negating of phenomena, cannot be understood easily. Much less can it be acceptable. But it is not impossible to understand. The Far Eastern philosophies can be studied and learned. Many anonymous and many quite famous minds from the West have crossed over the boundaries of Asian philosophy. Many of them were not just followers of their new teachings, but they even became their interpreters and propagators. Of course, we are speaking here of a philosophy, a philosophical conviction or, better said – of a way of life, about a view of life, and not about religion. And not about cultural tourism.

By chance, I participated in 'saving' one such exceptionally valuable life and mind from the dangers of cultural tourism. (The quotation marks here are necessary because, if nowhere else, in Buddhism one must take great care of one's humility and insignificance.) So, this is how that 'salvation' happened.

The story is about a man from Zagreb (actually an islander) named Čedomil Veljačić, a philosopher by education, a university professor by profession, a former diplomat by avocation, one of the greatest experts on Asian philosophy in the world, and a Buddhist by choice. And a wonderful person.

It was certainly not that such an expert needed the help of someone like me. Buddhism generally (and Professor Veljačić as a person) differs from the other, general theoretical and intellectual disciplines by the fact that it offered answers in practice as well. So, the life-path of Čedomil Veljačić consisted of testing his own philosophical postulates. He went to the outer limits of introspection, marked by abstinence from certain things in order to find new ones, so that something completely different could be put in their place. It seemed that he was losing, when actually he was receiving. Wherever there was no 'replacement', there remained an empty spot which, of course, was not an empty spot. So, it is certain that my help was not decisive, but our exchange of thoughts, and occasional consultations, whether spoken or written, our plans and agreements, were a part of his former world with which he remained in contact. I am talking about the time after 1965 when he had already given up his professorship at Zagreb University and at the Indian universities and taken vows in Sri Lanka in the most highly ascetic Buddhist sect of bhikhus (beggars). From then on, for the next thirteen years, he lived in an isolated community of these priests, far from the world and civilised (should I use quotation marks?) dwellings. Yet, even then, with his new name Bhikhu Nyanadjivako, he did not stop questioning his withdrawal: he separated himself from this community as well and spent the next eighteen years, up until his death in 1997, living completely alone ('real life with a hut and a cave' would be the title I would give to a picture about him). He received food from the local inhabitants who carried out that mission with conviction and respect, and his job was to meditate and write texts and books. In what way was he different from other monks in this operationalisation of faith?

The answer to this question is in the Preface to the three-volume edition of the capital work *Essays in Zen Buddhism* written more than half a century ago by the pen of the greatest expert and most deserving bridge-builder between East and West – Daisetz Teitaro Suzuki. In a moment of complete humility and modesty (as is appropriate in Zen), justifying himself (!) for the very idea of writing those books, and dozens of others, on this topic, he lamented about the greatest masters in the monasteries who persistently refuse to write anything about their unfathomable and unique knowledge, and who would never even consider doing so. They never went any farther than ultimately writing down a *kōan*. Although he doubted deeply the justifiability of what he was doing, Suzuki, thank God, threw himself into this work and – all humankind is in his debt. Now, from this great distance, we can see that he was not disturbed by the enlightenment that he obviously passed through several times. To the contrary.

So it happened that one of the small number of the monks who a decade or two later picked up a paper and pencil and enriched the world's knowledge was Bhikhu Nyanadjivako. To be more precise, he *continued* to publish and write under that name. Under his European name he had previously written and published two-volume 'wonders', every one: *The Philosophy of Eastern Peoples* and *The Boundaries of Asian Philosophy*, and a large number of other books. It is likely in his case that this mileage as an author was the deciding factor making it possible for him to continue his theoretical and scholarly work in his new identity, but with an equally precious description of *his* experiences in solitude. Maturity helped him avoid the traps and errors of hippy utopianism (of others), and his former professorship helped him not to become an itinerate teacher (instant guru?) whose honest intentions might come under suspicion with the passing of time.

Perhaps it was easier for him because Buddhism in itself did not accept Buddha as god, so that people can address him and themselves with a certain comfortable leisure. All introspection into the very embryo was thus relieved of the fear of God and of the otherworldly. That is why Bhikhu could deal in an unburdened fashion with Sartre's existentialism (well, Veljačić had been to the very source!) or with Nietzsche's slippery subjects (in Buddhism, the *übermensch* already existed).

I was in contact with Professor (I could not stop calling him that) Veljačić from the time when both the capital city of Sri Lanka, Colombo, and the closest city to him Kandy, were too close and so he left the Buddhist community and withdrew into complete solitude in a hut and cave, seeing almost no one, but receiving and sending letters and keeping up his correspondence. I felt privileged to be one of the few with whom he communicated. Veljačić made some of those personal experiences public in some of his books published later (like *From Nepal to Ceylon* or *Letters from the Deserted Isle*). *That* was the Veljačić – Nyanadjivako that interested me. So that there is no misunderstanding, all of his reception and comprehension of Buddhism was personal.

These books and individual texts outside of them were not of a scholarly, systematic character, but rather spoke of his intimate, personal story, of *his* withdrawal from the world, about *his particular* view of the famous Buddhist abhorrence of the world, which surfaced from the Indian absolute asocial, but not anti-social, ethics. Veljačić's disciple Rada Iveković writes well about this in the afterword to the professor's ascetic 'reader', *Poems of the Beggar and Beggaress*. This manifesto anthology – witness to a Buddhist retreat from the world, the hermit's life, asceticism, self-denial – is opened by a poem created more than two and a half thousand years ago, under the title 'The Rhinoceros'. Its repeating, concluding line to each stanza is the condensed truth of this philosophy, but also the adopted life and philosophical motto of Bhikhu Nyanadjivako: 'Alone you move like a rhinoceros'.

According to his own admission, Veljačić experienced his own transformation gradually, fundamentally and his whole life long, beginning it at the age of fourteen and finishing it (if that is possible) in death itself. This, therefore, is not the change of moving from socialism into a class society, from Yugoslavia to India, from Christianity to Buddhism. It is the movement from one state of being to another, an integral change of *one and the same* personality within itself, the transposition of abhorrence out of despising into a lethargic mercy. It is the movement into the state and profession of a beggar (bikhu) who gives.

CHAPTER 24

When he figured out that Sinan had led him into a third field of consideration, he realised just how much he missed the man.

In addition to the manuscript he received from the Sultan and the maps of Constantinople and Belgrade, he was now also reflecting on death. Josif had told him 'that everyone dies', but he surprised himself at being so taken aback by such a common and well-known truth. Then he stopped: why, the subject had been opened (like the other two) so that something would come out of it...

He asked Sinan: "What did you mean when you said *that everyone dies*?"

"What do you mean 'what'?" Well, everyone must be born and everyone must die. That is, I guess, a rule that everybody knows, one of those undeniable truths."

Mehmed looked at him suspiciously. Then he decided to outsmart him:

"No, a more correct or perhaps more precise rule than that one is this: not everyone has to be born, but all who are born... must one day die."

This was exactly what Sinan was expecting.

"There, now you see why you deserve all the good things that will happen to you in the future. People should listen to you, more than you do to them. Though, you say things like that because you actually listen to others carefully. I want to say, as far as you and I go, it seems that we cannot do without each other. Or, by the will of God, at least it should be that way."

Bajica stared at him for a while, and then asked,

"Do we need the Sultan's permission to go to Belgrade?"

More important than this surprise question was part of the answer, if Josif agreed, they could set off.

Mehmed-pasha left a message for the Sultan at the court in Sophia, in case something came up: he had gone to check Belgrade and Serbistan, and had taken his guest with him so that they could find some appropriate places for the Sultan's future endowments.

They went over to the Danube and headed upstream by boarding one of the auxiliary boats from the padishah's personal fleet. All of the ships, including the one they borrowed, stood awaiting their master anyway, anchored at a discreet distance from one another down the river, so that they would be available for the ruler whenever necessary. They were rarely used. Their river trip brought back memories to Bajica of his days commanding the entire Ottoman fleet. In truth, he only looked like one of the river captains, the commander of only one ship and the 'master' of one river for a few days. He enjoyed that partly ironic joke on his own account: it made him not forget either his days of glory or his days of misery. Neither his past nor his future.

After the leisurely, almost lazy sail upstream, after two days, they saw Belgrade on the left bank, and rising up behind it was its fortress. A little further ahead in the distance – the little town of Zemun. They dropped anchor at Dorćol harbour, which was constantly, and at that time as well, being enlarged by the craftsmen of Belgrade and the Ottomans. After all the battles, landings and destruction, it was worth the effort to do serious reconstruction on these moorings. Here, a bend after the confluence of the Sava and Danube made a natural windbreak for boats. It was the perfect place to hide. And to the two of them it seemed like they were sneaking up on the city, for this was the first time they had approached Belgrade by river, upstream on the Danube, from the backside of the image of Belgrade as they knew it. They truly liked what they saw here, and from here, and especially what they had foreseen.

What Josif had said was true: Dorćol both looked and felt like the Golden Horn, especially because of the wide variety of people who lived and worked there. And the view from Dorćol of the upper city and the plateau of Kalemegdan reminded them almost exactly of the view from Kadirga of the Topkapi palace and the area in front of it. Bajica connected this truly obvious similarity to his own weakness in terms of his background. Fortunately, the best possible expert for space and construction was standing next to him, so he could ask him about his peculiar obsession. Josif comforted him. And even more than that.

"In the first place, it is because of my influence that you're seeing these similarities. I was the one who pointed them out to you! My earlier trips to Belgrade convinced me that I was right. But I actually checked this out personally before I ever even told you my ideas about the similarities. Now from your reactions I see the extent to which I am was right, and I feel better. Because, at one point, I began to think that I was imagining non-existent similarities."

"And in the second place...?"

"Well, actually there isn't any second place. I thought that I, as I sometimes do, had convinced myself of something that I wanted to believe in but which is, actually, just my imagination. Just as I thought that we sometimes 'pull' so hard for something that we convince ourselves in the end that our side has won. But it hasn't. But we cannot see that. However, after I had weighed and measured everything in a variety of ways, I came back to the solid ground of provability. Then, all that was left for me was to enjoy these accidental or intentional similarities. And to share them with you, because they mean the most to you."

As a place for their sojourn, Bajica had decided on the home of Ferhad-pasha in the lower city, the son of the former administrator of the *sancak* of Smederevo, with the same name, from 1523 and 1524, who had their residence in Belgrade. Even though his feet and thoughts drew him toward Dorćol, he obeyed Josif from the moment when he heard him talking with their hosts. It was then he realised that Sinan was on some sort of assignment in Belgrade (which he was perhaps not given by the Sultan) and that it might be interesting. But above all it turned out that he learned quite a lot from the lesson.

Here is a part of their conversation.

"Do you remember, Ferhad-pasha, when your father asked the padishah to place his own name on the mosque here close to your home? He probably dared to do that because he knew how much the Sultan appreciated his contribution to the conquest of Belgrade. Still, he was surprised when it was allowed. On the other hand, he knew that it was possible to bend the rule that the first mosque in a conquered town be given the name of the magnificent sultan; your father made 'his' mosque from the church of a Franciscan monastery. Anyway, that's how many mosques have gotten their names from other administrators, both the mosques of Zeynudin-aga and Ahmed-aga. Those were converted churches and it would not have been good to grace them with the sultan's name."

Sinan wisely did not mention the following year in the life of this pasha, when he was suddenly invited to Constantinople and immediately executed there for a variety of abuses. The Sultan thereby deprived him of his gratitude, but he did not take the pasha's name from the mosque.

"Does that mean, oh worthy Sinan, that you've come to Belgrade in order to finally build a proper house of worship?"

"Not one, but two!"

"Is there such a great demand?"

Ferhad-pasha bit his tongue even as he was finishing the stupid, insolent and dangerous (for him) question. Who was he to question any number that was the business of his master?

Sinan did not take his question the wrong way. It was more important to remind him of the time frame in which the problem existed.

"You cannot remember, but you should know: in the days of your father, when Suleiman captured Belgrade in 1521, he had to designate one of the Christian churches in the lower town as a place – of the infidels, imagine that – to worship omnipotent Allah! Well, how many more such godless churches had to be converted into *musjids*[53] for the sake of the army? The army has to worship, too! Too much time has passed. So, maybe it would be a good idea to correct this horrible mistake by constructing new, proper mosques."

Bajica was practically eavesdropping on this conversation. He smiled at Josif's play with numbers. And then he chimed in.

"Sinan-Koca was the witness to the first worship service here attended by the Sultan. I was not. However, as former Orthodox believers, it was equally strange to both of us that the Ottoman ruler should pray to Allah in one of Christ's churches, just by *proclaiming* it to be a mosque! Even five years later, when we were both on the campaign against Hungary and passed through Belgrade, the situation was the same: all of the mosques were made from Orthodox and Catholic churches into places to worship Allah. Not a proper mosque in sight."

Ferhad-pasha the younger had forgotten that both of his guests had been in Belgrade several times. He was genuinely surprised.

"Well, then you know many of the details about... such things!"

He said 'about such things' because he was afraid of having to take a stand on questions of religion, and especially the mixing of one with another.

Mehmed-pasha answered him.

"Of course we do! After all, this is my country. Here, I am still known by many as Bajica Sokolović. And Mimar Sinan is not far from that: his ancestors were of the same religion and from deeper in the south. They still call him Josif."

Then Josif spoke up. He could not resist prodding his friend.

"Go ahead, Mehmed, show him what you know from your studies in the monastery of Mileševo! Teach our host something. It would do him good to find out something about the Great Mosque of Sultan Suleiman where he goes so often. To be honest, perhaps not as often as he goes to the one carrying the name of his father."

Bajica laughed again, this time out loud. As one of the leaders in the Belgrade *cadi* district, he was *required* to go to the Sultan's house of worship!

Still, he agreed to say what he intended.

"The great mosque in the lower town was made by converting the Serbian Metropolitan church of the Dormition of the Holy Virgin. When the lower town was taken, and after the surrender of the upper town on August 29, 1521, Sultan Suleiman went immediately the next day to pray the *namaz juma* there."[54]

"But, do you know who originally built it?" Sinan asked further.

"Of course I do. If anything, among the monks we learned about the endowments and the rulers. So, it was built by the Serbian King Dragutin, at the end of the thirteenth century. One of its founders (who also later renovated it) was the Serbian ruler Despot Stefan Lazarević: when he proclaimed Belgrade to be the capital of the Serbian state in 1402, he reconstructed the lower and upper towns, the ramparts, the towers and all the fortifications. He built the citadel, added new double walls separated by trenches, had a ditch built along the land side of the city, and he built moveable bridges, feudal homes, a library, a chapel, a treasury... Both it and the whole town was sometime later described by the biographer of the despot, Konstantin Filozof."

Sinan was glowing with satisfaction. He looked back and forth from Mehmed-pasha to Ferid-pasha, and as if speaking to the latter he said: "You see, my pupil has learned his lessons well!"

But he wanted to say that everything modern rests on top of something that was built earlier.

CHAPTER XXV

Veljačić did not desire to become ideal. He simply followed a path that led him to certain destinations where he stopped. There he would rest, take stock of where he was, and then head off again. The connecting thread of his journey was Ghandi's utopian and practically applied philosophy of non-violence. And in this, Veljačić seemed to be like another dear fellow, the American Gary Snyder. This was, of course, no accident. This anthropologist (among other things) was exceptionally well-educated. Although he was one of the greatest experts on the culture of North American indigenous tribes and on Tibetan and Zen Buddhism, he was mostly known in the world as a member of the Beat Generation, as an exceptional poet. And with reason. Among other things, he had received the Pulitzer Prize for Poetry.

Snyder prepared for his transformation for a whole decade in Japan, at a Zen Buddhist monastery. Passing through the rigid daily discipline of the ascetic he was thus able, in addition to his official diploma, to dedicate his life to turning theory into practice. Returning to his homeland, he returned to the inaccessible regions of the Sierra Nevada from where he set off to cruise America, maintaining his solitary familial privacy (his Japanese wife, children...). From that place he studied myths, ancient China and India, wrote lectures and ethnological essays. And he worked the earth. Nature.

I do not know how, but in my correspondence with Čedomil Veljačić (more precisely with Bhikhu Nyanadjivako), we both came to the idea of writing a book together about Gary Snyder. I suppose we both felt, at the same time, the need to shed light on this multi-linguist from our own points of view. One of Snyder's (and my) friends (Ginsberg, Orlovsky, Michael McClure, I do not remember) even gave me a hand-drawn map of how to reach his (Kikidza) hideout: the map looked like one of those one uses when searching for hidden treasure. It is a pity that I never found the treasure...

It is no wonder. The seventies were quite turbulent, and they offered an enormous number of ideas, accompanied by the desire to bring them to life. However, to do so for most of them would have taken three lifetimes. Which, on the other hand, did not mean that one should give up on everything.

Accepting also this humbleness in the choice of goals, at the end of the seventies several of us known for our persistence (D. Albahari, M. Ristović, B. Đoković, and a few others), started up the edition of 'Sveske' ('Notebooks') (not 'Books' – which is proof of our lack of pretension) in which we connected the ever connectable Far East with the West. And we enjoyed ourselves. The most important part of the work, not quite so visible, was our individual contact with various and varied creative and curious people from all over the world. After all, what could be nicer than widening your horizons and then sharing them with others? So, I used the opportunity presented by my already existing correspondence with Professor Veljačić (also on the occasion of the publication in Yugoslavia of the, at the time avant-garde, magazine *Haiku*) and in 1978 I got a text from him 'Rala-hamiyeva aranya' – 'The Holy Forest beneath the Black Stones' – which we published soon after. We thought that, for the everyday audience, not to mention for enthusiasts, it was of great importance that they learn something of the intimate solitary life of people who have completely rejected the currents of civilisation. Nyanadjivako, actually, even among all the ascetics there in former Ceylon, had become one of the greats because he went the farthest in many details and extremes. But, interestingly, not even he was bypassed by the 'illness' of aging and drawing close to the final numbness in human life: he started thinking about the *place* of his corporal rest. After decades of sojourning outside of his country, it seemed to him that it might still be one of those in the final selection. In accord with his beliefs, he was searching for his place of death, not for the place of his grave. Death was a part of the silencing, of the ultimate extinguishment, of Nirvana. He asked me for my opinion but, out of my tremendous respect for him, I did not answer him straightaway. Then, comprehending, he began to list some of the islands in the Adriatic as possible places. I expected that; he had indeed been an islander in his very essence (he spent almost the entire period of the war, in the forties, on the island of Vis). He thought that Mljet or Korčula might be some sort of continuation of his sojourn on Sri Lanka. The degree to which he had become dependent on islands and seas was also testified to by the fact that even on the island of Ceylon, inland, he managed to find a (real) islet for himself! Not symbolically, but literally. An island, even if it was just surrounded by rivers. As if it was not enough for him just to isolate himself. Ultimately that was why I gathered the courage to tell him what I thought of the idea. I did so in a rather rough manner: I expressed my understanding for his choice of the most beautiful, most isolated, most well-preserved and least populated island, and a place on it that would be far from the beaten path, but then I reminded him that Adriatic archipelago was a part of Europe and a Mecca for tourists. No matter what kind of cave he found, he would not be able to hide his location. With his will and permission, or without them, sooner or later it would become the main attraction for tourist groups who would put it on their routes (as a destination, as they like to say in tourism) of rare and exclusive spots of interest. And the fact that it became a destination, even if just a day trip, he would not be much different than the animals exhibited in the zoo.

He listened to me. When it came time for his final departure, he left us in 1997, as it should be – he did so in the place where he lived. So, from his house. From home.

CHAPTER 25

Bajica figured out later that even Josif's insistence that he actually say something about the Great Mosque and its distant past was an introduction to a plan that his engineer friend already had in mind, and had perhaps brought along not only to Belgrade, but even earlier, to Sofia.

The city commander assigned a few men who were familiar with the surroundings to follow them (not to lead them) discretely as they walked around. Although Mehmed-pasha and Mimar Sinan came to Belgrade without any pomp or a special entourage, practically incognito, thereby relieving their hosts of any obligations toward them, they actually made the agas shoulder a load of problems. First, in recent memory no such high officials of the Porta had arrived on a visit in such silence and, second, their behaviour was unrivalled. How did one guard them and not insult them? They would be equally bothered by too little attention, or too much. If they were not here so publicly, then a large entourage would be inappropriate, but then again they were not safe. Bajica and Josif did not know that the night before the city's Dīvān had met for hours over one subject – what should be done in such an unprecedented situation, with the strange visit of the Beylerbey of Rumelia and the head architect of the empire. The agas and beys of Belgrade even suspected that this surprise visit was perhaps a test. Even though they could not think of anything clever, even the not-so-clever did not add up: both of the guests, for reasons known only to them, rejected anything that even seemed to be official. For example, in the early morning they went almost alone (with a few discrete bodyguards at a safe distance) for a walk around the city.

Sinan suddenly told Bajica that he now had to admit that he was on orders from the Sultan: while in Belgrade he was to choose a place for constructing a mosque in honour of the padishah. And that he had set off for Serbia via Sofia because of that, and that Mehmed had proposed their journey together before he managed to tell him of the plans. And he allowed him to come up with the letter for their ruler and to justify their departure for Belgrade for amusement! And then he continued.

"For the construction of the most important mosque there is not much choice: there are certain places where it can be and by rule it must be in the most important, most dominant position and, if possible it must be the biggest and most expensive structure. There was not and could not be any competition. Therefore, I will find a solution quickly and easily. Second to that is the kind of plan I will draw for it. I won't be doing that while I'm here."

Bajica remained silent as he paused. It was clear that Josif was only introducing some other plan. Did it dare to be the most important?

"I think this is a wonderful opportunity to get to know this town better, though we've been here many times, but obviously not often enough, while there is nothing else to occupy our minds. At the same time we have justification for coming here under the highest orders of the Sultan, so that we can also make our own plans..."

Sinan now waited for Mehmed to react.

"What plans of ours are you talking about?" Bajica asked. "I have plans that you're going to tell me about?"

"Well, yes, as a matter of fact. I mean, they are your plans, but you still haven't said them out loud to yourself. You want them, but you're not sure if the time is right for you to think about them. You're cautious, that's they way most people know you. Perhaps too cautious. That's why it's easier if I say them out loud for you."

And so he did.

"You're connected to Belgrade and Serbia in many ways. Not just and only with Bosnia. You want to do something for this town and its people. You would, in fact, like to do a lot of things for all Serbs, but we're not talking about that right now. And that has nothing to do with me. What does is this – a few days of walking around the city and its environs. So that we see everything, memorise it, make notes, drawings, and you are to figure out what you would like to make better and more beautiful, and where. My gift to you is my offer of transforming your dreams from being wishes into reality. The ones that I know how to, of course. There you have it!"

Bajica was breathless. Josif was giving him his dreams! Could this friendship grow any deeper? What he was offering meant hard work and years of effort! And that at a moment when, after countless numbers of constructed mosques, bridges, hospitals, schools, inns, stables, imarets, hamams, turbehs, caravansaries, bazaars... that same Sinan was building, for his ruler, the largest of the biggest mosques in Constantinople (not counting the Christian Aja Sofia) and dozens of buildings around it. An entire complex.

As if reading his thoughts, Sinan went on instead of him.

"The Sultan has indeed ordered many things from me, and I can see that he's preparing for more... He's already asking me about the water supply to the capital, about the Roman aqueducts, about the Topkapi palace and many other things. However, even though I haven't mentioned to you a lot of the things I'm doing, that doesn't mean that I have to be personally present at each site, nor do I need to be there all the time. I know exactly where I need to be. And, anyway, it will take time until you become rich. Only then will you, as careful as you are, be able to ask me to build your dreams. I'm only giving you time to think about them."

Finally Bajica managed to speak.

"Well, you even foresaw my surprise! You allow me to remain silent, and you speak (instead of me?) so that you can also allow me to hide my excitement at least a little. For me to dilute the discomfort. There is almost no way for me to thank you! The only thing I can do is return your frankness. And perhaps to attempt to show you at least a little about this city and its people. After all, I do know some of its secrets; many people here are grateful to me for the good things I have done for this town, bringing to it all sorts of trade, innovation, skill, change..."

"There, you see, you have something to give back. And you're finally admitting that you've done something good. Not only do you have a right to that truth, but you also have a responsibility toward it. Perhaps even my proposal comes from a new sort of freedom – because I know that many owe me for my work, and so I have a right to my moments when I lack humility in, again, doing something for others – but by my own choice."

It was true. By constructing the Sultan's mosque, which was already rising high on the Golden Horn according to his orders, Koca Mimar Sinan had gotten Suleiman's complete confidence and thereby received the highest praise for everything he had done until then. That was the source of his freedom in offering his idea to someone he was very close to. That way he also managed to fulfil his need to make decisions on his own and which had to do with something beside his knowledge of his craft.

Out of their mutual sense of duty, they walked around the upper town first. The plateau it rested on was exceptionally large and it offered exceptional locations for the construction of the padishah's mosque. The natural position of an exceptional high spot above the confluence of the Sava and Danube was so suitable that any structure set there could be seen for miles in all four directions, if the weather was good and the air was clear. Sinan had never seen a spot like it anywhere: whatever one built there would become... a monument. He was right not to worry.

Mehmed caught himself looking at the same spot with the eyes of a soldier. The citadel in the upper town would seem to anyone to be invincible (although it had been captured by many). With certain improvements, it actually could become unconquerable. This remarkably suitable location would have looked like a challenge to any serious military leader. Indeed, that was the reason the fortification had been attacked so often: it was irresistible. As if capturing it had become a question of honour. From the very past of Belgrade, one could confirm the illogical claim that things that seem least likely to be made a reality brought out the courage in people to try even harder to make them so.

He also wanted to check with Josif if such challenges also happened to him when he was preparing to build something.

"I know about the great plans you made for the proper little town around the Sultan's future mosque in Istanbul. Of the things you planned, you already built two schools for the study of healing. You also started building a hospital. You're going to surround the mosque with two more schools and a caravansary. Probably a mausoleum as well. Are you putting off constructing the mosque till the end so that the challenge will be even greater or because you are afraid of the challenge it presents?"

Sinan was surprised.

"Well, that's a hard question. There is truth in everything you said. But there is something practical in the answer: this is the greatest and most difficult job I have ever done. And not just for me. Till now, no one in the Ottoman Empire has undertaken such an enormous risk and challenge. If something goes wrong, I have no doubt: my head will roll from my shoulders that very instant! However, my desire to build it is so strong that I'm not afraid. Building everything around the mosque buys me time for various other possibilities, to correct the professional mistakes in the plans, to organise the job better, to assemble all the necessary craftsmen and materials. Do you know what a job it is to harmonise more than five thousand people for construction, to make it all work together, so that every part of the job leads into the next one planned without stopping, and not by improvising on the spot. Everyone should be working without stopping, without making mistakes, without losing patience or running out of money. Harmonious and organised.

"There is no way for me to learn how to avoid mistakes except by practicing on those things that I've already done. Yes, Aja Sofia remains as a model to me, but I don't have its engineer beside me so that I can ask him at any time how to do the things I have never done before. The dream of creating a better structure than it can thus only become harder. Insolent. Almost unallowable.

"The only thing for me to do is *believe*. Still, a whole series of details in engineering are connected by practical matters. You have to put imagination and art together with calculations, numbers and precision. That saves you from panicking about failure from the start. For example, for work on the 'Suleimaniya' (as we call it among ourselves), I took three and a half thousand Christians and one and a half thousand Moslems. I have more confidence in the former. I tell the Sultan that they are partly slaves so they cost less. But they, in fact, do a better job. Among them, you should know, most are Serbs, already the second generation of those brought to Istanbul to build the waterworks after the fall of Belgrade. Since they did such a good job back then, they got permission from the Sultan to call the area of their district 'Belgrade Woods'. And I hired their sons because they carried on that work better than anyone else."

Bajica remembered what he wanted to tell him, to ask him, in the home of their host.

"Aja Sofia is the model for all engineers. You mentioned that just now as well, and it crossed my mind when we were talking to Ferid-pasha about the places of worship that were not originally mosques. But isn't that mosque of all mosques, the model of all models, also a transformed Byzantine church? For five hundred years, people prayed to Christ there, and for the last hundred they have bowed down to Allah. Everyone knows that, but they think it's normal that this Christian structure (that is so attractive in its size, beauty and significance!) has become and remained the model of Moslem architecture ever since the capture of Constantinople!"

Josif answered him cleverly.

"Perhaps because the model remains out of reach!? Why do sultans do whatever they wish? Because no one can catch them or match them, reach them or teach them."

CHAPTER XXVI

The inclination to be a supporter (not the sporting kind) I something I called 'overlapping'. And I see that, as time goes by, that inclination in me is growing. What do I want to say? I am terribly attracted to similarities that turn into coincidences in various situations that have no visible link between them, and perhaps no real link either. But I cannot resist, when the occasion arises, from connecting them. I am aware the whole time that this is just supporting the side that suits me (as did Sinan the engineer), but I go on in the game which can sometimes bring, albeit only to me, fascinating discoveries.

Luckily, I am not the only one.

For example:

In the early days of January, 2008, I headed for Austria with a pile of books and papers that were supposed to help me attempt to finish writing something that was supposed to be a novel. Why did I agree to do that? Just like when, back then, I decided which of the three books I would write of those I had planned (and I decided that when I found out that I was literally sitting on the foundations of Mehmed-pasha's caravansary!), the images and the details connected themselves. Sometimes the facts do their own thing, and sometimes it occurs to me that I make them that way by suggestion. So, it was a whole half a year before my departure, when I turned down several other, more attractive scholarships, and accepted the one I did because I found out the following: the place where I was invited, named Krems, lies 50 miles northwest of Vienna, on the banks of the Danube. Like Novi Sad, a city to which I am bound in many ways that lies 50 miles northwest of Belgrade, on the banks of the Danube. (Among other things, equally coincidental as the Golden Horn and the Belgrade confluence, the Topkapi palace and the Kalemegdan fortress.) There is more here than just the overlapping of geographic location and distance. I could give a variety of names to the reasons for such a decision, but I will choose the following: irrationality. And what else could be the justification when a writer turns down all other, remarkably better, conditions and situations just in order to accept something logically indefensible?

Just before I departed, I received a Swiss magazine, printed in three separate language versions – separated in order to link them (German, French and English), with one of my texts in it, but also the text of the Bulgarian writer Alek Popov – inspired by that very same place, Krems, where I was about to go.

Then I got in the car and, by chance, dropped by Novi Sad. No, I did not do anything crazy like staying there and telling myself 'This is Krems'. I continued along the road of the heroes in my book, across the Serbian-Hungarian Panonnian Plain, to Buda and Pest, then on to Vienna. This time, I also did not capture Vienna. I bypassed its imaginary ramparts and, following the Danube, arrived at Krems. In the apartment where I was staying, the Danube loomed through the window. The view was the same as if I were at home.

It all seemed like the repetition of the same pattern.

For, the Ottoman penetration into Europe was also the equally persistent repetition of their own actions: setting off on the campaign in the spring on the very same day as the previous time, passing down the truly long road again, and then the spring and summer sieges of fortified towns which lasted to the day as long as the previous ones, the battle with the oncoming winter and the successful or unsuccessful return to the starting point... Or, in the best-case scenario, to Belgrade for the winter. And then, everything started again from the beginning.

This Ottoman business was also connecting the un-connectable, wasn't it? Who in their right mind would ever connect Istanbul and Vienna in the same empire? Well, we see that such people did exist. And they were quite persistent about it. Who believed in something inside that idea. And I do not think that they attempted that connection through war just to capture, plunder and destroy. What good would Vienna be to them if they razed it? Well, they destroyed Belgrade as well, but then they renovated it. Among others, just like the Austrians and Hungarians did. For that matter, just like everybody else.

And I 'justify' connecting the un-connectable, both mine and the Turkish, and the examples are countless. Many of them are not so obvious. Especially if people are humble...

I remember the marvellous example of an exceptional man named

Vladimir Devide. He was a math professor at the University of Zagreb, an exceptional and renowned expert at that, but he had the unusual fortune of becoming famous worldwide for something quite different and, one might say, quite the opposite: he dedicated part of his life to traditional Japanese Haiku poetry. Let us be clear, he did not do so to the detriment of his mathematics (as we might say, to the detriment of his 'fundamental profession'). As an amateur student of Japan, he simply found much of himself in this medieval art form, and recognising it in himself, did not want to give it up. A person in such a situation, of course, begins to wonder: well, is there some kind of connection between mathematics and poetry? And immediately answers, of course there isn't. To be fair, in haiku there is a small game of numbers: a haiku is assembled from *three* lines that have a total of *seventeen* syllables. The first line has *five* syllables, the second *seven* and the third *five*. Japanese breaks words into syllables with ease and clarity. Serbian can also do this, as can some other languages. But some languages do so with difficulty, or even not at all. For Japanese this is important because this poetry and its unbreakable rules came from it, the rule that, to reach the peak in writing these poems, the number and order of the syllables must be respected without exception. However, all of that is surely not enough for the serious interference of mathematics in it. Here it could be reduced to the operation of addition (like in the lower grades of elementary school).

Professor Devide was somehow impelled to justify his dealings with haiku poetry, as an amateur – that is when you do not have a diploma in something – and he was not shy of that word; he often used it for himself. This was absurd because, in that somewhat larger country of Yugoslavia, in the mid-1970s, there was no one who could come close to him either in the theoretical knowledge of this poetry, or even in the very writing of it. And, we will see later, there were few of them even in the world. I had the good fortune that I worked with him quite a lot during that time, so I was an intimate witness to the absurdity of this forced self-proving and proving of oneself to others. So, because of his family and general upbringing, he began to publish texts about the connection between haiku poetry and linear mathematics in order to convince the unbelievers that he worked on this poetic pastime for a profound reason. And what happened? Since the texts were 'dead serious' (apart from the fact that all of this as an idea could have begun as a sophisticated joke to Zen), now the Doubting Thomases objected to the *existence* of a link between poetry and mathematics! They did not bother with the question of whether the texts *proved* that the connection existed, they (I mean the proofs) were taken for granted, but the connection simply could not exist. I want to say, there was evidence that the connection existed, but there was no connection. To all of this Vladimir Devide did not enter into any kind of polemics with anyone, but rather he wrote several books about that poetry, about Japan, about culture, about mathematics... In Japan, he received the highest awards in several global competitions for haiku poetry, meaning, even the largest existing one in the world for any genre – let's say, twenty thousand poets with fifty thousand poems. Not to mention recognition and awards from the Japanese government.

The magazine *Haiku*, that I edited with dedication under his Zen teaching rod/magic wand, without enough money – on poor quality paper, prepared on typewriters and printed with medieval technology (thus, amateur), was the first cohesive pride of Yugoslavia; it became one of the best in the world. There was even a famous catchphrase: finally the world recognised our country as a great power in something! Yugoslavia – a haiku power. It sounds good.

All, it seems, because of the connection between poetry and mathematics. Because of connecting the un-connectable.

Unfortunately, the country is not the same as the state. Those Doubting Thomases would probably recognise *that* particular connection with joy. And even fight for it, if necessary.

CHAPTER 26

It was only from Josif's answers that it became clear to Bajica how and by what means, apart from possessing enormous talent, he had become the successful Sinan Koca Mimar! Clearly, because he managed all of his jobs like a soldier! What was of crucial significance? The most important characteristic, again – apart from talent – was his ability to organise things well. Where had Josif learned that but as an officer of the Ottoman army, on campaigns, together with Bajica. That was how, not just by changing his religion, Josif became Sinan!

He learned to plan, to minimise risks, to risk when it was necessary, to create a strategy on the basis of foreseeing possible outcomes, to instruct others, to encourage by personal example, to gain others' trust, and then to demand and order, to follow up on orders, to check, to punish and to reward. To know beforehand what consequences were forthcoming, from where and what they meant. To know what victory is, and what is defeat. When a military leader reaches the state, with all of these tools at hand, so that there are no more surprises, then it can be said that his subordinates will eat out of his hand. If necessary, they will even die for him (and not just for the common goal).

Sinan now commanded an army in which everything was similar to a real army except ... death. If there was death among his troops, souls went to meet their Maker from sickness, sometimes because of accidents, but among the departing no one was... killed.

Comforted by these last thoughts, Bajica could concentrate on their further tour around the lower town. This was also done partly out of duty. Because, they already knew most of what was important about these two parts of Belgrade from their earlier visits. The lower town quarter was attractive to Bajica (no less than to Josif), belonging exclusively to the Danube section of town, called Dorćol. Bajica felt the need to be a guide and host to Josif here. He felt like Dorćol belonged to him.

The sounds were the first thing that caught a person's attention. The murmur and commotion from Dorćol could be heard in other parts of town. From them, one could already draw the conclusion that such a place could not be boring to live in. Then came the descent into Upper and Lower Dorćol, or even the Main or Lower district (the inhabitants used these divisions in order to say that this is in fact a separate town with its parts, but not to say that one was more valuable than the other). These 'separate parts' were separated, or rather joined, by the Long District. The name said it all; it was three thousand footsteps long. It backed up against the fishermen's market on the delta in the lower town, and ended up deep in the district, where one could take the road to Constantinople, all the way to the Ottoman capital. Since the Danube ran along the side, it imposed a name on the whole quarter (not just the lower town), and that was the Danube District. It was full of artisan workshops, booths, all sorts of stores, cafés, fountains and stalls, shops with confections, teahouses, tiny hamams...

So, it was only when they dove into this seeming chaos of people, animals, narrow streets, light and dark, only then did they get a feel for what makes up the soul of the place: after all, and above all, it was the people. Everyone greeted them here, but not imposingly like Arab traders, and not just to offer them merchandise. They greeted them out of some kind of neighbourly respect, some even recognised the beylerby, but then they pointed him out to their neighbours as 'Turkified', and 'that man who helps the Serbs'. Hearing this several times in passing, Sokolović was taken aback each time at first. And then he stopped and said to himself, "Yes, well that is me. Both of them. And what did I think I was?"

It seemed to him by the differences of the peoples living there, this city was in no means second to Istanbul or to any other big city of the world. By their dress, language, merchandise, speech and behaviour, one could recognise here, in addition to the Belgrade Serbs, those from other parts of Serbia: Serbs from Bosnia, and Catholics, Orthodox and Moslem, and also Turks, Greeks, Jews, Armenians, Bulgarians, Hungarians, Romany, people from Dubrovnik... They were all permanent residents of Belgrade. At separate, rented booths and shops they saw and heard merchants – newly arrived Arabs, Persians, Tatars, people of all the colours and languages of the Moslem east. Most of them came here intentionally and with a purpose, others were trading in passing, as they were on the way to somewhere else. As one of the traders called out to them, this was a 'real Misir of Rumelia'.[55]

When they would stray a bit next to one of the stores or behind it, they would see, surprisingly, one other beauty of this quarter: almost all the houses had their own gardens or vineyards. All of them were submerged in the vibrant and luxurious greenery of their yards. This backdrop calmed them – as if all the power of nature, just a few steps from the chaos of the bazaar, damped all the unrest of the hundreds of sounds and movements.

It had to be admitted, however, that there was incomparably more of all of this – sound and movement – now than there was in the time of their previous visits to Belgrade. This town had, in the meantime, visibly become a centre and the crossroads of many ways, partially thanks to Mehmed-pasha Sokolović: in politics and money and campaigns and knowledge.

Even wealthy Ottomans found good reasons to leave their mark here, like Mehmed-pasha Jahjapašić, the sancakbey of Smederevo, and his brother Bali-bey, the first aga of Belgrade in 1521 (both of them were Serbs by background). The former had left behind mosques, seminaries, schools, fountains[56] and so on. He even built a caravansary that was turned into an imaret – an inn. It was considered to be 'God's property' because anyone could stay there for up to a month and not pay a cent 'but just had to pray for the soul of the benefactor'. And it was not the only one. Here was also the caravansary of Sultan Suleiman the Magnificent (in the lower city, next to the River Sava) and his imperial hamam (on the bank of the Danube), but also the court and hamam of Piri Mehmed-pasha, the Grand Vizier from the time when the Sultan captured Belgrade, quite near Fehad-pasha's mosque.

Because of the commotion, the crowds and the noise, Dorćol seemed to be the most densely populated part of town. Driven by curiosity, Bajica tried to imagine it without all these people in the streets. And then they received a proposal that would enable them to see it like that. One young apprentice, presenting himself as a worker of Duke Radiše Dmitrović, delivered an invitation from his master for them to visit him that evening at the address he gave them. Bajica received it kindly, and sent a message back by the young man that he would come.

Josif, as if awakened from a dream, stopped drawing parts of the town, and asked in surprise:

"How come you accepted the invitation from a Serb so openly and without even blinking?"

"He's not just any old citizen, you know. He's a Serbian duke. But you obviously haven't heard that I, as beylerbey, on orders from the Sultan, authorised the local dukes in Serbian towns to share a part of the duties, or you might say authority, with the local agas. This duke is one of them! And one other thing: I understand your concern, but even if that were not the case, I would not fret too much about meeting with a Serb. As long as I do so publicly, that means the grand vizier does not have to worry."

At the agreed time, the two of them showed up at the address they were given. Dorćol was not asleep, but it was quiet. All parts of it were resting except a couple of the cafés that semi-secretly became taverns at night, from which came muffled voices not too similar to those during the day.

Their host welcomed them humbly, but was behaving somehow formally. He asked them not to hold it against him for hosting them according to Serbian customs, but they were free to refuse him. However, he figured, here they were not so official and public, especially since he wanted to show them something, and they would later advise him just how public it should be.

Now it was Bajica's turn to tell Josif a few of his earlier plans. When Duke Dmitrović stepped out under the pretence of introducing them to someone, saying that he was going to the other end of the house to invite him in, Bajica confessed to Josif:

"I have been corresponding with the duke officially and sometimes unofficially. This meeting has been planned for quite some time, but we were waiting for an occasion that didn't depend just on us."

Josif looked at him with his eyebrows raised and said nothing. Now they were even.

The duke returned with two other men. The first was young, dressed like a feudal lord from Dubrovnik, and the other was somewhat older, hidden beneath a long beard, and dressed like an Orthodox monk. Their host introduced the young man as Trojan Gundulić from Dubrovnik, from the famous Gondol family of Luka, and the other as hieromonk Mardarije from Mrkšina crkva near Kosjerić.

"Now, why are we here all together?" Dmitrović began. "Young Gundulić has taken over a printing house that I bought a while back, but did not use to the best of ends. Not that he's an expert craftsman, but he has cleverly begun to use his merchant skills in that business.

And it could be a good business, which nobody really thought was possible. Yet, for the past few years in a row, he and his compatriot Luka Dimitrović (you see, he has one letter more than I do in his last name, so we are not related!) have been importing leather-bound liturgical books from Ancona. Here, in the last delivery of two hundred, all of them in leather, in Serbian with the Serbian alphabet, printed in a foreign country – they sold every last one of them!"

The duke stopped, looked at the pasha, as if asking for permission to go on. Josif noticed this and began to grin.

"And then one day, knowing about our little business, Mehmed-pasha asked, or actually proposed: why didn't we print our own Serbian books? And I admit, at the same time as young Gundulić! So, we invited hieromonk Mardarija to prepare such a book for us. And after a lot of work, he made a Four Gospels for us, using Makarija's Bulgarian-Slavic gospels from 1512 as a model. He did the transcription alone, made the woodcarving moulds and letters and did all the calligraphy. And he printed each of the two-hundred and twelve pages personally!

"So, here you are on this August 15, 1552 for us to celebrate together the first Belgrade book, or better stated, the first book to have come from a Belgrade printing house."

Then the duke and the hieromonk brought in several copies of the large, beautifully bound book, the gospels written out in calligraphic letters.

Mardarije thanked them for their congratulations.

"Thank you, brothers. Please allow me, our guests, this time, among ourselves, to call you that. Don't hold it against me. I am satisfied because we managed to make people see the importance of the written word, ecclesiastical and literary language joined in the Serbian redaction of Old Church Slavonic. Since Gutenberg invented this contraption one hundred years ago, there are not many who can boast of a lot of printed books. After Venice and Cetinje, and then Teodosije in the Serbian monastery of Rujno near Užice fifteen years ago, and now we here in Belgrade! We didn't have cast letters of lead like those who are richer than us, but our wooden ones served us well."

Bajica was touched by these words. This was an important moment for literacy and knowledge, and not for the division into languages and religions. So he did not hesitate to remind everyone present that he himself was raised with this alphabet, that he was a Sokolović, and that was why he had proposed that something be done. If Belgrade had become a centre of trading and transport, then it should at least have its own books.

"Belgrade has also been the centre of wars for far too long. I think that, just as over the last thirty years, the waters of the Sava and Danube will go on being calm. True, during that time many armies have been in and around the city, but none of them disturbed it. And they will continue to depart from here and return here, to rest or prepare for the next campaign, but there will be no war here. At least for another hundred years. I'm saying all of this like some kind of dervish, so that I might give a name to these Gospels with a feeling of peace and prosperity: the *Belgrade Four Gospels!*"

Peace and prosperity have always awakened in people additional efforts toward harmony and tranquillity. So in Belgrade, in this peaceful period there, it was possible for the situation to allow a man from Dubrovnik to begin the tradition of printed books in Serbian. Moreover, for a whole colony of merchants from Dubrovnik to write in Serbian, in Serbian Cyrillic. The Christian (or Latin) quarter, stimulated by good profits, was the engine of a better life for all the other quarters. Even the usual fish-market offered a larger amount and greater variety of fish: from big and heavy white sturgeon, carp and beluga, to pike, burbot and kaluga, down to catfish, trout and perch. As if the Danube and Sava, flowing past the salt mines, had absorbed underground more of the materials needed for the spawning of fish than they had earlier.

Remaining several more days in Belgrade, both of them – each from their own position – implored the Ottoman and Serbian chieftains to build as quickly as possible: docks, customs offices, schools, inns and caravansaries because of the ever growing numbers of guests – both believers and infidels, to take the Dubrovnik Republic as a model which gave its merchants larger and larger loans to do business in Belgrade and Serbia, and to think about ways of supporting business people. Bajica would personally recommend to the Sultan that a river shipyard be built in Belgrade like the one that existed in Constantinople. That would employ a lot of people and bring in a lot of money. And the merchants should start seriously exporting goods to all of Europe and Asia, and not just to wait to see what would happen by itself, and especially what would just happen to arrive at the bazaar. And it is even possible, as one can see, that the Flea Market can look much more civilised.

Bajica had a meeting with several of the high priests in the Orthodox church, brought to him by heiromonk Mardarije. They explained to him that the Serbian church was in double danger: for one, because there was no Serbian state, the entire nation had turned to the church because they saw in it a replacement for that state, and for another, the church had no money to save the crumbling churches from complete dilapidation, and building new ones was out of the question. Moreover, the Patriarchate was about to disintegrate. They were afraid that the faith would not survive. For, how can you practice your faith if you do not have a place to do so. Faith in God cannot always be just in the soul. Especially when it should be shared with others.

Mehmed told them: let the church go on dealing with the faith and let it not get involved in the business of the empire and the state, and the Orthodox population can expect improved conditions soon. For his part, he would help.

CHAPTER XXVII

Perhaps I sometimes, with a wee bit of justification, bragged when I would manage to cleverly and artistically connect things that few people would ever even imagine connecting. But, I also, with equal justification, sharply criticised myself when I would overlook understood and obvious connections.

One of the last unpleasant things I experienced because of a lack of knowledge or mental agility was on the subject of my book about the question of identity in the Ottoman Empire of the 16th century, in a conversation with the Egyptian writer Gamal el-Ghitani. We saw each other at his home in Cairo in the autumn of 2007, when the end of writing this book was in sight. But, the book would not have the same meaning for me now if I had not brought up a part of that important subject in my conversation with him – how other Moslem peoples viewed the overtaking (my word) or confiscation (his word) of parts of their national and cultural identity once they had been enslaved by the Ottomans.

The reasons for conversing on this subject with Ghitani himself were manifold. He was a confirmed top expert on the history of Egyptian civilisation, and especially that of Cairo. He had written plenty of books with various perspectives, from historical, precisely factual, to those of the *belles lettres*, based on an artistic vision of the past.[57] At that moment, without the presence of Nobel Prize winner Naguib Mahfouz, Ghitani had become the most respected living Egyptian (and perhaps even Arabic) writer.[58] In recent years he has gathered popularity also among the illiterate (!) because since not long ago they have been able to watch a TV series on Cairo and Egypt that Ghitani has been filming for ages, and in which he appears as the guide. I was a witness to that widespread ('written and oral') respect while we walked the streets of Cairo, when people approached him constantly, kissing his hand and thanking him for the gift of the history of their city and country. Such a show of respect I have not seen anywhere – except, to an extent, in the case of Orhan Pamuk in his own country, but I know that at the very mention of that example everyone will remember the threats that Pamuk receives from his detractors. Of course, that dark side of an opponent's opinion cannot be avoided. To the contrary, I will reinforce it using Ghitani as an example. So, in spite of his indubitable patriotism, being even fortified, I would almost say slightly exaggerated, in which he argues for a clear, pure and healthy attitude toward Islam, he is also the object of threats like his Turkish colleague. Moreover, the police are on guard in front of Ghitani's house twenty-four hours a day. For at least half of that number of hours, I witnessed their shift changes. The automobile and driver/bodyguard available to him day and night are not a luxury: the state has resolved to show religious extremists that it stands behind him! Reasonably so because, communicating with the world, in the very least by translating his works into the languages of the world, he does good for his culture and his faith which he neither rejects nor even brings into doubt. Not even the enormous love with which he explained the details of Islamic architecture to me while he, like the most highly prized possible tour-guide in the world, led me around Cairo by night, not even that is enough for the fanatics to respect him. In order to go out that night, in order to go out at all, he had to sign a voluntary statement that he was refusing a so-called security detail.

Anyway, to get back to our conversation. The occasion was indeed my sentence about coincidences from, indirectly, the common past of Serbia and Egypt that were of interest to us both. Belgrade had fallen under the authority of the Ottoman Empire in 1521, and Cairo only four years earlier – in 1517! His novel, *Zajni Barakat*, speaks of the replacement of the Mamluk rulers by the Ottomans, and about the early period of their rule in Cairo, and therefore in Egypt. My novel (in process) speaks partly about Belgrade and Serbia of that time under the Ottomans. I heard a lot of useful things in that conversation, but what surprised me – and I am returning to the question at the beginning of this chapter – was his very sharp and negative reaction to the consequences of that occupation. This presupposed stories about murders and oppression, but the thing that had the strongest effect was the following. In order to give a memorable example, he added a fact in a *real context* that already existed in one of his books, that the Turks took

239

and transported thirty five crafts to their own milieu, but not just the knowledge of them: the Turks actually took all the craftsmen who did those crafts. Every single one! From the masters to the assistants, apprentices and students. In that way, they obliterated the tracks of the existence of an entire field of knowledge and its history! They wiped it out of existence! (The exclamation marks are my attempt to at least partially indicate the rage with which Ghitani spoke about this.) I tried to comfort him by telling him that there are indications that when the Ottomans captured Belgrade they sent from one-third to nearly the entire population of the city to Istanbul in slavery (the numbers differ – depending on the source)! The evidence of this is the existing waterworks in the Turkish capital that were built by an army of civilians from Belgrade, and who were rewarded by being able to call the quarter were they settled... *Belgrade*. For everyone's information.

When he saw my unhidden surprise at his fury, he gave me a reasonable explanation.

"I have a right to be more angry with them, because we are of the same faith. It just makes things worse when someone of your own faith does evil to you. Do you think just the Christians have such examples from the past, not to say privilege, that they oppressed each other?"

I agreed with his rhetorical question: "There are examples from the present as well."

CHAPTER 27

They returned to Sophia together. Sinan also made sketches and determined places where two mosques could be constructed in this town. Then he went back to Istanbul where he continued supervising the construction of the Sultan's mosque, or rather, the complex that preceded it. At the same time under his occasional supervision, a complex for the Grand Vizier Rüstem-pasha was going up in Tekirdağ (a mosque, caravansary, school and so on).

A messenger arrived for Mehmed-pasha with the Sultan's orders for him to appear immediately at the Topkapi court and to leave all of his business in the hands of his underlings for a longer period of time. He understood. A new war campaign was being prepared.

At the court of the Grand Vizier Rüstem-pasha, whom the Sultan had proclaimed the high commander of the army, he found out all the details. While the Ottoman army was busy with Rumelia and drawing close to Vienna, in Asia Minor the Persian Shah Tahmasp was taking back the cities he had lost earlier to the Ottomans. He did so cruelly, killing entire army units, but also civilians. In addition to all that, using his cleverness, the Shah's son Ismail Mirza managed to defeat the pasha of Erzerum, Skender, and to kill several thousand of his soldiers. Angry and determined to end this conflict once and for all with infidels of the same faith, the Sultan ordered the second vizier Ahmed-pasha to guard the borders with Austria, and he extended Mehmed-pasha the honour of ordering him to go immediately to Tokat and spend the winter there, and, well equipped, to begin war operations against the Persians in the spring.

The Ottoman court, however, suffered changes that also caused a halt in the plans of state because of the increasingly bad relationship between the Sultan and Sultana, who had once been so deeply in love. Actually, horrifying things began to happen. Sultan Suleiman was ever more often on outings, in the unreasonable behaviour of an old man which he still was not completely, and his wife, Roxelana, falling ill quite often, began to worry about the heirs to the throne, in a selfish motherly way, but without any kind of moderation. Since Roxelana had two sons with the Sultan, Selim and Bayazit, she was seriously irritated by the third, a favourite of the army – Mustafa – born from the Sultan's relationship with another woman. The problem with her plans was that he was the oldest of all of them, thereby meaning that he was ensured in advance to inherit the Ottoman Empire. But the Sultana would not give in: she interfered more and more in the business of state, and in this case she came up with an intrigue that blamed Mustafa for making the army rebel against the Sultan himself and, persistent in this idea, she managed to convince her husband of the truth of this news through mediators, managing to keep herself out of the picture altogether. For the empire, such an act of rebellion meant an attempt at overthrowing the existing ruler from the throne, and as such was the most direct threat. So, the Sultan stopped all other plans, deciding what to do. And he made the most terrifying possible decision. He suddenly changed his former opinion about staying out of battle, and he appeared on the Persian battlefield to personally stand at the head of his army. He invited Mustafa with all the viziers to the army encampment. His son, ready to help, not suspecting anything, found seven mutes in his father's tent instead of his father, men appointed to be his executioners. Although unjustly accused, the prince was strangled while his father listened to his cries for help and waited behind the tent flap for the end of the execution. Immediately thereafter, several of Mustafa's most loyal commanders were murdered, and at the same time, in Bursa, a eunuch strangled Mustafa's tiny son so that with his death the lineage would die out and would no longer be a threat to the Sultan's throne.

Soon after this event, wracked with sadness at the death of his favourite brother, another almost unheard of son of the Sultan, Prince Djihangir, died; he had been mortally ill from birth and completely isolated from the public. Melancholic and depressed because of his brother's murder, he simply refused to take the medicines that, along with his brother, kept him alive.

Although Bajica continued to observe this tragedy from the wings, it did not give him any peace. However, from the wings it was easier and to better judge the roles, influence and abilities of the people in the court. He figured out that this was not the end of the madness in the ruling family. And how could it be if a mother is able to plan the murder of her husband's son, and he was able to have his own son and grandson murdered? The continuation was quick in coming. He saw that the public cleverly calmed down. In order to distract everyone and shift the blame from this event, and to stop a rebellion among the janissaries who really revered the prince as a soldier because of his remarkable bravery, Suleiman suddenly had the seal of the state taken from his son-in-law, Grand Vizier Rüstem-pasha. Rüstem-pasha did not understand what was happening (so it seemed), except that he had done something wrong. The seal was given to the second vizier Ahmed-pasha who was instantly recalled from Rumelia.

In fact, Rüstem-pasha wrote a letter to Bajica offering quite a different explanation and different reasons for his own replacement. Yet, soon returned to his former position as the first vizier, but as a short-term replacement, Ahmed-pasha was, it turned out, just a temporary toy in the hands of his very shrewd owners.

Even among the Turkish enemies in Europe, this murder resounded as an unreasonable act. Prince Mustafa was the very incarnation of goodness, loyalty, respect and learning. He supported scholarship and art, he protected poets and scholars, and he even wrote poetry under the name Muhlisi. Occupied with serious philosophy and poetry, he even personally assembled a Persian dictionary and wrote commentaries on the works of Rumi, Saadi, Jahja, Hāfez and many others. Learned people especially grieved for him, openly criticising the Sultan and Grand Vizier, thus even risking their own lives.

Mehmed-pasha tried to learn something about parents and children from this. Although he had not yet gotten married publicly, he decided to take much better care of his two sons, Hassan and Kurda, who were born to his concubines. Though he did not manage to see them often enough because of his obligations, he thanked God that he did not have to hide them, especially not for the same reasons as his master. But regardless of that, not even he knew at that moment what might still await him as far as they were concerned.

Authority sometimes really did manage to take on terrifying forms.

What finally returned normal life to the empire was the already customary continuation of another war. Now, with a new wartime commander, the Sultan in person, Mehmed-pasha received one more recognition of the Sultan's profound trust: heading far east toward Kars, at the beginning of the end of the Persian resistance, he led the left flank of the Ottoman army, and Prince Selim, the older son of padishah Suleiman and Sultana Roxelana, led the right. This campaign was preceded by an interesting moment that was recorded by many chroniclers. Namely, it happened that in the celebratory parade as the army set off for battle, the troops of Anatolia and the Karaman troops of Prince Selim were left completely in the shadows by the magnificent appearance of the soldiers of his wartime equal. "All eyes were fixed on the fancy Rumelian army brought in by Beylerbey Mehmed Sokolović. Leopard skins hung from their shoulders, wolves tails hung from their spears, they wore long spurs on their boots, their shields were huge, their gauntlets were dark blue and blue, their gloves of iron, their banners red and white, their horses all dyed with henna..."

This was indeed an external symbol, but it meant something – that Mehmed-pasha had quickly made the part of the Empire under his control richer, and thereby fancier. The Sultan praised his commander with this barefaced strutting, but he also wanted, simultaneously, to show off his own ability to judge people.

All the following victories over the Persians, from Syria through Armenia to the Caucasus, were routine. And Bajica fulfilled his responsibilities in like manner. He used everything he had learned about war and from fighting wars. But he also knew where heroism came to an end and where commanding by whim began. He took careful stock so that everyone knew and respected their place.

The satisfied Sultan did not wait for the return to Istanbul in order to reward his subjects. In Amasya he held a Dīvān, and there led Mehmed-pasha into the Great Council: he appointed him as the third vizier of the Porta. In Bajica's place as the Beylerbey of Rumelia, the Sultan appointed another Serb by background, an aga of the janissaries till then, Pertev Mehmed-pasha.

When he returned to Istanbul, there was a choice of several places for his own court. Now, as a member of the viziers' council, he had to be close at hand and at the service of the Sultan and the state every day. He chose a humble abode and the most distant of the places offered from the Topkapi court, on the banks of the Sutlija on the periphery of the harbour, near Eyüp's mosque. And he was not sorry. His next-door neighbour was an old acquaintance, efendi Ebussuud el Amadi. He was a highly educated man who especially liked that part of the Ottoman

Empire where he spent a lot of time as the military judge (*kazasker*) of Rumelia, after 1537. Since 1545 he had been the sheik-ul-islam.[59] He was perhaps the only man Sultan Suleiman actually listened to. He even publicly recognised the efendi's new interpretation of the Quran and of all Islamic tradition.[60] He accepted his new laws, and admired his education. He respected his care for the consistency and dignity of the law in the state, and not for the needs of the moment. Probably out of affection, the Sultan called him Amadi.[61]

Both Amadi and Bajica showed unbridled joy at the fact that they would be able to spend certain amounts of time together in the future.

The first visitor to his new home, even before his closest neighbour – the great mufti – was Josif. He dropped by actually to prove that he had known ahead of time, and had hinted to Bajica, that he would quickly be very close to the imperial family. At the same time he also showed Bajica a special honour, because he brought his sons and daughters along. In order to justify the short visit, he told him how he had, in the meantime, finished the Sultan's mosque in Damascus with, as he boasted, a beautiful Syrian garden. He had also finished the hospital near the future 'Sulemania' and was now under pressure from the Sultan because the job was naturally taking longer than expected. Everything was going to plan, but the plans were quite grandiose. Before his quick departure for Damascus to preside over the opening of the mosque for believers, he managed to see Bajica's sons who had finally settled in with their mothers at Bajica's new court. He had also employed a new secretary, the learned and faithful Feridun, on the recommendation of his next-door neighbour. Now, he had finally gathered everyone he wanted to be around him.

Departing, at the door, Josif whispered in his ear:

"Your heart seems to be full of joy."

He quickly answered,

"My heart, yes, my soul – not yet."

CHAPTER XXVIII

When Pamuk and I toured the former home of Ivo Andrić in Belgrade, now a museum, it was serendipitous that our hostess was Tanja K., one of my friends from university days. An expert from the institution known as the Municipal Museum, she was an excellent authority on the past (for example, the life and work of Despot Stefan Lazarević, especially his Belgrade library from the turn of the 14th century), and she skilfully told us unusual things about our Nobel prize winner and pointed out some of the important details. With all her charm, and probably in response to it, Pamuk turned out to be very interested in everything: as he listened he took pictures of all sorts of objects and papers in the showcases and on the walls. This focus on the life of one of his favourite writers (as he well should be when such a talent from Serbia/Yugoslavia wrote so masterfully about his culture!) led me to put off showing him the Nobel award that Andrić got in 1961 until the very end, and I then accompanied it with words that made him burst out laughing, especially considering the date (May, 2006):

"Now I have to tell you why I really brought you here."

Then, a dramatic pause. And he, taken aback, waited.

"Because this is the only chance in your life you'll ever have to see what the Nobel Prize for Literature looks like."

The joke was a winner, but so was Pamuk. The very next prize bore his name. He held it in his hands just a few months later.

In between those two awards, we walked around Belgrade, visited bookshops, tramped about the fortress of Kalemegdan, from its terrace (accompanied by tough, subtle, stern and amusing Vida Ognjenović, the president of Serbia's PEN) we looked across at the confluence, Zemun and the plains of Vojvodina, just as Bajica/Mehmed and Josif/Sinan had. Now and then we mentioned the two of them.

This was the actual topographic spot where I remembered a description of that place *where we were standing*. The author of the description was

Konstantin Filozof. And the book was his famous *Biography of Despot Stefan Lazarević*, the namesake of the man who renovated Belgrade and proclaimed to be the capital city. As it is surrounded by water on three sides, to him Belgrade *shared some of the masterly design of Constantinople above the Golden Horn and the Bosporus.*

Letting our imaginations run wild, but keeping true to some of the existing facts, we connected some of the unproven situations of the past.

Pamuk spoke about a little known ruler of the Mughal Empire, Jalaluddin Akbar, from the second half of the 16th century, the younger contemporary of my heroes, a Turk by background. His people conquered India in 1526 (about the same time as the fall of Cairo and Belgrade) and proclaimed Delhi the Mughal capital. After all the crimes, which that war certainly included, a time of peace and prosperity arrived. When young Akbar took the throne, he succeeded in making his dream a reality: he united the Christians, Buddhists and Moslems.

Why was Pamuk talking about that? Because he was certain that Mehmed Sokollu and Jalaladdin Akbar must have known each other. Perhaps they met during one of Suleiman's war campaigns in Persia when Mehmed-pasha with his troops charged the enemy down the path of Alexander the Great. It seemed to him that they were both warriors who went into battle in order to unify, and not to divide. Like men who were convinced that a variety of nations can live within one man. Just as one (the same) nation can live in several (different) people.

"In the year of Mehmed's death, you would say Bajica's death, 1579, Akbar issued a proclamation written with a tolerant view of Islam – a Divine Faith – under the intolerant title 'Decree on Infallibility'! This example, as well, truly looks like the irrational unification of a precise philosopher and a dumb soldier! But it also seems that he talked about it several times with Mehmed-pasha before it was issued. All right, I won't say that they wrote it together. But I will say that they talked about religious freedom and the right to differences in identity."

I had my own example.

"The town and harbour of Caesarea, south of Haifa in today's Israel, was founded by Herod the Great at the end of the first century B.C. The Roman Empire proclaimed it to be the seat of the Roman province of Judea. Through battle and killing, Herod conquered Jerusalem and became King of Judea in 37 B.C. And then, for unknown reasons, he killed his wife and his two sons. And he went on living: he renovated the Temple in Jerusalem, built a theatre, amphitheatre, a fortress and also some new towns. He remains famous for his uniquely varied actions: from the exceptional architectural undertaking of building the harbour at Caesarea to the resistance of the Jews to his forced Hellenisation; from the slaughter of children in Bethlehem (connected to the birth of Christ) to the successful unification of the Romans, Jews, Greeks and Arabs."

"Certainly the fifteen centuries of difference with Bajica's time made it impossible for them to meet, but that doesn't mean that something about him wasn't read by the great Mufti Ebusuud el-Amadi, when he was thinking about helping his friend Mehmed to save the Serbian Patriarchate from dilapidation"

"Not only was it probable, but certainly he did read something. Knowledge depends completely on what came before. Do you want better proof of the inheritance of knowledge from that very same era? The first builder of Roman thermae from the year 33 B.C., Agrippa, raised them in Rome and in all the larger cities of the empire. And all the other baths, from Cartagena to the Ottoman hamams, came from them! But, of course, he did not invent them. He got them from the ancient Hellenes. And they?"

"From such a great distance in relation to such important events," I philosophised, "I'm ever more certain that all of those people had hearts made half of ice, half of honey. All their greatest secrets were poured into the latter. You see, when I think of all those Ottoman agas, pashas and viziers who ruled here, at this confluence, and left so many endowments behind them (to be honest, most of them have been destroyed), I get an intuition for the reasons behind their actions. It was not just to leave something behind, or to get rid of their wealth which would, if it weren't spent in benefaction, be taken away and given to the sultan's court after their death. Nor did they do so from conceit or from ignorance."

"Well, fine. From what? From that other half of their heart?" Pamuk joked, giving the correct answer.

"Yes, that's right. From the one that melted. Therefore, from love, locked away behind seven gates, because they were afraid to love, publicly and openly, to show others that they could be vulnerable. And all of them, the ones I'm talking about now, simply fell in love with this town and, as if they were in debt to it, left endowments behind to pay off that debt."

"That's an interesting position to take. Belgrade as a bank. Hmmm, all right. Anyway I think that, after the sun and the wheel, the bank is perhaps the third most important invention in the world, of course, depending on whose it is."

"Yes. One of the Christian yuppies would probably turn such a triad into a new Holy Trinity. The bank is probably clear to you, but why you would accept the other two-thirds, you're wondering." I was showing off. "Well, the sun so that we don't leave out ecology, and the wheel because it represents technology, no matter how primitive it may seem as an invention."

Then, I returned to our location.

"To an extent I understand all those imperial effendis who were Serbs by background. They must have had some kind of strengthened feeling for their relationship, depending on the person, with the country, the language, the land, their family... But that wasn't crucial for them. For example, the famous family Jahjapašić! They were most famous for their exceptional skills as soldiers: they were brave, decisive, cruelly determined to win, unshakeable in their new faith, but somehow honest in that faith. They rejected Christianity, and they never, not even once, brought their new faith into question. Neither the father, nor even one of the three sons. Bali-bey was the first Ottoman 'governor' of Belgrade after its capture in 1521. Sultan Suleiman appointed him to that position not fearing his new conversion 'back', because the Jahjapašić family were stricter Moslems than the strictest of the others. On the other hand, he avoided at all costs sending them back to the areas from which they came! Gazi Mehmed-pasha was even the sancak-bey of Smederevo twice (1527–1533 and 1536–1541), became the beylerbey of Buda in 1543, and a year later he captured Višegrad. He left so many endowments in Belgrade that the number of them is not even known (as a folk poet would embellish it), but why? Well, you already know, because in the hamam of his namesake at the baths in Višegrad, you cleansed your body from the things others tried to dirty you with. I was cleansing the same things from my soul, then. A good deed, such as a hamam, is left for others out of pure love!"

"I would love it if you are right. Because there are so many mistaken ideas, and thereby ignorance, about our world today, and even more about the expanses of the past." And then he offered one more example.

"In any case, our modern vocabulary is not suitable for these stories of ours from history, but Istanbul and Belgrade were much more open, as they would say today – cosmopolitan – cities than anyone imagines or wishes to admit. People do say that occasionally of Constantinople, though prejudices continue to reign. But you'll hardly hear of anyone saying of Belgrade that, for example, in the time of your Mehmed/Bajica, 1557, 'his' shipyard (the one founded by Sokollu/Sokolović) annually produced eighty-five ships, no small feat, galleys with three rows of oars; the so-called triremes. In terms of size, we would call them destroyers by today's standards! That number could be equalled only by the arsenal in Istanbul! To be fair, such a large number could be achieved because of the great experience Mehmed Sokolović had as the admiral of the entire Ottoman navy. He taught both cities how to quickly create or, if needed, rebuild a seagoing or river-going armada."

I was happy that Pamuk knew that. I added something.

"Did you know that, in the books of the Protocol Registry in Venice, among the coats of arms of significant ports one can find the coat of arms of Belgrade from the 15th century? That means that the port of Belgrade already then held a reputation for being a so-called world renowned port of call!"

As if we were competing in this search for curious forgotten titbits, Pamuk went on pulling gems from the bottom of the barrel. Like children when they start unconsciously competing, not waiting for the end of the on-going story, rather jumping in with their own, "And did you know..."

"Did you know that it was only in the 1970s that the public was informed of the *six-language* parallel dictionary that was compiled in the 14th century, more precisely sometime between the years 1363 and 1377? It was compiled by the ruler of Yemen, al-Afdal al-Abas, of the Rasulid dynasty. In it, there are one thousand two hundred parallel concepts in Persian, Turkish, (late-Byzantine) Greek, Armenian, Mongolian and Cilician (a branch of the Armenian language that was spoken in what is southeast Turkey today, in the coastal region of Adana). Even today it is kept in Sanaa, in Yemen. Can you imagine the trade routes of the times, the culture and all of the civilisations of that period that drove someone to connect those languages? He certainly didn't do it out of idleness or on a whim, but because it was needed!"

He continued to test me.

"What term do you think the dictionary starts with?"

Taking into account the time it was made, it was not hard for me to conclude.

"Most probably with the word 'god', the common and most important word to all of them?"

"Clever answer. They are generally all listed: from the Arabac Allah, Persian Khuday, Turkic Tengri, Greek 'O Theos, Armenian Astuats, to the Mongol Tengri (as in Turkish, so he didn't list it). However, there are interesting conclusions to be drawn from some words. For example, for the concept of raincoat there are adequate words in Mongolian – *daqu*, in Persian – *barani*, in Turkish – *yagmurlug*... while in Arabic, not surprisingly – there is no word!"

"You mean, because they didn't need the thing, because of the heat and sparse rainfall, then the word itself was unnecessary?"

However, as much as he surprised me and made me happy with these facts, he also made me sad:

"But for years I have been searching for such a five-language parallel dictionary from a similar period, which would be exceptionally important to me, especially if it's true that, in it, besides (Ottoman) Turkic, Persian, Arabic and Latin, one can also find old Serbian. Up till now, I've had no luck. Either the story of its existence is untrue or I am not skilful enough in searching and finding, so it constantly escapes my grasp."

Such facts, it must be admitted, were exceptionally important. They went far beyond the need for comforting or for overemphasising a particular culture. On the contrary, they spoke of those other cultures who, for a variety of reasons, forgot about 'the forgotten' ones.

CHAPTER 28

'When have I ever felt like a creator?' Bajica wondered, thinking of the period since he had become Mehmed. Thinking about Sinan gave him no peace because it constantly reminded him of his irreconcilable attitude toward destruction. No matter how he tried, he could not uproot his envy of Sinan's building, and he sincerely felt it without any kind of malice. Almost desperately, he quickly ran through the years behind him, searching for a straw of creative work to grasp. Why, just now when he had been appointed to a truly high position, had he once again begun to torture himself with this question that he usually managed to suppress? Well, precisely because he had become a part of the council that made decisions on all-important matters in the lives of individuals and directly administered the entire empire! Since he never concealed his own responsibility, it could not just disappear in this situation either. It forced him to weigh his current situation. But looking at the entire organisation of the administration of the state from a safe distance (so far), told him that he had boarded a ship where there was no voluntary disembarkation until the admiral of all admirals said that they had docked at the shore. The trip seemed to be a long one, and jumping ship was not recom - mendable. The passengers, no matter how important they were, could only be thrown overboard. By the casting of a single vote.

The water helped him again! He remembered when he used to be a creator! Well, at that time not a lot was known about doing battle on water, and it was then he had inherited the spot as fleet commander and took the responsibility of doing something after the death of the legendary Greek Hayreddin Barbarossa, the pirate and then head-commander of all the Ottoman naval forces. Then he had indeed done a lot for the Empire and for the Sultan himself: he had *built* a new shipyard that had in turn *built* an entire new fleet in just a few months. He had proven that he knew how to prepare everything, from ships to the reorganisation of the entire armada, for those crucial moments of conquering or defence. But he had left doing battle to those more experienced and better at it than he. It was probably then that the padishah saw what kind of person he had at his side – who did not lose presence of mind even when there was fear in his eyes. It was in those eyes the Sultan recognised a trait stronger than fear: responsibility toward given trust. Even if it was forced responsibility!

Now at last with greater ease, with less jealousy, he remembered Sinan's mentioning of the names of the engineers, craftsmen and assistants who had built with him or continued to build and finish up jobs that he had started, planned, sketched or for which he had simply offered an idea. His head assistant was Hidayet, and he was the only one with special permission that meant he could supervise all jobs while Sinan was away, from professional ones to those that included making decisions about things that might be called artistic. His builders were Mehmed Chavush and Mehmed Mustafa. His head marble-worker was Kassim Mermeri (his family name even meant 'marble') and with him was Mustafa Nebi. Hachi Mustafa was in charge of glass, Sefer, Ahmed and Ali ran the craftsmen's shops, Baki was the horse handler-landowner (*spahija*) in charge of transport and Hussein, another landowner (*spahija*), was in charge of the regular workers. There were others such as Tachir the merchant who oversaw material supplies; the Greek Jorgi and the Serb Simo whose jobs were... confidential assignments. From time to time Emre was also present as an additional assistant to Sinan when the work began to back up from sheer volume.

Bajica remembered these names not just because Josif mentioned them so often in their conversations, but because of one very special reason: it was his desire to have such dependable experts around him, connected by a good common goal, that would also bring out the best in them. That was, after all, the most certain way for a man to surround himself with people he could trust. However, on his path, certain other rules applied. Since promotions depended on wartime conquests (by the way, meaning the taking of others' things on those campaigns, from both the living and the dead), the concept of conquering was built into the characters of the participants. Such people also saw their own men as possible enemies and therefore treated them that way. In connection with its irresistibly attractive feeling of ruling over others, and the flagrant use of wealth, government and military service seemed like a skilfully hidden battlefield. On it, using different methods, the same injustices and evil were done as in the campaigns. The only difference was that this evil occurred here and among one's own people, and that the evil deeds were not preceded by killing but by intrigues, interference and scandalous lies. Occasionally, in fact, the whole ruse ended in someone's death. To be honest, on all these issues, those loyal career officers and high clerks had role models for such behaviour as of late in the Sultan's own family.

In addition to Feridun, his secretary, Bajica also now had his sons beside him. Perhaps his neighbour, Amadi, might become a real pillar for him, just as it seemed to him that Josif had found someone similar in his ever more frequent visits to the old poet Sai Mustafa Çelebi, who had once been the teacher of Sultan Bayazit II at the school of Enderun. The present Sultan Suleiman was also not immune to him because, like Bayazit, he also supported poets and artists. He even wrote some poetry himself under the pen name Muhiba, and talked about his work with Çelebi. Both Amadi and Çelebi were much older than the head engineer and third vizier, and it seemed that their enormous experience actually meant a lot to both Mehmed and Sinan in their attempts to remain lucid and practical in their work. On the other hand, both of these wise men thought that Bajica and Josif were the best possible chosen partners in conversation because they were different from others in the fact that both wanted to learn!

However, Mehmed could not keep near at hand all those individuals with whom he wanted to be close to like Sinan did. The people he respected, and there were not that many of them, held a variety of positions in jobs that were not related to one another. He figured out that such closeness must be the result of serious and long-lasting effort. So he began to observe even more carefully, though he had done so anyway his whole life. He was excellent at it, in any case. Evaluating the knowledge, behaviour, experience, temptations and goals of those he considered worthy of his attention, he slowly began to make plans to bring them closer to him. And again, this meant that from that moment forward he had to look much more practically at himself and the things he needed to do. This meant to begin to have an effect on events, to not surrender everything to chance and to not act like one does not take part in things. This did not require any kind of special establishment of new desires or a change in any of his own character traits. It did mean to watch and act with a new focus that would occasionally remind him that his actions had an influence on his future. Two facts were of great aid in all of that. The first was that to the most powerful man of all, on the basis of Bajica's actions – that was clear, he had evaluated Bajica's qualities very well so far, and his new appointment only proved it. The Sultan's good will and affections were obvious: it could be seen with what kind of consistency and persistence – in almost thirty years of service in the ruler's vicinity – he had rewarded Bajica with new appointments. Quite methodically, slowly but without stopping, punishing or demoting him. His advancement lasted an exceptionally long time, the rewards were handed down step by step, not a single one of them was big and not a single one was skipped, especially those in the lower ranks. Each new promotion had been deserved because of the enormous effort put into it. In this, the Sultan showed a strange relaxed attitude to time; it was as if he were certain that they would both live a hundred years!

Sitting in the peace of his new home, in everything he summed up as having done, Bajica saw a long but straight line. Now it was best to think of something that would link both the past and especially the future to some greater certainty and security.

And he drew some conclusions. The link was his wider family. The Sokolović family. Especially the younger ones. The ones back home! They should be here. Because when they were all here, then they were all on our side. And when they are all on our side, they are strong. That was his thinking.

Now when he had arrived at the position of the third vizier of the Empire, that number in front of the name of his office had to have some kind of meaning. He did not forget the numbers he had skipped over. But he also had to think of those numbers that still stood before him. Perhaps some of them were meant for him, too.

The plan that he immediately began to carry out by bringing the sons and all the males, both younger and older, from Bosnia and Serbia to Istanbul and Edirne, proved to be not only smart but also very practical. As the rumour was heard around Constantinople about the arrival of more of Allah's Christians from the Sokolović family, Bajica noticed a newly created disturbance in the court, and then an increased fear of him. Although he was not happy with this, he accepted this new state of things because it ensured him a measure of peace: people did not approach him so easily and drag him away unnecessarily from his work.

Surrounding himself with his relatives, this seemed to others that Mehmed was setting up a new wall behind which he was building the new foundations of future power. They helped him, it quickly became clear, in the upcoming and truly stormy years of his life.

He spent all his free time walking the shores with Mufti Amadi discussing the system of the state, the law, the future, relations with Europe and Persia... But they also enjoyed conversations about artists and poets, and especially about Sinan's enormous part in the building of the empire. Sometimes they would go together to walk around the plateau where, in the Sultan's honour, buildings were going up one after the other, a public kitchen, a hospital (with a pharmacy, a hamam and a bakery), a caravansary, a public bath and four schools, a monastery for dervishes... In the middle of it all rose a proud mosque that was already nearing the end of its construction. The only things rising above the enormous structure were four minarets. From the plateau itself, the view stretched to the port of Istanbul and Üsküdar across the water.

As the completion of the 'Suleimaniya' drew near, this began to cause a new nervousness in the Sultan. New events in the ruling family had even more seriously disturbed his normal behaviour. His wife Roxelana, now seriously ill, feeling that her end was near, made haste in her new obsession: on the throne of the Ottoman Empire, she wanted to see her younger son Bayazid who seemed to be more capable than his brother Selim. However, the law stood on the side of the elder son. The irrefutable right to the throne was held by the oldest son; and that was Selim. Yet, the mother could not make peace with that and placed them at odds by praising the younger son and encouraging him to fight for the throne. Her son-in-law, Rüstem-pasha, the husband of her daughter Mihrimah, withdrew this time from the new family discord, having learned from his recent experience. However, this made room for others to get involved in the whole story, pursuing their own interests. The ambitious Lala Mustafa-pasha, the younger brother of Deli Husrev-pasha, cousin of Mehmed-pasha Sokolović, the one whom Bajica had taught skills and protected in Edirne, saw a chance for himself in all of this. Whether he was still angry because the Sultan had long ago taken away the state seal from his brother while he was the grand vizier, in favour of Rüstem-pasha, which had led to the death of Deli Husrev, or whether for some other reason, he became the lynchpin in the Sultana's intrigues. So that no one would think that he was taking revenge for his brother the former minister,

Rüstem-pasha came to ask Bajica for help. He specially asked Mehmed-pasha to treat him as a relative and to warn him. Bajica agreed, but he went to see the Sultan with Amadi, and the two of them reported to him the intrigue that was going on behind his back. The Sultan received the news quietly, obviously not wanting to destroy the last traces of his regard toward his former love Roxelana. But then he unloaded all his rage on his favourite, Mimar Sinan! Sinan now came to the two neighbours to complain about the irrationality of the ruler. He told them that the Sultan had threatened him with death, and that he had promised the keys to the 'Suleimaniya' within the next two months. In addition the padishah ordered (!) him to complete the türbe (domed mausoleum) for his wife Haseki Hürrem and himself. And then, without retracting the threat, but somewhat calmer, he told Sinan that he was allowed to build a türbe for himself just next to the courtyard of the mosque, because he could clearly see that Sinan deserved it: it was to be the most beautiful mosque that the Empire had ever seen. Sinan was not to be tricked. When Bajica told him, "Well you see what an honour the padishah bestowed on you, allowing you to be near him in death, even if at his feet, and you are even worried that he will have you killed!" He answered, "That doesn't mean anything. I can build a grave for myself in a place of distinction and then he can still have me killed and have me buried there with honours! I'm not sure what an honourable killing would look like, but he is capable of coming up with such a thing if necessary."

Although he said this as a joke, these words indicated the extent to which, in spite of all his strange behaviour, Suleiman was still the most powerful ruler in Asia and Europe.

And indeed, Sinan reported the completion of works to him on the day he had promised. Then came yet another surprise from the great padishah. At the grand opening, a celebration like Constantinople had never seen, in front of all the courtiers and other people, the Sultan handed the keys to the mosque to Koca Mimar Sinan and told him to open the doors. Moreover, in front of everyone he asked him aloud:

"And why didn't you put your name on the mosque?"

Suleiman was serious. He wanted to praise Sinan in front of everyone in all possible ways, and perhaps he even went too far in his beneficence.

Sinan was not to be confused:

"Who am I to put my name on the house of Allah?"

The Sultan swelled with pride because of the subjects he had.

CHAPTER XXIX

I can no longer remember how many times I went to Turkey to gather materials for this book. Even when I travelled there with my family on vacation, in addition to the great enjoyment we had every time in that exceptional and marvellous country, almost every time I stole a moment or two from my right to be a tourist and to rest, in the attempt to find a few more materials. The conclusions I reached during those years of research were sometimes unexpected. Like when I, once upon a time, in one phase of my life, lost my faith in literature because I managed to find myself more easily in music, which seemed at the time to be more attractive. So it was that on this assignment of searching for my heroes, I was often fascinated by what I *saw* more than by what I *read*. It is quite fortunate that my main character was, already back then, in addition to Koca Mimar Sinan, a politician (we would say so today), Mehmed-pasha Sokolović, and not a writer. If that had been the case, today that writer would be in a very poor position in this book in relation to the architect. Because standing stolidly before me, the incredible strength of the constructed buildings won out convincingly, as I, like everyone else, would try to describe them afterwards. And I would fail. Because the words could have no effect on them. Those living images before my eyes were so magnificent in relation to all else, regardless of their dimensions, and especially because of the details that they comprised. Perhaps the visible and the experience were joined in some sort of new art that I did not know of. Which did not exist. Which could not be created because it was made up of too many different media. How can one create something new from a hamam, and that it not be a photograph of it or a description. And that it still be art.

The particular music that once turned me back from writing did not have that problem because it was created as something new, but *within* its own art. Even though it also was made up of words, to be fair, unwritten ones. Well what kind then? Non-existent! At the end of the

1970s, the Welsh composer Karl Jenkins, after the tradition of the classical music he was educated in, introduced completely new elements into what was known then as the ethno style of modern music. Like every creator of notes who is skilful and a bit shrewd, he knew that perhaps the subtlest touch with the soul comes from the instrument most similar to the human voice – the cello, and he used it profusely, but he also added voice to it. Using the tradition of female choir *a capella* singing from Africa, the tribal one, he transferred that together with solos within the framework he was building. But he intended the voice for singing only, not for understanding. The language, or text, which was being sung, was non-existent, made up. So, risking that something might not be well done in his composition, he took the usual concentration of the totality of listening and interpreting and funnelled it all into the discipline of just listening, and not the standard division of listening to and understanding the text. Perhaps because, as far as I understood, he actually dedicated it all to God: to any of the gods, to the one common one, to all of the gods individually. 'Adiemus' as a word has a Latin root perhaps so that one might somehow recognise the tradition from which the composer took the background. All right, he at least had the right to do that if he had subordinated everything else to a common denominator. Because, as the subtitle of the composition says, those are 'Songs from a Holy Place'. He developed that music (in this case the proper word is 'project') over several years and in several volumes of it. The world was a better place because of it. And even if the world was not better, at least I was.

Like Jenkins in front of the image of some kind of god, so I stood enchanted before some of Sinan's buildings. My childlike amazement was not diminished by my detailed background knowledge about what I was seeing. The excitement was probably raised by the search itself, which sometimes grew into a real adventure. I was especially left breathless by structures that I would suddenly come across in open spaces or when they were tucked away among others, appearing in an instant from a particular line of sight. And especially those that I sought out for years, without any success in finding them. And when I did find one of them... Yet, the happiness at discovering them often turned into the superficiality of a tourist: I would have to photograph the 'object', to write something down then and there, to study the details as much as time or the rules allowed and to absorb most of that without knowing if I would ever be able to write something intelligent about it. With the passing of time, I turned into a huge archive cabinet that was too heavy to move. Still, the megalomania of gathering a mountain of facts was not worrisome in itself. In the liberation from that cabinet, one always uses very little of what is there. I am experienced in that. Hundreds of facts, some would say in excess, act like the airbags of an automobile, in order to protect us from the blows of failure or helplessness. Thank Goodness, a writer is an obstinate creature and does not surrender easily either to failure or to helplessness. At least he tries not to.

As time passed, I learned to look at the buildings like music. I would completely shut myself off from reality, and then I would see the music. When the string instruments resounded (not to mention the cello), the notes spread far and wide, the complexity would grow into pure simplicity and – the building would find its natural place on the shelf. The archive cabinet was gone. Writing could once again flourish, unburdened.

Whether he wanted it to be that way or not, Sinan remained most famous because of those buildings that are largest. That is understandable: the mosques were places for talking to God, their greatest benefactors were either sultans and grand viziers who were the only ones then to humbly offer their everything to that which was greater than them. The monumental character of the 'Selimiya' in Edirne and the 'Suleimaniya' in Istanbul is indisputable. The knowledge, wealth, faith and skills of the entire Empire were invested in them. Because they are monuments to the All in Everything. A gift of one era to another.

Moreover, just as his houses of God connected eras, so did Sinan's bridges connect towns, countries and people. Over a period of about ten years he built two completely different but equally magnificent bridges: at Büyükçekmece and at Višegrad. One came about out of necessity when Sultan Suleiman, returning from a hunting trip to the Topkapi palace, was almost killed when he fell into the lagoons with his horses in the outlying area of Istanbul, where the lagoons feed into the sea of Marmara. That was the occasion, but the reason lay in the following: that was the route the Ottoman army had taken for years as it set off on its campaigns in Europe. And the next campaign was already planned for the following year. And the return. So, out of urgent need, Sinan built – as the Sultan's endowment – a 'mountain of a bridge' whose name says why it is different from all the others: 'four donkeys' backs'!

Composed of four arches, actually, four individual bridges connected to each other, with each having a surface, where the traffic goes, that rises gently along its centre and then slants toward the edge, all four being the same. Over six hundred and sixty meters in length, it rests on twenty-six arched columns, such a remarkable bridge unlike any other anywhere, seems only at first glance to be a less attractive structure than the others. (Probably because it looks like four humped backs.) However, beside the fact that it was an architectural wonder in the 16th century, it is also a true, essentially beautiful structure, built with originality, elegance and stability.

The Višegrad bridge in Bosnia is a work of love from the Grand Vizier Mehmed-pasha Sokolović to his birthplace, a love that he shared with his friend, originally an Orthodox Christian, Mimar Sinan. The bridge was, and still is, of exceptional significance because it connects not just the two banks of the River Drina, but two parts of the world. It should be said; it was never even for a moment strategically important to the Ottoman Empire. This bridge seems to be more solid, stronger and more massive, but it has a special line of elegance that is, in accord with its entirety, less refined. Just as the Drina is, as well.

Both bridges have, in different ways, the signature of their maker. The *one* work of around four hundred structures (according to some sources, more than four hundred and seventy!) spread across three continents *where Sinan left his name* – is indeed the bridge at Büyükçekmece. Moreover, his sentence about the bridge has also remained: "Amongst all the things I have constructed, this is a masterpiece."

On the bridge at Višegrad, his friend Bajica Sokolović left a message instead of him. After building it, Josif left the forthcoming affirmation and fame of this bridge to Bajica and retired into the shadows.

All of the other things the two of them did together (where one of them was the benefactor and endower, and the other the maker and engineer) are known both to their contemporaries and to those who came after. That is why it interesting to know where they wanted to leave personal traces behind. There is one other place, though to be fair, contested or not proven well enough, where Sinan's intimate thoughts about one of his buildings are cited. It is not, as some might think perhaps, in his confessed text *The Book of Building (the Memoirs of Sinan the Engineer)* which was written down as Sinan dictated by his friend the poet, Sai Mustafa Çelebi, a book that remained unknown for centuries and was only recently made available to the public. In and of itself, both in text and in appearance, it is a real work of art. However, the citation I have in mind is found in the work of another namesake of Sai Mustafa, Evliya Çelebi, a famous traveller in the 17th century. His travelogue about all the countries of the Ottoman Empire under the rule of Murat IV is entitled *Seyahatname* and is the result of his continuous journeys that lasted about forty years! Thus it is no surprise that it comprises ten notebooks (volumes). There is, in fact, a problem with Çelebi's text in that he sometimes feels the need to 'reinforce' the truth, so it happens that some of the numbers are exaggerated, or two names are confused. But this should not be seen as strange if we only try to imagine, or better calculate, the number of kilometres he travelled, the places he saw and noted down, and the people as well. Therefore, in essence, that sort of mistake does not lessen the significance of what he did for the history of the world in his book.

Just because of this feature of the subtle shift of a fact or two, and as a result of the non-existence of other written sources, some reserve is held about Sinan's quote in this travelogue where he speaks of his own handiwork, Suleiman-han mosque in the upper town in the fortress of Kalemegdan: 'With this minaret in the land of the Alman[62] in Belgrade, the capital city of the Ungar lands,[63] I reached the peak of my craftsmanship. It is an enormous skill. Let the other engineers, if they can, make even of wood such an artistically constructed minaret.' (According to the translation of Hazim Šabanović, and further.) One more reason for doubt: all things considered, Sinan knew very well to which country Belgrade belonged, and whose capital city it could not have been.

Çelebi himself praises that minaret as well, actually in an exceptionally original way: 'It is a mosque full of light with an elegantly high and symmetrical minaret which is so lovely it is like it is magical.' And anyway, his whole text is bubbling with praises of Belgrade which he obviously really liked and where he returned many times. For example, he talks of all five towers that frame the Belgrade citadel (Kula Nebojša, Crvena, Krvava, Zindan and Šahin), saying that 'they reach to the clouds' and that they are 'as high as the Galati tower in Constantinople'. From comparing these two descriptions, his 'poetic license' can be seen, which was obviously not meant to repudiate reality. For him, Belgrade is 'a city that is similar to Heaven on Earth'. Therefore, it is clear, if he exaggerates, he does not do so because someone or something is forcing him to. His exaggeration is based on, mostly mildly said, his great esteem.

Çelebi, actually, a hundred years later, did the same thing that our two predecessors, Mehmed and Sinan, did: he leaves his own mark which, as you can see, is most often linked to the concept of identity. For, what is achieved by this mark, or at least what was he trying to achieve? The answer is self-evident: he protects or is even protecting his own identity.

That is the same reason why both of them built the caravansaries. They were built so that, having travelled the roads and bridges, people could rest there. Both of the men were especially famed because of them: many of the thirty-one known caravansaries that Sinan signed as an engineer and Sokolović as a patron, were built on the road of the Ottoman campaigns from Stambol toward the Balkans (most of them up to Belgrade), thereby linking the municipal centres. A similar merchant route (of silk) was fortified by the caravansaries in Asia from the Caspian Sea, via Aleppo, Bursa, Istanbul, and all the way to the northern Mediterranean.

Mehmed-pasha Sokolović (again with Sinan's engineering support) found it convenient to build exactly that sort of multi-faceted caravansary (next to the mosque) just next to the Sultan Suleiman bridge at Büyükçekmece. He did the same next to his own endowment, the bridge at Višegrad. Without a mosque. Although he bore his Ottoman name Mehmed-pasha Sokollu, whenever he built something in Bosnia or Serbia, he behaved like Bajica Sokolović, and he was wise: as a patron, a giver of endowments, he did not build any mosques there.

On the other hand, all of the caravansaries and inns he built, with equal effort, made it possible to travel more comfortably, to trade, to inform, to perform better diplomacy, but also to make war. Judging from the specialisation in engineering, probably this Sinan-Sokollu partnership (with a helmsman, it is obvious which one) would today be the makers of the strongest hotel chain in the world. And the owner? Well, their helmsman, who else?

CHAPTER 29

Time changed speeds.

As if in an unstoppable whirlpool, events started rushing one after another, it seemed – even faster, also because more things were happening, because things happened more often, the things that happened were big... Afterwards they began to catch up, to forge ahead, and were even forced to trample over each other. Many could not keep their feet in those times; the whirlpool sucked them down, threw them to the side, threw them off centre and left them wounded, with unhealed scars, and some never managed to return.

Bajica felt the storm coming in good time. He prepared himself as much as his knowledge and his opinions would allow him. In this situation he could not depend on his experience, like everyone else for that matter, because no one had experience with situations like these.

It was not in vain that Sinan, as an afterthought and very quickly, built a tomb for Sultana Roxelana. She died without seeing the results of her insatiability: the battle of the whole Empire between her two sons, two brothers from the same mother. Not to mention the consequences of the war of the princes! She did live to see her tomb, just next to the emperor's greatest act of devotion – the magnificent 'Suleimaniya'.

No matter how the wise viziers attempted to remain outside the conflict in the imperial family, the moment came when they had to choose sides. The mother of Haseki Hürrem was right when she ascertained that her younger son Bayazid was more capable of running the sultanate. Privately, her son-in-law thought so, too, the Grand Vizier Rüstem-pasha, and Sokolović with him. But law and order must be respected in the Empire. Thus, Bajica, who was one of those who was supposed to carry out that order, chose the side of the young emperor Selim. The highest law on the inheritance of the throne exclusively supported the principle establishing the oldest son as the heir to the throne. In any case, respecting the law should be the easiest solution.

Although, unfortunately, it often turned out to be the most difficult.

Sultan Suleiman gave his sons the chance to make peace. As peacemakers he chose the purest of his underlings at that moment, whose sense of justice and loyalty he did not doubt, and who, still unspoiled, had proven to be decisive enough and never capricious. He summoned in the third vizier Mehmed-pasha Sokolović and Pertev Mehmed-pasha who he immediately appointed as fourth vizier. He gave them the task to reconcile his children or discipline them, and if it became necessary – to have one of them put to death. So it happened that two viziers, both Serbs by background, unexpectedly, found the destiny of the entire Ottoman Empire in their hands.

Before departing on this assignment, which would obviously take a long time, Sokolović did two things: he managed to bring his first three nephews from Bosnia and Serbia and to proselyte them to Islam, leaving them in the school at the Topkapi palace. Their hosts were his sons Hassan and Kurd who had been going to school there already for a long time.

The second important thing he did was with the great Mufti Amadi: he received complete support from him about an idea that they had discussed several times on their walks and had worked out thoroughly – that the Serbian Orthodox Church began to renew its work in an organised way and receive a special kind of independence, all with the Sultan's permission. Within the church, of course, it would recognise its own subordination to Constantinople, but it could begin to represent a sort of replacement for the non-existent independent state in the eyes of the Serbian people. Now, of course, neither Sokolović nor Amadi counted only and purely on the padishah's generosity. That would be naïve. Yes, his enormous good will was necessary, and it seemed that this was the proper time to utilise it because the ruler was expecting enthusiastic aid from his third vizier (with the help of the fourth) on a truly sensitive question related to his children. In addition to that, he had already approved Mehmed-pasha's proposal that Lala Mustafa-pasha be quietly banished to the outer reaches of the empire because of his participation in the conspiracy. From Bajica's reports on convincing this pasha to stay away from such impure and fickle affairs, Suleiman remembered the sentence: "You see, my lord, that even in the Sokolović family there are scoundrels. I taught him and helped him, and it seems that he doesn't like me precisely because of that!" In this, the Sultan not only liked the vizier's honesty but also the coincidence that he spoke this truth at a moment when Suleiman could say the same thing about his very own son!

To the padishah it was clear that, among the conquered peoples, the best and most numerous soldiers were the Serbs. They participated in all the Ottoman campaigns and fought courageously in them. And even when they had been on the opposite side – the enemy – they had earned respect as warriors. From the moment when Mehmed-pasha Sokollu had taken over as beylerbey of Rumelia, all praises had been more than deserved. Mehmed was exceptionally respected among all Serbs and his conversion to Islam was not held against him. The Sultan had silently approved his concessions to the Serbs, and even more importantly, he respected Sokolović's frankness: he did nothing clandestinely. All of the decisions that were up to him, he made them and carried them out openly, and those that he considered to be too important – he had asked for approval from the Grand Vizier or the Sultan personally.

He had exchanged letters with his brother Makarije who was serving as the archimandrite in the monastery of Hilandar on Athos, consulting with him on the idea of renewing all of the Serbian churches and monasteries and preparing him for these new tasks. All of those preparations were known to the Porta, as were several meetings of the two brothers in Stambol and in Belgrade.

Suleiman, for his part, took counsel of the great Mufti about the gradually legalised concessions he gave to the Serbs. That was the reason that Mehmed-pasha and Amadi presented the plan together to the Sultan about the independence of the Serbian church.

The Sheik-ul-Islam presented the idea from the standpoint of the law and legislation, but also from the aspect of the Moslem faith. In no single area did he see a barrier to the great ruler offering thanks to his subjects and offering them such an important comfort in their god and in their faith. Moreover, the Serbs would in every way be better organised through the church, and thus would cooperate more easily with the Turkish Dīvān. As members of the most numerous Christian nations within the Ottoman Empire, the Serbs were also those who accepted Islam in the largest numbers. However, equal respect was shown to those who wished to remain faithful to Orthodoxy. Even cases of differing faiths within one family were tolerated, a blind eye was turned if the rites of both faiths were carried out, to be honest, some of them secretly, in one faith. In ruling the vast territory, the Empire needed the Serbs, regardless of their faith, because they could be employed as administrators at a local level and thus greatly reduce the number of Ottomans necessary, which was something that was a problem anyway. In reality, the Serbs, whether completely or not, were administering parts of their own country, thereby establishing the comforting feeling that was most important – that they were in charge of their own destinies.

The third vizier guaranteed by his own authority that the agreement and law would be carried out.

And indeed, the Sultan immediately ordered Amadi to prepare all the legal, legislative and religious papers and interpretations for the secretary so that he (the Sultan) could issue a firman with a bulla. Bajica's brother Makarije[64] was singled out and appointed as the patriarch of the Serbian Orthodox Church. In a special order, a large sum of money was approved for the renewal of the work of the priesthood, with the rider that the Serbian church and its congregation continue to organise the further collection of funds for its further work.

The Sultan was certain that this news would resound loud and clear throughout Rumelia, but especially among the Christian empires and kingdoms all over Europe. It was a politically useful move.

Under orders, Mehmed-pasha set off with the main body of the army toward Kütahya, to Prince Selim. Pertev Mehmed-pasha headed to Konya and Bayazid in one final attempt to convince him to dissolve his squadrons of Kurds, Turkmen and Syrians that he had gathered, and to obey the law. Since the prince turned down the pasha's proposal, the Sultan, angered, crossed into Asia Minor in order to show he meant business, and ordered Sokolović to attack his son Bayazid with the army and artillery. The prince did not accept even the last offer to lay down his arms and surrender, so the vizier began the battle against him. In two days the rebels were defeated, but Bayazid managed to escape. Sokolović harried him to the Persian border and came into conflict just before it with him and his four sons. Losing this battle as well, the prince, with the help of Ayas-pasha who did not like Sokolović or Prince Selim, transported him over the border to the land of the Persian shah Tahmaspa. He was saved temporarily, but Ayas-pasha, the beylerbey of Erzerum, was caught immediately and punished by strangulation.

Another, perhaps more serious, opponent of Bajica, Lala Mustafa-pasha, continued to act as an adversary toward his cousin; he went on getting involved in all ways possible in the intrigue over the sultan's sons, using the sympathy of Prince Selim toward him. Selim even promoted him to the beylerbey of Temisoara, and then sent him back to Asia to appoint him as the administrator of Van.

The negotiations with the Persian shah went on for a long time, but they were successful in the end: after over a thousand of the prince's most faithful followers were killed in short order, his protector sold him together with his children for four hundred thousand gold pieces. Bayazid was killed along with his four sons. Even his fifth son, only three years old, was strangled in Bursa on the orders of his grandfather. The cruelty of the Dīvān and the court was not called into question: the destiny of the Empire must be certain and secure.

Mehmed-pasha Sokolović carried the largest part of the job on his shoulders, while Pertev-pasha sealed the deal by delivering the money to their enemy-ally. The heir to the throne, Selim, would be in debt to both of them forever, especially to Mehmed-pasha.

Using his benefits for preserving the throne, on return to the court in Constantinople, Bajica continued to bring his family to the capital. Already the first one he had brought and had trained in the palace school, his uncle's oldest son Mustafa, was appointed by Bajica to administer the Bosnian sancak, thus creating a lasting and stable bridge between the old homeland and the new one. He used this time to set his affairs in order, to plan his first endowments, to appoint his people to as many influential spots as possible and create a network that promised security in his rule. Then, his and Sinan's constant protector, Grand Vizier Rüstem-pasha died during his second term of office, overcome by illness. Sinan had already built him a grave, and also a caravansary in Edirne, and he was well underway with a mosque in Stambol, in addition to the elegant one in Tekirdağ. He had paid him back with honour.

Josif used the chance to show Bajica the plans for the mosque that, according to him, his craftsmen had already built in Bosnian Mostar, on the request of Mehmed-pasha Karajoz. And he told him:

"No matter what, you will be the next patron in Bosnia. Do you see how your steps are reaching the top of the tower?"

And indeed: immediately upon the death of the first minister, his place was filled with the second vizier Semiz Ali-pasha, a Slav. Bajica took over the place of the second vizier. Pertev Mehmed-pasha was moved to the place of the third vizier. The fourth vizier was Ferhad-pasha (married to the Sultan's granddaughter Rumaya, the daughter of his favourite son Mehmed who had died before his time), and the fifth vizier's place was taken by a man who was also of Serbian birth, the beylerbey of Rumelia, Mustafa-pasha Kizil-Ahmedović.

Mihrimah got involved in Bajica's further destiny, the widow of the Grand Vizier Rüstem-pasha, the daughter of Sultana Roxelana. She was not as ambitious as her mother; she had gotten burned as one of those participating in her early bad judgments, and now she carefully chose the move she would make. So, she limited herself to the important plans of the Empire, but to those less direct ones. She calculated who would be good for whom in the state, and on the basis of her figuring she got permission from her father Suleiman and the agreement of her brother Selim: to organise a big celebration. And what a celebration! All on the same day, spending her own money and gathering the most important people of the Porta, she scheduled three weddings! That day, the heir to the throne Selim married off two of his daughters: Ismihan (Esma) took Mehmed-pasha Sokolović as her husband, and the other – Gevher – took Piyala Mehmed-pasha. In addition to them, the janissary aga Abdulkerim married the daughter of the executed prince Mustafa.

The wedding was also a part of the speed with which Bajica's life went on. Still, such an offer was not to be refused even though the young sultana at the age of sixteen could have been his daughter and perhaps even his grandchild, and by year of birth she could have been the bride of his sons Hassan and Kurda who were among the courtiers present at the wedding. Esma's mother was Nurbana, from Venice and the famous family Bafos, the wife of the future ruler. And she was also the granddaughter of Sultana Roxelana and Sultan Suleiman. With this connection, Bajica's further lifeline was clearly drawn. There was not much more he could even question about it. But he had no reason to complain. He had agreed to this life-path long before. At that time he was still in a position to change something about it. Now he could only try to be the best possible at what he was.

In becoming the son-in-law of the present and future Sultan, Bajica had ensured himself the greatest possible security in every possible way. It could only be taken away by the word or decision of *only one man in the Empire*! No matter how much the word of that very man tailored the life of everyone with incredible ease and difficulty at the same time, he had to admit that no one had ever been able to reach the kind of achievements he had. But, for that reason he noticed a new danger: certain highly ranked courtiers, whether out of envy, great personal ambition, unhealthy mind or out of simple filthiness of character, showed fear at first toward Sokolović, and now began to turn that into intolerance and even hatred. Of course, they understood the extent to which he was the greatest possible barrier to them for all their impurities, and that especially now as a member of the ruling family he was slipping out of their sphere of influence. Thus, they covered their more or less open hostility with a new veil – of shrewdness. A circle of flatterers formed around Mehmed, people full of empty ideas and plans, offering good services, non-existent cousins and whatnot. He figured out that he must defend himself with a character trait he did not have – cunning. Even worse, building that trait into his character was no easy task. When he saw that the evildoers were attempting to lure him even into a marriage bed with their intrigues, he gave up on trying to change himself. He told himself that he would stay the way he was as long as he deserved to and was able to. He explained to his wife, so young, that he did not want to force her to love him just because the family had decided to put them together. He would respect her and he would not be involved in public scandals with other women. Esma understood this as his goodness and honesty. She already respected him without reserve, and she was very close to even possibly falling in love with him. When Bajica heard that, he was not sorry for his decision to be consistent.

Now Mehmed-pasha could dedicate himself to enemies within the empire calmly and without making drastic moves. He needed to prepare the ground ahead of time for the inevitable, for the time when he would be appointed first vizier. If he waited till it happened unprepared, it would be too late. First, he focused on *his* opponents. As the most passionate, he summoned Lala Mustafa-pasha and openly asked him why, without any visible reason, he was working against Mehmed-pasha. The answer, which he interpreted as an honest one, was a bit disarming. But he did not show it.

"Because, Mehmed-pasha, I constantly see Bajica in you. I am not afraid of your duality or of you betraying Islam, but I can't stand the ease with which you take sides with the Serbs and the Ottomans, the Christians and the Moslems. The fact that you openly aid the Orthodox Church and participate in the hajj at the same time. Everyone, even the great Sultan himself, thinks that this is not duality of religion, but it looks like that to everyone. It is actually because I am a Serb by birth that I can't understand how to be Allah's Christian! You are either one or the other!"

"But I don't wish to be either one or the other. I wish to be myself. And since I have never presented myself as anything other than what I am, I've taken the risk of being punished for it. The greatest ones after Allah, both the padishah and the Sheik-ul-Islam, those who interpret the laws of heaven and earth, they have never ever begun to think what you are thinking. I am ever at their disposal: whether in the deeds that I do, or with my head if it needs to be severed."

"But I want to free myself of that duality! I want to no longer be that which I was. I want to forget what I was. And you, there among those at the forefront, the one whom everyone is watching because in you they see your future and their own, you constantly remind me of the past!"

"I'm sure that you couldn't forget who you were, even if I were not around. Do you know why? Because that is impossible! No one can help you there. However, you could help yourself if you would just take things as they are. But that takes incredible strength. You must see whether you have it in you."

And so the conversation ended. Bajica respected Lala Mustafa's honesty, but he realised that he would never make a friend of him, and that he might not even manage to change him from being what he was – an enemy. Well, at least, if nothing else he figured, out of fear of Bajica's growing influence, Lala Mustafa would less publicly or less loudly encourage others to rebel. Even though Lala did not dare to tell anyone else of the content of their conversation, especially not those who shared their background, it was enough that everyone knew that the conversation had taken place.

Most important of all was that Bajica had guessed what the essential truth of the problem was that Lala Mustafa-pasha bore within himself: he could not forget the love, care and wisdom that Bajica Sokolović, so young, had shown him in the school at Edirne when he taught him everything – from the defence against losing himself to the physical protection of his own life. Bajica was actually too exposed and visible, and was an unpleasant witness to what Lala Mustafa had essentially been in actuality. This probably put him in the uncomfortable position that he felt like a man who could be accused at any time for actions that only he – the guilty one – knew that he had ever even done.

Bajica never blamed anyone, for example, for either changing religions or not. He might criticise someone for the impure motives behind something they did, but not for the actions themselves. If one left aside the forced proselytisation that destiny had ordained for him, an entire series remained of reasons, examples, and ways that the Ottomans quite skilfully used in the Islamisation of the Serbs. That was strange because the Serbs' resistance was actually the strongest and most persistent. But the conquerors figured out that it was easier and less expensive to get as many followers as possible through peaceful means rather than war. And it actually proved true that it was easier to fight against the Serbs by making them Moslems than with weapons and battles. In this kind of war, everything except killing was used: blackmail of all kinds – from material to moral, buying people off – from bribes to tax relief, from the offer of small privileges to high positions. Once in the other faith, many Serbs pulled their entire families and all their friends into Islam. The Turks knew that it was actually those who would more easily, quickly and massively take in others with them because, living among their own, they would know better how to unify or divide the rest. This all suited the Ottomans fine: the Serbs did the work instead of them, the results were visible, and they were able to save their own, leaving only the minimum necessary number of Turks among them. This suited the Serbs because they stayed on their land, and as to what was 'theirs', that is another story. Many of them who did not leave their land to move to Turkey considered themselves to be the same as they were before converting to Islam. And those who did not convert, and who were still their neighbours, it was still easier to put up with them than with real Ottomans. If nothing else, they remembered them as being their own. In fact, there were many of those tough Serbs who, sometimes individually and sometimes in great numbers, escaped conversion to Islam through larger or smaller migrations. That was a nomadic resistance to the Turks. However, regardless of the fact that the whole and varied resistance among the Serbs lasted the longest, the persistence of the other side did its own. The Islamisation of all peoples under Ottoman rule was carried out most fundamentally among the Serbs, no matter where they lived. Understandably so, when it is known that the Serbs were the most numerous of the enslaved Christian peoples of Europe.

CHAPTER XXX

I was concerned about whether I would actually be rewarded by finding the multi-language dictionary that, at one moment, I thought I had just imagined. Above all it was important that I see what it was like to be a witness for myself in something that could seem like a complete fabrication, but also as a magnificent and real, even scholarly, discovery. This dichotomy was not foreign to me: I had had such experiences earlier as well. I had felt on my own skin that amateurism is not to be underestimated.

Here are the examples.

Long ago, when I had enrolled to study South Slavic and world literature, officially existing at the time, an unusual and for me unexpected love was born between myself and the literature of the Serbian medieval period. By educational accident and not personal choice, I was among the so-called English studying students, so at the Department for Serbian Medieval Literature I had a serious problem because I did not have the necessary linguistic education for the interpretation of original texts: in order to properly understand texts written in Church Slavonic or in one of the other variants of the old Serbian language (and Russian Church Slavonic...), one has to learn Old Church Slavonic. And in order to do that, it was desirable to know Russian. All cards were stacked against me. But my amateur love toward reading these ancient texts (produced in the 12th century and afterward) translated into modern Serbian did not wane. I continued to educate myself in this field with the enthusiastic support of Professor Đorđe Trifunović. I read, studied and wrote texts, and at one moment – was totally surprised! Professor Trifunović called me in for a conversation in his office, after I had turned in my research paper on the topic 'Dialogue forms in the 'Life of St. Sava' by Teodosije Hilandarac' (from the end of the 13th century). I was certain that, as a truly strict teacher, he would have serious objections about my paper in that conversation, or that he would, in the best possible case, give it back for me to re-work. But no. He did not even have the paper in his office! He had invited me in to tell me that paper was at the editorial board of the periodical 'Language and Literature' at the Serbian Academy of Arts and Sciences, where it was to be published immediately! But not because the paper was good, rather because it was revolutionary! But how? Well, because in it, writing about dialogue forms, I had apparently uncovered the roots of drama in Serbian literature! I could not believe it. Even though a student-beginner, I refused to be that naïve. Of all the questions I asked him that day, I still remember the one that he did not answer: "But how is that possible, with all the dozens of unsurpassable experts for old Serbian literature, and with all the centuries of them studying it?" Yet, I had to believe in my discovery when the periodical appeared in public, with my text inside. When so many people began to pat me on my nineteen year-old shoulder. When I was invited to stay on at the faculty after graduation as an assistant at the department. I did not. But, I did hold on to my love for the field and to my right to quote the works of my brilliant professor. And to read ancient literature. And to my amateur intuition.

This is retroactive assurance. But it has the role of proving that amateur presuppositions are sometimes acceptable. Even mine. Perhaps when love and childlike naïveté retain their authentic properties. My medieval double would say – that's how it is when you sing in the dark times.

The story goes on.

In January of 2008, while I was sitting in the apartment that I had gotten to use as a scholarship from an Austrian foundation, bringing the final chapters to an end in my novel about the time of shared Serbian and Turkish history, the story about the search for 'my' dictionary had taken its own course. The only existing copy of it had somehow unnoticed moved from the library of Aja Sophia to the library of the 'Suleimaniya'. As if Istanbul did not want to reveal its secret to me immediately. Well, among other things, not even Pamuk answered my question about this dictionary (is anything known about it?), asked at that same time, from the other side of the world. Only that question. He answered the others.

Then there were several telephone calls from Belgrade. The person to be most credited with this discovery, Mr. Sava Anđelković, an expert in another field, but who is in love with Istanbul and with the *story*, called me. He reported each leg of the journey of the package that was supposed to get to me: a copy of the manuscript was previously lost in Sarajevo, then copied again 'from the original'... had left Stambol, arrived in Niš... and was now in the cab of a truck headed for Belgrade... (he was worried that the 'uneducated truck driver might put it by the heater and deform the CD!'), and should he send it to Krems, in Austria? No, we would pass right by each other. I arrived in Belgrade quickly.

And finally... we met at Terazije, in the café of the Moskva Hotel (where I had left Pamuk in the garden to make sketches in his green notebook of the city and of the faces). I turned on my laptop there on the table because I could not wait to get home to see what our destiny had brought us: and my first disappointment! This multilingual dictionary was supposed to contain Serbian as well! But it was not there. I recognised Arabic (as the dominant language), Persian, Rumi (Greek), then Arabic again... but no Serbian. There was no text with the disk, not even with the elementary data about its archiving. I felt helpless like never before. Dejected. Discouraged. My dear friend was disappointed. On the other hand... there in front of me was surely one of the rare examples of cosmopolitan linguistics, probably produced somewhere between the 14th and 16th centuries that could not be everyday in any way, either then or now. Because there were several languages there that explained the same world in parallel! A glossary of linguistic brotherhood! Proof that the world of that time was open, that attempts were made to join and not only separate. Or at least attempted to join as well and *not just* to separate.

Afterwards I had an attack of persistent intuition. In one of the four books that this entirety was made up of, on one hundred and sixty-eight pages, I saw that, next to the Greek concepts (written here in the Greek alphabet) Arabic ones were added, afterwards, like 'singing from the dark times', like marginal comments by the copiers or students. Someone had *in that place* (unintended for that) written a translation of the Greek concepts in Arabic! Aside from the place foreseen for that and aside from the consistent parallel language structure by which the glossary was conceived. This made me think that I was not seeing what I wanted, perhaps, because it was hidden by another alphabet!

It turned out to be so. Mirjana Marinković, an Orientalist, immediately tried to interpret the Sultan's seal and signature (the only place where Turkish appeared!), but they were indecipherable, tiny and faded. The colours of the various languages were also not recorded, so the languages

– in the original, each was in a different colour – in this black-and-white copy were just varying shades of grey. The last one in the series, the fourth, was the lightest and least visible. But, it seemed to be Arabic (again). My Orientalist friend took a copy I made for her home to study it more carefully. The next day she called me, all excited, and immediately came to see me. Among the other languages she found 'lugat servi' or 'lugat serfi' – the *Serbian language*! It was written out in Arabic letters! And so it was hidden on all (the most faded) one hundred sixteen pages. The largest whole (book) of the four in existence.

The content was even more interesting than the structure: it was made up of concepts (in the broadest sense), phrases, sayings, half-sentences, bits of dialogue... it was more like a sort of parallel glossary, language instruction than an example of the standard idea of a dictionary. All of that in four languages! And the choice in it was interesting: 'I watch you because I seen ya', 'How long have they been here? Several day', 'Houring sit', 'What are you doing?', 'I spake, I didn't sayed', 'I love you from me h(e)art', 'A lot I hits', 'Don't cry, don't cry, go ahead and cry'... and other such odd stuff all in Serbian.

Who was that written for? Well, I thought of the victims of the blood tribute; they might have studied this in schools for janissaries and court clerks. Who else? Well, probably everyone who cried, loved, was punished and was forced to turn to the Other. Both male and female. Both the conqueror and the conquered. Both the old and the young. Both the master and the slave. Whoever it was, they became more educated and wealthy with the aid of this dictionary. And more useful, to themselves and to others.

And all of that was true for the present time as well.

This was one more of my amateur contributions to scholarship. It is obvious that our experts (and it seems many others in the world) did not know that this dictionary existed. Now they will be able to study it carefully and offer it to public display. So that our past and present can be wealthier.

This brought my amateur episode from the fifteenth century perhaps to a slow close, but fortunately, there are others. An entirely new one appeared in the newly obtained fact (that remains to fully proven) that, in the Aja Sophia there are two manuscripts from a similar period, written exclusively in Serbian, written in the Arabic alphabet, but without any other accompanying language. So to say, Serbian books.

Now I really had some research to do!

Still, this not the end of that sometimes absurd mixture of languages and alphabets. A drastic example of the connection of these in an impossible combination is found in a prayer book compiled in Belgrade in 1567. A member of the Dubrovnik colony, the merchant Mato Bora Božidarović received a prayer book written in the Latin alphabet, but since this merchant had grown accustomed to Serbian culture and even its alphabet, he asked his friend Marin Nikolić to copy this prayer book into Cyrillic. All of that would be understandable, even the degree of patriotism shown by a 'Latin', if the copyist had not gotten lost in the non-existent rules for the various dialects of the language. So he turned the entire prayer book into Serbian Cyrillic, including all of the parts of the Latin text, without translating them into Cyrillic! So, in the text there are entire sentences in Latin, written out in Cyrillic like this one: 'Ано салутис новстере 1567...' ('Ano salutis novstere 1567...').

I can just imagine all of the things that experts are forced to be ready for.

In the meantime, I headed off in another direction. And actually, all the directions were open. It was that freedom that was the real challenge to my research. Perhaps all of the things in the margins, alongside the goals that I had imposed on myself, the things that poured out over the 'main' events, perhaps they were the essence of the events. For example, the way that the customary guards of grandiose monuments played an important role in my conceptualisation of new truths.

I remember my first meeting with the beauty of the 'Selimiya' at Edirne. I was suffering from excitement that grew unstoppably with every meter I drew closer to it from Belgrade. Like the meeting of lovers in puberty. When I stood before it the first time, so gigantic and elegant, it was already late in the evening. I could not hold myself accountable for the fact that I was late getting there; I had crossed a thousand kilometres at once, passed over the borders of three countries but was kept at one for ages, waiting for God knows what. And then when I reached my goal, I could not go in! I paced around outside God's house on all sides, like a cat pacing around its milk, trying all the doors in the hopes of finding one open... And then on the east side of the wall, I saw a guard in the courtyard through the gate. I did not say anything to him. I just stood there looking at him. He looked at me, and then walked over. Standing there across the way from a chain as thick as those for ships' anchors, dividing us into two worlds, he stared me right in the eyes without saying a word. My stare must have told him everything because he unhooked the chain, unlocked the gate, and beckoned to me to come in. He took me to the rear of the Selimiya and opened the door for me.

If I had tried, I do not know how, nor whom I would have asked for help, to get such a privilege ahead of time, I certainly would not have succeeded.

I was allowed, or better said – enabled, to enter that beauty all by myself.

A second, similar, experience occurred in Istanbul several years later. The long-lasting search for details that were important to me did not lessen my enthusiasm. To the contrary. That was how, after a long time had passed, I had finally gotten on the trail of the small mosque that Sinan had built 'for himself': this was a house of prayer that he ordered to be built for himself when he was already very old. Because of a variety of circumstances, I did not manage to find it for years. It even occurred to me that the government was hiding it intentionally. So, I was already starting to think like a paranoid. And it was, actually, just small, without a dome and high minaret. It was tucked away among some other buildings, in a street named 'Koca Mimar Sinan'. Perhaps it is, objectively speaking, believed to be unimportant, but to me it was of incomparable importance.

I arrived there at a bad time as well. It was closed, no one inside or anywhere around. It was not even a day of prayer. The only thing I could do in my helplessness was, like a kid, to peek through the glass of all the windows to see whatever I could and tell myself that I had not come in vain. But in truth, I was desperate. I believed, with profound justification, that this humble structure was Sinan's testament (and I will say more about that later), to something exceptionally important in his life and work. And there I was, again to use the symbolism of the cat, able only to lick the pan on the outside.

Then somebody said something to me in Turkish and I realised that the guard had been watching me the whole time from somewhere, probably from the tiny house to the side, which was perhaps even his home. Most certainly he thought that he had not seen such a persistent and bothersome tourist for ages and – he took pity on me. Talking the whole time, even though it was clear that I did not understand a word, he unlocked all parts of the little mosque and waited patiently, allowing me to remain in each of the rooms as long as I wanted.

The goodness of everyday people who, in their simplicity of conceiving the world, were able to recognise someone's irresistible and insatiable need, made the world a better place. This was proof that every *why* does not have to have its *because*. It is enough to have *that*.

CHAPTER 30

Together with Great Mufti Amadi, Bajica guessed the direction in which the problems of the Ottoman Empire would go in relation to Europe and in relations with Europe. Not military problems, but those broader ones that had to do with the advancement, stagnation or regression of the entire culture and civilisation of the sultanate. Within the state, an imminent battle loomed between the old and new understanding of the world. Between staying the same or entering into change. Between blindness and foresight, devolution and evolution.

The result of the finished battle of the princes – the favour of the heir to the throne, Selim, and of the present ruler Suleiman, so of both of them, toward Mehmed-pasha, offered him the security that he could think fundamentally and plan for the long term about the paths of the Empire. These preparations to become the grand vizier gave him the chance, immediately and at least temporarily, to discourage most of his possible opponents from acts of enmity. Because even to such people, all the signs indicated that this man was waiting to become the highest minister of the state, and when he took the position he would stay there for a long time: it had been a long time since two rulers simultaneously supported one person so enthusiastically – both the present ruler and the one to come. To be sure, Bajica wisely did not consider that anything was said and done until it actually happened. He had witnessed often enough the surprising and ultimately unexpected plans both of individuals and of the entire empire. He remained consistently careful and firmly focused.

With the help of the great mufti and with the Sultan's silent support, he participated in the making of new laws, and especially in their proper interpretation. He used all places and chances, using appropriate language depending on where he was and who he was talking to, from the religious schools to various public appearances, to explain the dangers the empire did not dare fall into, and which it was already showing tendencies of sliding into: this was about the attempt (intentional or not) at falsely understanding the role of education. Namely, certain backward oriented courtiers, viziers, ulemas and other public servants had begun, loudly and emphatically, and above all mistakenly, to equate education with religious studies, but not with the study of scholarship. This was leaning to the side that could drag all the accumulated successes of the entire empire into a real catastrophe. So, general scholarship was replaced with scholarship of the faith, thus depriving the Ottoman Empire of new scientific achievements, precisely at the moment when Europe was emphatically edifying knowledge and proving it to be the main generator of advancement. From this, already visible conflict arose another as well: various religious fanatics began to associate into sects and to influence believers and the army, goading them against all the so-called infidels in their ranks, especially those in high positions. They were all fairly confusing and unclear in their explanations, but even such people did some damage. Bajica, and the entire Dīvān as well, began to be bothered by the *hamza sect*, founded by Hamza Bali Orlović. This dervish, from Bosnia by background, asked his followers in one moment to do the impossible, mixing Christ and Allah in a single religion, and in the next moment demanding extreme Islamic orthodoxy from them. At times among his followers he had the craftsmen (in one period just the producers of embroidered cloth), and at times they were mostly janissaries. One moment he presented himself as a Shiite loyal to Mohammed and his family, the next moment he was loyal to his Bosnian roots. Precisely because of that religious and ideological confusion, and also because of the rapid spread of his influence to all corners of the Empire, he became exceptionally dangerous. When the Islamic priesthood in Bosnia could take no more, he was arrested and sent to Constantinople. Even though in 1561 he was killed secretly so as to avoid public outcry and even a possible rebellion, that event created something even worse than an uprising as its consequence, something that no one wanted: his death turned him into a martyr and therefore he obtained even more followers.

Members of the sect had gone to Bajica and Mehmed-pasha several times over the years, using his names in alternation depending on which stage of religious fanaticism they were at the time. In alternation they praised him and asked him for help (for money, support – publicly or privately) or they cursed him as being Turkified, a compromised soul and demanded that everyone flee from him like the plague. Bajica took none of this personally because he understood that they were a sect of inconsistent and unclear ideas, but he did not discount the sect's followers in the least.

The carefulness with which he entered all his work became his trademark. He retained it as one of the most valuable character traits that he had developed and which would, as it had so many times in the past, save him from destruction in the future. He often used it to save others as well. Over the next few years he led the Sultan's army in several of its campaigns, already now in the company of one or both of his sons, and with many others of the Sokolović clan placed in high positions of authority with the padishah's approval. In equal measure with the battles, Bajica advanced all aspects of life in the Empire, from trade, shipbuilding and legislation, to supporting poets, including the highest ruler among them.

His years of loyalty led him to his inevitable enthronement in the position of Grand Vizier of the Ottoman Empire in 1565. Suleiman the Magnificent Kanuni entrusted him with the state just a year before the thirteenth and largest campaign against the Austrian Empire. Passing through Belgrade and Zemun on June 27, 1566, the Sultan was seen for the last time in public on horseback, because thereafter he was more of an old man on his deathbed, carried on a stretcher and cared for in his tents, no longer a feared ruler. The siege of Sziget remained in history thanks to Bajica and his incredible cleverness when the Sultan died during the siege, on the night between September 5 and 6, just one day after the fall of the bravely defended town under the command of Nikola Zrinski. Mehmed-pasha continued to serve *under the command of the dead sultan*, reporting the ruler's death neither to the viziers nearby nor to the army. In doing so, he managed to maintain the morale of the soldiers and, regardless of the fact that he did not fulfil the padishah's dream – of conquering Vienna, he brought the campaign to a successful end. He also managed to keep the secret of the death and of the now preserved body of his ruler among the army for more than six weeks (!), more precisely until October 24, 1566, when he was on the fourth day with the army headed back to Istanbul, four nights till Belgrade. He made the death public when he was certain that, on his immediate report and summons, the Sultan's son Selim was hurrying toward Belgrade from Asia. (It only took the Prince ten days to reach the Hill of Reflection, as the Ottomans called the fortress in Belgrade). Selim was waiting for him there, in Bajram-bey's house. The proclamation of the new sultan of the Empire was carried out beneath the ramparts of Belgrade. The new ruler simultaneously proclaimed Mehmed-pasha Sokolović as his Grand Vizier. Thus Bajica's title was confirmed for the second time in two years.

The period that followed proved that all of Mehmed's preparations for the position of bearer of the great seal of the Empire had been warranted: he did not have to adapt anything especially new or different under this rule than what he had prepared and was already using. In any case, before he met with the heir to the throne in Belgrade, upon returning from Sziget he managed to appoint two of his relatives to two the two strategically most important positions in Rumelia: Mustafa-pasha Sokolović was appointed as the administrator of Buda, and his younger brother Mehmed Sokolović became the sancakbey of Bosnia. He successfully carried out all the business of the Empire, and the new Sultan, not really anxious to run the country, left it all in his secure hands.

Bajica ruled uncontested for all eight of Selim's years as sultan. How could he fail when he possessed experience in serving the Empire over more than half a century! Of that time, during at least half of it he had been making decisions. He transferred his experience in the service of Selim II also to his son and the new sultan, Murat III in 1574. Even though Mehmed-pasha was almost seventy years old, no one could still outdo him in running the country. Even Murat, who never liked him from day one, did not want to renounce him voluntarily. At least for now. Neither the son nor grandson of Suleiman Kanuni measured Mehmed-pasha's experience and loyalty to the highest Ottoman ruler by the year when Mehmed was his right-hand man. They measured his abilities according to all fifty years he had spent next to the sultan and they understood that, of all the titles the ruler had bestowed on him, most of them meant that he had to be *very close, as close as possible*, to the ruler, almost at an intimate distance. It was clear that the sultan wanted him nearby and chose offices that would not send him too far away. Even when he became the Grand Vizier, by Suleiman's command while he was still alive, in order to be as close as possible to the Sultan, he had to move to the court at Mejdan, at the foot of the Topkapi palace. It was hard for Bajica to leave his good neighbour, the Sheik-ul-Islam Amadi and to give up their tranquil walks together.

Such a faithful and dedicated servant had not been seen for ages in any country. For, when he was (re)instated as the Grand Vizier to the *third sultan* in a row, wasn't the country showing him an honour and trust that no single man of the Dīvān had ever experienced, wasn't the message clear enough?

And was there anything else he could want?

To leave behind a legacy in stone.

Where?

In *his* places.

AFTER THE END (WATER)

With the passing of time, the relationship between Sinan and Mehmed took on a new, slightly strange dimension. Because of their high positions, their obligations began to multiply and so they were able to spend less and less time together. On the other hand, since they understood each other well and did not want to weaken their friendship in its essence, they had to resign themselves to the inevitable. But they did not surrender to it: they came up with a way to be together more often even when they were not. In what way? Well, by each of them doing his job within the framework of the plans and agreements they had made: Bajica was to be the endower, and Josif the builder. Now at last, just as Sinan had foreseen, Mehmed was able to afford to pay for his ideas. Somehow they realised that water was to connect them in most cases. In addition to being the source of life and the sustenance of life, water had the magnificent ability to affect mans' physical and spiritual purification. That is why it seemed to them to be the perfect connective tissue (Sinan would call it 'adhesive material') for their shared life, but also for the lives that they individually once had and for the lives that they now led.

At the time when, with Sinan's help, Mehmed-pasha built the *sebilhan* in the centre of Belgrade, Bajica's hamam was finished and still brand new (in addition to the already existing one), and they named it the Yeni hamam.[65] Not even one hundred years later, in 1658, French travel writer A. Poulet composed quite an interesting praise of the waters, but also of the inhabitants of Belgrade while trying to explain the more profound meaning of public baths, using Belgrade as an example: 'The spas in the Levant, which are actually steam baths because a man does not bathe there although he is still cleansed, show that *these people succeed in things for which they have the greatest inclination* and that the spirit of these people... is so delicate in the perspective of these baths that it would be difficult for us to emulate them.' (emphasis V.B.)

Poulet's words, practically a definition, having a philosophical harmony, actually identify one of the shared characteristics of the Serbs and Ottomans of that time (and other times, as well): such waters and their use played a role in enjoyment. It was part of the truly important inclination of the Balkan peoples toward hedonism which was composed of exceptionally subtle variations on the theme of (self)satisfaction, even to the point of the masochistic fulfilment of one's own desires (starting with food and going further). Just as Evliya Çelebi said in about 1660: 'Those are all people who like pleasure and merriment, who are friends to strangers. Their meal times are hospitable and their doors are open.'

Both Sinan and Mehmed had long and rich lives.[66] Yet, even at the time when they reckoned that their lives *were going to be* long and rich, that did not turn them away from the idea that they should stay as close to each other as possible. Just as they had remained close in their early lives. By staying close, they only increased the chances that they would create even stronger 'ties'.

I had to reveal my presuppositions and potential discoveries to Orhan Pamuk. He was a good standard for objectivity; he knew the East and West well enough that he did not make the mistake of going to extremes on one 'side' or the other.

Speaking of water, Pamuk reminded me of the fact that Sultan Suleiman put Sinan to work in fixing the water supply in Istanbul. No matter how pragmatic that sounds, because no large city can survive without a lasting solution to water supply, the Sultan's view of water was far from ordinary. In a proclamation to Sinan, and to the people, he said: "I want there to be water in every part of the city. Let fountains be built wherever it is appropriate. Let wells be dug wherever, even where it is not appropriate. Let there be fresh water everywhere. Let all my subjects use it, and let them pray that my rule be everlasting." In any case, thanks to both of them, the capital city got its aqueducts: Kağithane (1557) and Kirkçeşme (1564), Mağlova and Uzun. To be fair, also thanks to the citizens of Serbian Belgrade who, after its fall, were relocated to Stambol in order to construct the earlier waterworks and these aqueducts, and who founded their own Belgrade in the middle of Istanbul after the first resettlement. Their hosts, probably in the honour of those Serbs, added similar names to places in the local environs: Belgrade Gate, Belgrade Forest...

"Water was also involved in his work on the Aya Sophia," Pamuk picked up my story. "Sinan reinforced the structural supports on that building, a structure which was the dream of every architect of that time, and thus managed to leave his mark on this Christian – Moslem house of prayer, today the building of a conciliatory institution – a museum, and into the entirety of the complex he introduced something new as well. Namely, Suleiman's love and wife, Haseki Hürrem, long before that in 1557 had asked that Sinan build a hamam there just beside Aja Sophia, of all places, with separate areas for women and men. And she succeeded! Can you guess why?"

"Well, I have a good idea. She used the opportunity so that this was done for her by a (former) Christian, just as she had been till not long before, 'in her former life', when she was Roxelana, the daughter of a Russian priest. The proximity of a former Byzantine church helped her keep a sort of balance with her new life. Among other things, do you think it is also a coincidence that in 1573–74 it was Sinan/Jusuf/Josif in person who was ordered, or better said permitted, to do the rather serious restoration work on the Aja Sophia? In addition to reinforcing the supports, he also raised two new minarets, and even built a tomb for Sultan Selim. All of that just because he was the best?"

"It is true that he built hamams all over the Empire. Although, I really like the one built for Suleiman's daughter Mihrimah in 1565 next to the school at Edirnekapiya."

"You know," I added, "I really like the fact that he never slowed down in his building. Not so much because of the energy that is easily recognised in the constructions, but because of the ease with which he built anywhere – whether in the capital or in the provinces. The complex I visited in Lüleburgaz, halfway between Edirne and Istanbul, looks so enchanting and unpretentious, and still it fits perfectly into its surroundings in the cramped provincial city. I think Sinan's secret was that he knew that engineering isn't just the construction of a single building, but that its job is to occupy a space available in the best possible way and thus become an authentic part of the environs. I never used to look at architecture that way, but I learned to see these things from him. Just like when I realised long ago that sculpting does not have to be the creation of a work by *adding* materials, but rather, by actually *removing* them."

"There is also something in the fact that he lived to be nearly a hundred. You can see exactly how time allowed him to comfortably study what he wanted, just as long as he wanted. I think he understood this use of time way back when he was on the campaigns in Hungary, proving to himself and others that he could reconstruct something that had been destroyed. When, as an engineer-officer, he successfully and quickly re-built a fortress in Banat (a well-known method in a campaign: destroy something in order to occupy it, and once you've occupied it – immediately rebuild it), and the commander wanted to leave him behind in charge of the outpost as the army retreated, he adamantly refused and risked his life for disobeying the order. However, he was so certain in his vision of his future that he somehow got to the Grand Vizier even from the battlefield, and managed to get him to rescind the order. Many decades later, in the same way, through observation and dedication, with fourteen thousand workers in just six years he managed to build his most beautiful mosque, the Selimiya (even more elegant than the Suleimaniya). Construction was just the execution of his observations."

I had more to add.

"In my opinion, that is the most beautiful mosque in the world. Why, just look at the minarets! The idea of making three staircases in each in such a way that three people can climb up at the same time and never meet! Still, before I remind you of something related to that beauty, I want to say that Sinan had developed a spirit of competition in relation to Aja Sophia. He kept his obsession hidden for a long time – to build a dome bigger than that one on one of his own mosques. When he finally did so in 1575 at the Selimiya, that victory, consisting of several dozen centimetres, meant more to him than the fact that the Ottoman Empire, and probably the whole Islamic world, had never seen a more beautiful house of Allah."

But Pamuk had his own addition.

"I think that he achieved the most he could. The Aja Sophia was too heavy a load both for the Christian or the Islamic shoulders of all later architects; it was hard to build anything that could outdo it. History could not give Sinan a greater compliment than this one, a sentence widely accepted in Turkey which, actually does not even try to compare them: *Aja Sophia is the sun, and the Selmiya – the moon.*"

"But I think you wanted to tell me something about that beauty?" Pamuk inquired.

"Well, yes. Some compare the Selimiya to the Taj Mahal in Agra.

I'm not mentioning it now because of our comparisons, but because I remembered that that pearl of Persian architecture in India is actually the heritage of – Mimar Sinan! Among the main builders of that wonder among *the seven wonders of the world*, the Taj Mahal (1632–1648), there are Ottoman and Persian names: Mehmet Isajeri, Isa Muhamed Efendi, Ustad Isa – who were all Josif's/Sinan's students."

Now Pamuk and I were competing. He gave the final blow.

"Well, also the creator of the famous Sultanahmet mosque, better known as – the Blue Mosque at At Meydan, just next to the Aja Sophia – was Mehmed-aga, who was Sinan's last student!"

Just when he thought he had won, I finished him off with one more fact.

"It wouldn't have even been there, at least not on that spot – the Hippodrome[67] (and it is known that the Sultan demanded that it be built *only* there) if Sokolović hadn't gotten involved."

Pamuk was surprised. He did not know that.

"How so?"

"Well, because on that very place was the palace of the Sokolović family that he had gotten personally from Suleiman, when he had taken the position of the Grand Vizier. Respecting the relationship between his predecessors and one of the greatest among sultans toward one of the greatest grand viziers of all time, Sultan Ahmet had to bargain with Mehmed-pasha's son over the price he would have to pay for this palace. When he finally did buy the palace (for an enormous amount of money and without any kind of privileged pricing) – he immediately tore it down so that he could build the Sultanahmet mosque on its foundations, and with his and Mehmed-aga's recognition – on the model of Sinan's Suleimaniya.

"But let's talk more about water," I suggested. "Do you know how else our two friends came together 'in the water'? By the fact that Bajica, since he had redeemed himself so many times in the eyes of those fanatical and dubious Moslems by going on the hajj, he asked Josif to build him a hamam in the holy city of Medina. Not mosque, a hamam! He asked for the same thing in Konya and Karapinar."

We parted ways. Pamuk went to Princes' Island, and I remained in the Istanbul heat to finish my search for Sinan's *last will*. He would be near the water, and I would – if I found what I was looking for – receive the testament like an award.

On my way I crossed the Galati bridge for the hundredth time (at its northern end, where the Genoese always had their quarter – fortification, from a cart vendor I would always buy hand-squeezed orange juice with the best taste in the world). This time I remembered how easily it could have happened that this bridge be built by Leonardo da Vinci when Sultan Bayazit II announced his plans to build a bridge on the Golden Horn. At that time the Venetians proposed da Vinci who drew up a project for him in 1502, according to him the largest in the world – between 240 and 350 meters long and 24 meters wide. The Sultan rejected the plan, and then sent the order to another artist – Michelangelo. Uninterested, Michelangelo rejected the offer. So, this chain of rejections would put off the construction of the bridge for three whole centuries.

Now, the last will of 'my' engineer I called the *mesjid*, the little mosque, ordered by the patron Sinan from the engineer Sinan. Or, as it will be seen, perhaps it is better to say – the client Josif from the engineer Sinan. Or the customer Sinan from the secret architect Josif. It makes no difference.

When I finally found it among the residential buildings of the densely settled outskirts of downtown, I realised why it had been so hard to find: it was even more than modest and tiny. One of the two most visible symbols of every mosque in this case did not exist, and the second barely existed. Namely, there was no dome on the roof: instead of it – the roof was made of four vaults like a family home just about anywhere. A mosque without a dome! No matter how small it was, I found that strange. And the minaret! It was hardly even there. It was so short that at first I did not even recognise it for what it was. Of course, it was not that I was looking for something big. I was just surprised. In the courtyard, there was long series of taps for ritual washing, and next to them was an additional yard in the pleasant shade of a tree. On the wall next to the entrance, the inscription *Mimar Sinan Mescidi Serifi 1573*. Next to the entrance a wooden shoe rack. Inside – everything to the measure of a man. And actually just the way it should be. Monumental structures serve other purposes. Here, one man sent a message to other people, not the sultan to the whole world.[68] This one, 'mine', chose a way of interpretation. Just as I was leaving and took a photograph I realised that it was built of bricks in two colours, horizontally laid in alternation. Like in Byzantium.

Were these the messages of duality that he could not let go of? Of one – yes, of the second – yes. But of both – no.

Later, quite recently, I watched a documentary film made in Anatolia in Sinan's – more precisely Josif's – village Agirnas, in his time settled by Greeks. The film was actually not made in the village, but *under* it! The pictures showed endless tunnels and many subterranean rooms with a surface area of four thousand square meters (!) that were uncovered during the renovation of a house, which is of historical import, during 2003 and 2004. The little building under which they found an entire village, was the house where Josif was born. The home from which he had left to become Jusuf Mimar Sinan.

It seems ever more to me that this underground world beneath his feet (the purpose of which has not been discovered) determined Josif's destiny and his profession.

Just as the subject of my book was determined for me by the foundations of Bajica/Mehmed-pasha's caravansary, under the foundations of my building on Dorćol, right under my feet.

THE END OF THE END

At the time when Sinan started to humbly pay tribute to his birthplace, the land where he grew up, by building things, most often by making fountains in Kayseri and the regions of Haslar and Vize (because fountains had a daily, useful value to the common people), a similar nostalgia overcame Mehmed as well. And he also began humbly and had a fountain built in Belgrade's upper town, just next to Suleiman's mosque. He had another built in Sokolovići where he had come from. For his larger plans, the ones he had been preparing for Belgrade over a longer period, he took counsel with Sinan. After all, the two of them had walked around the city and measured it together so many times.

He presented Sinan with his idea.

"I've thought long and hard about the story you told me so long ago: about the strange similarity of the position and shape of the Golden Horn in Istanbul and Kalemegdan and its surroundings in Belgrade. To be more precise: the Topkapi palace with its surrounding ramparts in Istanbul is in an identical spot like the Upper Town in Belgrade with its ramparts! So, I got an idea that gives meaning to these similarities, and gives me – with your help and confidentiality – the opportunity to leave a more personal and intimate message behind."

Sinan was pleased.

"I'm glad you thought about it. Some of the landmarks we leave behind have to have a more profound meaning or more serious message than most of the others. I was the one to make you think about all this. What's your idea?"

And when he heard the idea, it left him gaping.

"I found a small open spot at Kadirga to build my mosque. Since the place is hilly, you'll have trouble with the slopes, but I reckon that will be a real challenge for you. Because, no matter how much you level the place, there will still be a relatively steep part that will have to be used. However, when you see the view of the Sea of Marmara from there, you won't back down. Even though the spot is small, I would like you to build a school next to the mosque. And a fountain, of course, in the courtyard. I'm handing all my ideas over to you because I know that you don't see me as squanderer or as an egotistical great man, and so you will show your moderation and mine in accordance with that. The only thing special I want is that the mosaics be done in blue – something between that of the Sea of Marmara and that of the Danube and Sava."

He laughed.

"Come on now, you've got something more up your sleeve! Come on, out with it."

"Do you remember Donji Dorćol in Belgrade, the part near the Latin quarter? Well, there, in the part that opens up on the long street I want to build a caravansary and a covered market. I've seen that many travellers and merchants are coming there, and there will be more and more of them because Belgrade is becoming an important town..."

Sinan interrupted him with a question.

"And why don't you build a house of Allah there, like you are here?"

Bajica scowled at him.

"Are you kidding me? Why, isn't it enough that I converted to Islam, and now I should openly invite others to do so as well? No, the Serbs will keep living there, believing in their own God. I will not be the one to change that. Don't you see, that would make all of my effort in helping the Serbian church a waste of time. And one other thing: don't you think that it would be as if I were gouging the Serbs and other Christians in the eye? No, they should have some use out of all of this, too."

"But I only said that because I noticed that the places you propose to build on are similar in Stambol and in Belgrade!"

"They are not *similar*, they are the *same*! *Identical*! That's the very reason why I'm doing it. I measured all the distances precisely and then I saw the sense of it: that *according to their place* in both cities, my endowments will be exact copies of each other! Their south sides are at an identical distance from the Sea of Marmara, that is, from the Danube. On the East side, one of them has the bay alongside, the other the Sava... and so on. All the distances are the same. But I have one more request in the spirit of this."

Sinan marvelled at him. What an idea!

"Request of me? What is it?"

293

"That you make all the plans and preparations so that you build both at the same time!"

Sinan was left speechless. God in heaven, Bajica had actually turned his original idea into a masterpiece!

"Fantastic! Even if I were unable to do this, I would still agree to it. What a message!"

The engineer got down to work and, being highly motivated, he prepared everything very quickly and in two years of work, simultaneously, he built the two structures. One was a gorgeous little, but not too little, mosque.[69] It had a steep, arched entry upward into the courtyard, across a staircase *above* which was the school. The solution to the problem of the steep terrain now looked quite simple. The blue of the tiles was victorious over all other existing ones. The classrooms, the courtyard, the seven small domes on the roof of the mosque, the interior of the prayer room – it all looked humble, yet gave the impression that it were made of love, and not of material.

At the same time, Sinan's architects finished the caravansary and covered market, according to his plans, at the foot of the Hill for Reflection in Belgrade. Although less solemn, these structures appeared in the town like two new real beauties that no one could take their eyes off of. And many went even further. The inhabitants of Belgrade began to dress up when headed for these new spots: they freed the people from the long-lasting habit of wearing nicer clothes at home than when they went out. With the aid of these two structural beauties, they overcame their existing pride in not showing their own beauty to the Ottomans. Now they wanted to show it. They used the buildings enthusiastically and became known all over Europe: there was not a foreign traveller who did not describe them in their notes, reports and travelogues (depending on what kind of traveller they were and what they were writing for).

Sinan brought Mehmed a present, a plaque identical to the one set above the entrance to the Belgrade caravansary, the text of which was written by his friend and poet Mustafa Sai Çelebi. It read: 'Everyone who spent the night in this caravansary has gone.'

Then Bajica began to use the word 'city' for Belgrade, thus teasing Sinan who loved to argue with him over the differences between, for example, hamlet, village, kasbah, and town. And now he had even brought in this 'city'!

When the work was done, Sinan asked him: "And what else do you think you have achieved by reproducing your endowments in two *cities*?"

Bajica had prepared an answer.

"Now, whenever I like, I can look at your work *here* and think that I am *there*. And vice versa. Now isn't that magnificent?"

"That's right. If it were only comforting, that wouldn't be good."

After five years, they repeated their conversation.

Bajica asked Sinan to build another mosque for him, somewhat larger than the first, at Istanbul's Azap Kapi. And, *at the same time*, to build a marvellous stone bridge in Bosnia, on the River Drina, at Višegrad.

The preparations and work lasted long enough that people could see two more lovely structures made from the ideas, emotion and hard work of two friends.[70]

Having never seen him so satisfied, Sinan asked if it just seemed that Bajica looked like someone who had fulfilled his most intimate wishes.

Mehmed answered affirmatively, and then asked him for one more thing.

"Apart from my children, you are the one who has brought me the greatest happiness in life. Because of that, it's your own fault that I will now tell you one more of my secrets that you will be responsible for keeping."

"Do I hear the hint of a bad omen from the way you are telling me this?"

"Indeed. I did not have the good fortune of being born earlier, when you were, nor will I have the good luck to outlive you. Though, I should be satisfied with the number of my years when I compare them to yours, you who will outlive us all. You're already ninety, and it seems you'll live forever! That's why you're the best choice for keeping my secret. You know my young wife Esmahan, I call her Esma, the daughter of Sultan Selim, the granddaughter of Sultan Suleiman the Magnificent, I call him the Master of the century, and the Sultana Haseki Hürrem, I call her Roxelana. Well, she will soon be left alone and no matter how safe she will be after my departure, because she is a relative of all the sultans, I would like to know that one of my friends looks in on her from time to time. She still must not have male children because she is a sultan's daughter, and if she had them, they would be a danger to the throne. However, I could not take motherhood away from such a young bride when she gave birth to our son in secret. Yes, he's alive and well, a long time now! I kept him with us, he's pretending to be one of our servants. His name is Ibrahim, I call him Jovan. There, I just wanted you to know. No one will ever touch him, even if they found out whose he is, but in any case you check up on him sometimes. It won't be too much trouble for you. Indeed with that passel of kids of yours, five daughters and two sons with two different wives, you're surely quite skilful at it. Kurd and Hassan are already grown, and I'm not worried about them. Oh, yes, and I call them by different names as well."

Sinan feigned surprise. In fact, he was not.

"So, you've done everything on time, it seems, as far as I can see you're still alive, and you're leaving quite an inheritance behind – in children, endowments, victories, good deeds... After all this I'm expecting some kind of will and testament from you. Though, I must admit, it's a bit strange that I'm not leaving all that behind to you."

"You'd like to joke, but I have indeed left behind a few words that you ought to read when I am no longer here. I know that with Sai Çelebi you are also preparing a book with a registry of your legacy, and perhaps with a testament. You also have the good fortune that your friend is a man of the quill, so he will embellish some of your bad sides. I will leave myself to the interpreters."

"All right. I got it. And you are teasing me about my bad sides. But why don't we save some time and you just tell me what's in the letter? On your deathbed you won't have time, or I might not be around. And I don't like to read messages from my dead friends."

Bajica thought it through and decided.

"All right. But only if you understand these sentences as just another part of one of our conversations. I'll try to avoid emotional words, though I would hope they are at least wise. I will tell you some of the thoughts that have haunted me for years, or those that are the conclusion from such reflections.

For example, I know that I tried to avoid having an excess of fame as a warrior, because I never came to terms with violent death.

I like to see myself more as a wise person who is careful about what he says than as a great statesman who is careful about what he won't say.

I know that I felt a constant struggle for survival inside myself. I believe that is because I was forced to leave home. But that side of me made me skilful at guiding myself and others. I always had my guard up, and inside I felt two different ways of finding my way through: the internal one and another secret one that I did not understand.

From my experiences of the reign of all the sultans and many superiors close to me, and including my own reign, I realised that rulers can be classified in two groups: there are those who rule by the sword, of whom there are immeasurably more, and those few who rule by the shield. Such a ruler – a shield-bearer – was the Serbian King Uroš Nemanjić.[71] He was practically my role model. Perhaps that was just the way he was, perhaps the circumstances made him that way, perhaps there was some other reason... In fact, I'm inclined to think that it was somehow related to his wife, Queen Helen of Anjou. She, who converted from Catholicism to Orthodoxy of her own will. Out of her love toward her faith and toward her husband. Because it seems that, above all other reasons for his choice of the shield over the sword, stood love."

"And now, concisely, in one sentence, what did you learn is the essence of those who rule exclusively by the sword?"

Sinan did not hold back in the demand to give a full answer.

And the answer was biting.

"Almost all of them would end their rule, and often their lives, with an unspoken sentence intended for their subjects, but which was a symbol of the weakness of that kind of rule, and perhaps even its failing: 'I order you to love me!'"

Post mortem:

Statistics

KOCA MIMAR SINAN-AGA

The final list of Sinan's architectural works, and therefore their number, is difficult to establish with precision. The reasons for that are, above all, the historical distance from the time when he lived and worked, the non-existence of many things he built that have disappeared since, and also the large number of scattered archival sources, and finally the degree of their (un)reliability. The most precise and probably most accurate are made up of three lists in the following sources:

1. *Tezkiretu'l-Bunyan* (a text dedicated to the Grand Vizier Siyavush-pasha 1582–1584) and
2. *Tezkiretu'l-Ebniye* (a text dedicated to the author of both these texts, to the writer Mustafa Sai Çelebi, died 1595).
3. *Tuhfetu'l-Mi'marin* (anonymous author, the text probably came about during the 1590s).

The first two manuscripts are unofficially considered to be Sinan's autobiography because, purportedly, Mimar Sinan dictated them himself to his friend Sai Çelebi. Certain parts are written out in someone else's hand, besides Çelebi's, so it is supposed that they were written by Sinan himself. It was only recently that these two texts came out of the library of the Suleimaniya to the public, and were published as the *Book of Buildings (Memoirs of Sinan the Architect)*.

Unfortunately, these three lists render differing numbers of the total of Sinan's constructions: when all three are added up, the result is 477 projects. Of those, 314 appear in all three lists; 40 in two, and 123 only in one. Here is an example of a (fourth) list of those structures by type (the total of which is 370) for which it is claimed that Sinan planned and built them:

- 94 large mosques (*cami*)
- 57 colleges
- 52 small mosques (*mescit*)
- 41 bath-houses (*hamam*)
- 35 palaces (*saray*)
- 22 mausoleums (*türbe*)
- 20 caravansaries (*han*)
- 17 public kitchens (*imaret*)
- 8 bridges
- 8 storehouses or granaries
- 7 Koranic schools (*medrese*)
- 6 aqueducts
- 3 hospitals (*darüşşifa*).

Projects that were never built but planned:

- Opening the Suez canal
- Connecting the Don and Volga rivers by canal

HAJJI MEHMED-PASHA
SOKOLOVIĆ THE TALL

Without a shadow of a doubt, the apex of the Ottoman Empire occurred during the time of the reign of Suleiman the Magnificent Kanuni (1520–1566). By the inertia of the size of the empire he created, his heirs continued that legacy, his son Selim II (1566–1574), and his grandson Murat III (1574–1595).

The period of Sultan Suleiman's reign, lasting forty-six years, was marked by a total of ten grand viziers (more precisely nine, because one of them was appointed to this office twice). On average, each of them remained in this premier position four and half years (more precisely 4.6 years). Suleiman inherited two of the grand viziers from his father Selim I in the period from 1520 to 1523. They were the only ones from non-Slavic backgrounds. All eight (in fact seven) of the following first ministers, up to his death, were Slavs by his own choice.

1. Hadim Suleiman-pasha (the descendant of the White Eunuchs of the imperial palace)
2. Piri Mehmed (member of the *ulema*) till 1523
3. Ibrahim-pasha (1523–1536)
4. Ayas-pasha (1536–1538)
5. Lutfi-pasha (1538–1544)
6. Rüstem-pasha Opuković (1544–1553)
7. Kara Ahmed (1533–1555)
8. Rüstem-pasha Opuković (1555–1561)
9. Semiz Ali-pasha (1561–1565)
10. Mehmed-pasha Sokolović (1565–1579)

Rüstem-pasha Opuković held the place of grand vizier the longest (in two terms with a break, fifteen years total), and then Mehmed-pasha Sokolović (fourteen years). Next came Ibrahim-pasha (thirteen years). All of the rest held the office for a much shorter period of time.

The period from the death of Suleiman the Magnificent Kanuni, through the death of Selim II and all the way up to the reign of Murat III (1565–1579) over a period of fourteen years, belongs in its entirety to Grand Vizier Mehmed-pasha Sokolović. He is the only one of the grand viziers to whom was entrusted the seal of the state during the reign of three sultans (his life and office cut short by violence, at that).

From his murder in 1579 (after his fourteen continuous years of running the country), through the death of Sultan Murat III in 1595 to the reign and death of his son Mehmed III in 1603, so over a period of twenty-three years, there were a total of twenty-three grand viziers, on average one per year.

In the period from the capture of Constantinople in 1453 to the end of the reign of Mustafa I (the son of Mehmed III) in 1623 (a total of one hundred and seventy of the most significant years for the Ottoman Empire) there was a total of forty-seven grand viziers. On average each of them reigned for three and half years (more precisely 3.6 years). Mehmed-pasha Sokolović, with his fourteen years in the position of grand vizier, held it almost four times longer than the average. A position which was, moreover, brought to an end and taken away – by violence.

NOTES

1   In the practice of the *devshirme*, boys of non-Turkish background were taken to Ottoman courts from the conquered countries; through intensive schooling there, they were trained to be elite troops in the Turkish army – the janissaries – or to be servants of the court.

2   In Serbian, the word *estrada* (translated here as "Popular Stage"), especially since the early 1990s, has carried a derogatory connotation signifying the tawdry new folk music and other performance arts that reigned in that period, cajoling audiences by appealing to the lowest of aesthetic and other urges. They falsely presented themselves as folk art, using the vague truth that their distant roots could be found in the national ethnos. Their abuse was used as accompaniment to the short-sighted, populist goals of the nationalist politics of the day. This word did not apply to an entire sector of artistically resistant styles and works that existed at the same time, including some of the performance arts.

3   Slave, servant, vassal.

4   In Turkey he is known by this name (in Turkish it is "Kanuni"), but in Europe as the Magnificent.

5   A small galleon with 16 to 20 oars. A very fast, mid-sized ship.

6   A ship used as a carrier for heavy artillery at sea.

7   The Italian, *galeotto*, an oarsman, must be differentiated from *galliot*, though they are clearly connected etymologically. Here, galley slaves are surely in question. (cf. footnote 5)

8   The chief commander of all naval forces in the Ottoman Empire. They were Heyreddin Barbarossa, followed by Mehmed-pasha Sokolović, and at this moment Ali-pasha Muezzin Zade.

9   An official diplomatic interpreter, translator, most often with foreign missions in Turkey. In this case, it is more likely that an emissary was the person being talked to.

10 A *ferman* or *firman* is a written order from the Sultan carrying his bull (the sultan's seal: it has his monogram composed of his name and title).

11   In Turkish, *fiçir bayir* means "hill for reflection". This is the Turkish name for the plateau on which the fortress is built.

12   In Turkish, Kalemegdan means City Field, where *kale* means city and *megdan* means field.

13   Latin, Antemurale Christianitatis.

14   The Slavic tribe of the Serbs, according to the Byzantine emperor and historian Constantine Porphyrogenitus, settled Byzantine Singidon at the beginning of the 7th century. The Serbs called the place Beli grad, Beograd, "the white city" because of the white colour of the limestone crest it rested on and because of the white fortress they found there which was built of the same geological materials and colour.

15   Turkish, the Home of Holy War.

16   As in the case of Sinan, whose family lived in the Ottoman Empire, janissaries were taken by force exclusively from children of foreign birth, conquered Christian peoples, and Islamised Bosnians and Albanians.

17   Sokolović was indeed called the Tall (in Turkish, "Tavil") mostly because of his lean figure, which made him seem even taller.

18   From the Turkish *terazi* (meaning "scales" – either the object or the place where one measures weights and ratios. Both the weights and the object being weighed).

19   *Page* (in French page, from the Greek παιδίον – small child, small slave, young slave; in New Latin – pagius; in Italian – paggio). Earlier meaning: a young nobleman who was preparing to become a knight or young nobleman in the service of a lord; a young one who carries the train of a nobleman's robes.

20   The beylerbey was an administrator (today he would be some kind of governor) over a *beylerbeyluk*, in this case the largest military-administrative region in Turkey.

21   *Serasker* was the title for the Commander-in-Chief on a military campaign.

22   In Turkish it is called *Meriç*, in Serbian and Bulgarian *Marica*, and in Greek *Évros*.

23   Today it is Svilengrad in Bulgaria.

24   Members of the light cavalry, composed of Turks and the domestic Moslem population in the Balkans. These were units formed exclusively in the border areas of the Ottoman Empire. Their existence was regulated by strict rules. In times when there was no great war campaign in motion, their job was to constantly attack over the borders and harass the enemy.

25   A unit of the janissary corpus. One orta was 400 men.

26   Radovan Samardžić, *Mehmed Sokolović*.

27   In the language of today, the High Defterdar was the head of finance in the central government. In addition to him in Constantinople, the state also had local *defterdars* in each province and *pashaluk* (a region governed by a pasha).

28   Çelebi(ya). Although this is a title for an educated man of noble birth, indeed for a nobleman, as time passed it also took on an informal, class signification for a prince. Later, in certain cases, it even took on the feeling of a personal name, a surname.

29   The Caliph is the religious ruler of all Moslems.

30   The padishah (Persian), the lord over kings, autocrat, a unifying synonym for ruler, emperor, sovereign, great sultan (one of the titles of the former Turkish sultans).

31   A *haseki* was equal in title to a janissary aga.

32   *Rikabdar* is a title for a personal courtier to the sultan whose task it was to help the ruler mount his horse and to follow him on his journeys by walking at the sultan's side as he rode. It was literally not possible to be closer to the sultan's train. This seemingly unimportant and almost insulting court role actually indicated something quite the opposite: the rulers unbounded trust in the person to whom he assigned it.

33   The main duty of the *çohadar* was to take care of the ruler's raiments.

34   The *silahdar-aga* was the imperial shield-bearer whose job it was to take care of the ruler's personal weaponry.

35   The *çeşnegir-başa* was the administrator of the refectory, the man who tasted all food and drink intended for the sultan.

36   The high *kapidzi-başa* was by rank the oldest among all the commanders of the court guard.

37   The *katil-ferman* was a decree or order that one of the subjects was to be strangled or otherwise executed.

38   The military and administrative office of a single *sancak* (or *sandzak*). Several *sancaks* made up a beylerbeyluk (or pashaluk).

39   The highest builder/engineer/architect; one of the words that signified this office – *mimar*, in Sinan's case, with time became Mimar, that is, part of his personal name.

40   A large military property.

41   An endowment whose income from ownership was given to the maintenance of religious or educational institutions. Or for the general good, that is, for purposes of charity.

42   The administrator of a *vakuf* according to Shariat law, or a *vakufnami*.

43 The head barber in the Ottoman courts carried the title *berberaş*.

44 In the period 1548–1549.

45 The *alaybey* was the leader of the landowners in a *sancak*.

46 The place is significant because her son took his name from it, and became known by that name, as the Turkish chronicler Ibrahim Peçevi (or Peçuyli).

47 The word madrasa signifies all sorts of secondary and high schools, while *mekteb* is reserved for primary schools.

48 He means Suleiman's famous great love, the former slave Roxelana, the daughter of a Russian Orthodox priest.

49 A *reis* was a commander of a military (or merchant) ship; the commander of one part of a fleet or the whole thing.

50 Precisely because of his appearance in the court, first the women and then all the others began calling him "the Tall", and often they added this as an official part of his name: Mehmed-pasha the Tall.

51 A provincial administrator in the Turkish Empire.

52 Published in 1526 under the title *The History of the Rebellions in Hungary and Erdelj*.

53 A *musjid* is a house of prayer like a mosque, but of less meaning and significance. Moslems can do all their prayers individually, except on Friday and for Bayram when they need to go to common prayer in a mosque. So, in the lands of Turkish civilisation, *musjids* were small neighbourhood mosques in which one could bow and pray, but not on Friday or for Bayram. Often, they did not even have a minaret.

54 Obligatory Friday prayer. In this case, in the *Journal* about the Campaign of Sultan Suleiman against Belgrade, the content of which was dictated by Suleiman himself, the following appears about this event: "With God's aid, the fortress of Belgrade was taken today... The town muezzin sang out the evening prayer." It continues: "Friday... The honourable Sultan happily crossed the newly built bridge and entered Belgrade. He did the Friday prayers. He turned the lower church into a mosque."

55 Just as Rumelia is the old name for the European part of the Ottoman Empire, the name Misir is the old name for Egypt.

56 *Sebilhan or sebilya* – a fountain of water.

57 Of the former, I would set apart the monograph on the capital city of Egypt, *One Thousand Years of Cairo,* and of the latter the novel *Zayni Barakat*.

58 He wrote two books about Mahfouz. They spent the years of their childhood twenty yards from one another in the same street (which we walked

down together on one of our walks). As he told me, now he was his oldest living friend.

59 In Europe, this position is most often known under the name "Grand Mufti". He is the leading interpreter of (religious) law. He personally did a lot to make jurisprudence superior to the army. His reforms of Ottoman state law led to the solid ensconcing of the *uleme* (scholarly and religious learning) into the entire system.

60 Many claim that he is actually the greatest interpreter of the Qu'ran of all time.

61 The Pillar.

62 Germany.

63 Hungary.

64 For the next thirty years, the patriarch of the Peć Patriarchate, indeed the head of the Serbian Orthodox Church, would exclusively be a member of the Sokolović family: Makarije (1557–1571), Antim (1571–1575), Gerasim (1575–1586) and Sava(tije) Sokolović (1586).

65 New hamam.

66 Sinan only lacked one year to have lived an entire century, he lived to be ninety-nine. Mehmed would probably have also survived to a similar age, or at least deep old age had he not, still vital and quite active, been killed in his seventy-fourth year of life by the hand of a fanatic member of Hamza's sect.

67 The Greek word "hippodrome" which means the place where horse races are held. In Turkish, the adequate term is "At meydani", coming from the words "at" – horse, and "meydan"- field.

68 For building all the large and small, but immeasurably important structures that have survived these five centuries, with which he incurred the debt of the Ottoman Empire and Islamic culture, and indeed world culture, Sinan was graciously rewarded by his ruler. A *vakuf* (a document – a decree establishing ownership) has been preserved from Sultan Suleiman in the year 1563 by which Sinan was allowed to possess wealth including eighteen buildings, thirty-eight shops, nine houses, one field, a mill, three fountains, a small mosque and a school. The "small mosque" on the list is this very one.

69 The Mehmed-pasha Sokollu Mosque, at Kadirga, was finished between 1571 and 1572. So were the covered market and caravansary at Dorćol.

70 The Mehmed-pasha Sokollu Mosque, at Azap Kapi, was finished between 1577 and 1578. So was the Višegrad bridge (the Bridge on the Drina), in Bosnia.

71 He ruled Serbia from 1243 to 1276.

BEST OF THE BALKANS
ISTROS BOOKS' TITLES FOR 2014

Odohohol & Cally Rascal by Matko Sršen (Croatia)
Translated by Celia Hawkesworth
Odohohol is a boy with special powers, living in a future world in which Evil has prevailed. And being a boy with special powers, he represents new hope for all life in the universe – through his travels in parallel dimensions, he links up with others from the Secret Resistance and joins forces in the fight for Good. (January, 2014)
ISBN: 978-1-908236-15-9

Mission London by Alek Popov (Bulgaria)
Translated by Daniela and Charles Edward Gill de Mayol de Lupe
Combining the themes of corruption, confusion and outright incompetence, Popov masterly brings together multiple plot lines in a sumptuous carnival of frenzy and futile vanity, allowing the illusions and delusions of post-communist society to be reflected in their glorious absurdity! (April 2014)
ISBN: 978-1-908236-18-0

Death in the Museum of Modern Art by Alma Lazarevska (Bosnia)
Translated by Celia Hawkesworth
Avoiding the easy traps of politics and blame, Lazarevska reveals a world full of incidents and worries so similar to our own, and yet always under the shadow of the snipers and the grenades of the recent Bosnian war. (June 2014)
ISBN: 978-1-908236-17-3

False Apocalypse by Fatos Lubonja (Albania)
Translated by John Hodgson
1997, a tragic year in the history of post-communist Albania. This is one man's story of how the world's most isolated country emerged from Stalinist dictatorship and fell victim to a plague of corruption and flawed 'pyramid' financial schemes which brought the people to the edge of ruin. (October 2014)
ISBN: 978-1-908236-19-7

The Great War by Aleksandar Gatalica (Serbia)
Translated by Will Firth
In the centenary year of the start of WWI, we finally have a Serbian author taking on the themes of a war that was started by a Serb assassin's bullet. Following the destinies of over seventy characters, on all warring sides, Gatalica depicts the destinies of winners and losers, generals and opera singers, soldiers and spies, in the conflict that marked the beginning of the Twentieth Century. (October 2014)
ISBN: 978-1-908236-20-3